£6.44

T x/2

Scientific thought

New Babylon

Studies in the behavioral sciences

9

Mouton/Unesco
Paris · The Hague
mcmlxxii

Scientific thought

*Some underlying concepts
methods
and procedures*

Mouton/Unesco
Paris · The Hague
mcmlxxii

Q
175
.S424

Preface

'We have always found that whenever a postulated symmetry principle was appearing to fail in natural phenomena, this must be due to some still deeper symmetry, with which it must be in conflict. We may, at a given time, fail to comprehend the aesthetics of nature. When, however, the full and final picture emerges one has invariably found that the symmetries this exhibits are profounder still.'

This extract from Professor Salam's contribution to this book neatly sums up the history and one of the purposes of science and philosophy. There is always an ultimate beyond the ultimate: perhaps the ultimate will at last be reached when man gets to infinity...

Moreover, science is many-sided, and each tends to regard it from the standpoint of his own particular experience and interests. The Bronze Age and the Iron Age, clearly, were named by technology. But, asked in 1886 whether the nineteenth century would be known as the century of iron, of steam or of electricity, the eminent physicist Boltzmann had no hesitation in declaring that it would be known as the century of Darwin.

The philosophers, on their side, have always tried to think beyond science, and to provide a framework which invites the human mind to think about science and, thereby, about itself. Aristotle's categories provided an early systematization which Kant, digesting new knowledge acquired meantime in mathematics and many other disciplines, transformed. Hegel attempted a synthesis in which all the partial and contradictory philosophies of his predecessors would be contained and transcended... one thing is certain: as thinkers, scientists and philosophers continue to add their contributions, the sum of human knowledge increases, and so, likewise, does the layman's difficulty of keeping apace.

Not alone have there been tremendous developments in physics, chemistry, biology and mathematics, but wholly new disciplines, such as cybernetics, have appeared. Mass communication techniques have transformed our concepts of information. Economic planning is the rule in nearly all countries. The moon and other planets are being explored.

But, according to the Chinese saying, there is always a first step in a journey of ten thousand miles...

This book is a collection of articles by eminent scientists who were invited by Unesco to explain ideas, methods or procedures which underlie many of the extraordinary discoveries and developments of the twentieth century. The views expressed are those of the authors, and not necessarily those of Unesco. The articles are obviously not exhaustive, and in most cases do not deal with other views that may be held on the same subject. But each contains a bibliography so that readers specially interested in any particular article can see where its subject matter can be studied in greater detail.

In publishing this book, the Unesco Division of Philosophy believes that readers will welcome it as a series of authoritative statements, conveniently brought together between two covers, on diverse subjects which have in common their immense importance in modern scientific thought.

Contents

Notes on the authors

YEHOSHUA BAR-HILLEL. Born Vienna 1915. Doctorate (1949) from the Hebrew University of Jerusalem. Research and teaching in the United States (Massachusetts Institute of Technology; California and Ann Arbor), Europe (Konstanz and Berlin), and Israel (teaching logic and the philosophy of science at the Hebrew University).

Past President of the International Union of the History and Philosophy of Science; member of the Israel Academy of Arts and Science.

Publications include: *Language and information; Aspects of language: essays in philosophy of language, linguistic philosophy and methodology of linguistics;* with A. A. Fraenkel and A. Levy, *Foundations of set theory.*

STAFFORD BEER. Visiting Professor of Cybernetics at Manchester University, and of General Systems at the Open University, London. President of the Society for General Systems Research, Washington; member of the United Kingdom Automation Council. Consultant to government and industry, and a regular broadcaster on radio and television.

Publications include: *Cybernetics and management; Decision and control* (Wiley-Lanchester Prize); *Management science; Brain of the firm; Platform for change* (in press).

MARIO BUNGE. Born Buenos Aires 1919. Doctorate in theoretical physics. Research in atomic and nuclear physics. Has taught physics and philosophy in Argentina and the United States. Now Professor of Philosophy and Head of the Foundations and Philosophy of Science Unit, McGill University, Montreal.

Publications include: *Causality; Metascientific queries; Cinemática del electrón relativista; Intuition and science; The myth of simplicity; Foundations of physics; Scientific research.*

ARNOLD KAUFMANN. Professor at the Institut National Polytechnique of Grenoble, France. Has taught at the Ecole Nationale Supérieure des Mines, Paris, and at the Ecole de l'Air, Salon-de-Provence. Consultant on various Unesco projects.

Publications include: *Les cadres et la révolution informatique* (Centi Prize, 1970); *Des sous-hommes et des super-machines* (with J. Pèze); *L'inventique – nouvelles méthodes de créativité* (with M. Fustier and A. Drevet); *Mathématiques nouvelles pour le recyclage des parents* (with G. Cullmann); *Introduction à la combinatorique; L'homme d'action et la science; Introduction à la théorie des sous-ensembles flous.*

MIHAJLO D. MESAROVIC. Professor of Engineering and Director of Systems Research Center at Case Western Reserve University, Cleveland, Ohio, United States. Continuing to work on the mathematical theory of general systems and the application of the multi-level, hierarchical approach in environmental and socio-economic problems (in particular in the 'Predicament of Mankind' project of the Club of Rome, of which he is a member).

Publications include: *Theory of multilevel hierarchical systems* (with D. Macko and Y. Takahara); *Foundations for a mathematical general systems theory* (with Y. Takahara); *Systems approach and the city* (ed., with A. Reisman); *Theory of non-numerical problem solving* (ed., with R. Banerji); *Systems theory and biology* (ed.).

ANDRZEJ MOSTOWSKI. Teaches mathematics, logic and foundations of mathematics at Warsaw University (since 1946). Now engaged in research on models of extended systems of set theory and of systems of arithmetic.

Publications include: *Constructible sets, with applications.*

JEAN PIAGET. Born Neuchâtel, Switzerland, 1896. Taught at Universities of Neuchâtel, Lausanne and Geneva, in Switzerland, and at the Sorbonne. Pioneer of research on child psychology. Former Director of the International Bureau of Education, in Geneva, and various research agencies. Honorary doctorates from various European and American universities including Harvard, Yale and the Sorbonne. Recipient of several prizes including the American Psychological Association Prize (1969).

Publications include: *Mémoire et intelligence* (with H. Sinclair-de

Zwaart); *Le structuralisme; L'épistémologie génétique; Psychologie et épistémologie.* Contributed Introduction and chapter on Psychology to *Main trends of research in the social and human sciences* (Unesco, 1970).

ABDUS SALAM. Director of the International Centre for Theoretical Physics, Trieste, Italy. Professor of Theoretical Physics at the Imperial College of Science and Technology, London. Specialist in particle physics and gravitation theory.

Publications include contributions on the following subjects: Theory of groups and the symmetry physicist (London Mathematical Society); The role of symmetry physics; Weak and electromagnetic interactions (Nobel Symposium 8); Fundamental theory of matter: a survey of results and methods; Gravitational ward identities (with J. Strathdee); Computation of renormalization constants; Finite field theories (Rochester Conference).

HERBERT STACHOWIAK. Professor of the Philosophy of Science, Free University of Berlin.

Publications include: *Denken und Erkennen im kybernetischen Modell; Rationalismus im Ursprung. Die Genesis des axiomatischen Denkens.* Editor of 'Cybernetics' paperback series. Co-editor of *Schriften zur wissenschaftlichen Weltorientierung* (vols. I-VII); *Lexikon der kybernetischen Pädagogik; Teorema* (Universidad de Valencia); *Grundlagenstudien aus Kybernetik und Geisteswissenschaft.*

LADISLAV TONDL. Born 1924. Research and teaching at the Czechoslovak Academy of Sciences on the methodology of science, and logical semantics.

Publications include: *Methodology of experimental sciences; Contemporary western philosophy; Problems of semantics; Man and science; Scientific procedures.*

NICOLAI N. VOROBYEV. Born 1925. Doctorate (1961) in Physics and Mathematics. Professor of Theoretical Cybernetics; Chairman of the Department of Operations Research, Central Institute for Economics and Mathematics (Leningrad Branch) of the USSR Academy of Sciences; Professor at the Leningrad State University. Specialist in game theory.

Publications include articles on coalitional games, extremal algebra of positive matrices, modern state of the game theory; *Fibonacci numbers; Theory of series; Development of game theory* (all in Russian); *Grundlagen der Spieltheorie und ihre praktische Bedeutung; Grundfragen der Spieltheorie und ihre praktische Bedeutung.*

SATOSI WATANABE. Born 1910. Doctorates from the Sorbonne and Tokyo Universities. Taught philosophy, electrical engineering, physics and information sciences at various universities including Hawaii, Fordham, Yale, Columbia and Tokyo. President of the International Society for the Study of Time; member of the International Academy of the Philosophy of Science.

Publications include: *Knowing and guessing – a quantitative study; Methodologies of pattern recognition* (editor); *Frontiers of pattern recognition* (editor).

1　Sets

ANDRZEJ MOSTOWSKI

We shall deal, in this paper, with the concept of a set. Our chief concern will be with sets occurring in mathematics, because it is in mathematics that the concept of a set has most applications and the modern philosophical controversies about the nature of sets have originated. While it is true that many scientific concepts based on the concept of a set do not belong to mathematics, the methods of using sets in their construction derive from mathematics, and so it can be safely stated that the concept of a set used in science is not essentially different from that used in mathematics.

It will be seen below that many subtle discussions concerning very abstract mathematical problems have their origin in the way we speak of sets in ordinary language.

1. SETS IN EVERYDAY LANGUAGE

1.1　*Collections*

We very often speak of collections of objects as of entities consisting of these objects. Various words are used to denote these entities, e.g. collection, group, set, class, aggregate. Sometimes very specific words are used to denote certain collections (e.g. constellation), whereas other words can be applied in various situations (e.g. a group of demonstrators, a group of buildings). We cannot treat all these words as synonymous: 'group of demonstrators' is correct, but 'class of demonstrators' is hardly acceptable. Nevertheless, they all obviously have a clearly related meaning. To avoid linguistic difficulties we shall use the neutral word 'collection' to denote any entity (sets, groups, classes, teams) consisting of individual objects. These objects are called the elements of the collection. Thus we have a collection of football players (a team), a collection of stars (a constellation), a collection of the inhabitants of a given city whose age is below 20 (a group), and so on.

1.2 *Operations on collections*

The above use of words is fully sanctioned in everyday language and there is not the slightest difficulty in understanding it. It is very helpful in classifying objects and in handling elementary problems in statistics. Thus, for example, when preparing statistics on city dwellers we divide the whole group into various collections by age, sex, occupation, income, etc. Even at this very elementary stage, various useful operations (see Table)

Table

Collection A =	$a, c, 8, 4, z, y.$
Collection B =	$b, e, 9, 4, x, y.$
Union A, B =	$a, c, 8, 4, z, y, b, e, 9, 4, x, y.$
Intersection A, B =	$4, y.$
Difference A, B =	$a, c, 8, z.$
Difference B, A =	$b, e, 9, x.$

can be made with collections, e.g. the union of two collections (defined as a collection consisting exclusively of elements which belong to either of the given collections or to both of them), or forming an intersection of two collections which consists of elements common to both. The difference of two collections A, B, consists of elements which belong to the former but do not belong to the latter collection. The general laws which govern these operations form what is usually called Boolean algebra. One word of caution is necessary here: if we use the word 'collection' or similar words in everyday language, we always assume that each collection has elements. Also we are inclined to exclude collections which would have just one element, the reason being simply that the basic idea of a collection is that of an entity consisting of several elements. If there is just one element there is no need to apply the process of forming a collection. However, it is clear that such restrictions are very inconvenient: even in the simplest applications to statistics we must extend the concept of a collection by allowing collections without elements and collections consisting of just one element. For instance, if we divide a population into groups according to whether they have certain properties, it may very well happen that there is just one member of the population who has a property or that there are no such members at all. The laws of Boolean algebra specifically assert the existence of an 'empty set'.

1.3 *The principle of abstraction*

A theoretically important method of constructing collections is provided by the so-called principle of abstraction. Let us consider a collection and a two-termed relation which may or may not hold between any two given elements. We assume that the relation is reflexive (i.e. each element of the collection bears the relation to itself), symmetric (i.e. if x bears the relation to y, then y bears it to x) and transitive (i.e. if x bears the relation to y and y to z, then x bears the relation to z). Such relations are called equivalence relations. The principle of abstraction says that under the above assumptions the given collection can be decomposed into subcollections, no two of which have common elements, and so that two elements are in the same subcollection if, and only if, they bear the given relation to each other. The subcollections into which the whole collection decomposes are called the equivalence classes of the given relation.

As an illustration let us consider the collection of all ships and the relation which one ship bears to another if they have the same mode of propulsion. The equivalence classes are then the class of all steam-ships, the class of all sailing-ships, etc.

1.4 *Abstract character of collections*

We shall now discuss the problem whether collections whose elements are physical objects are themselves to be considered as such objects. The problem is not very precise because the meaning of the words 'physical object' is far from clear, but we shall not analyse this concept here and shall try to use it as it is used in everyday language. It is customary to require that a physical object fill a well defined portion of space and that it be in some way connected. In this sense most collections are certainly not physical objects; for instance, a constellation is not a single connected entity. But, even if we admit that physical objects need not be connected, we still cannot consider collections as physical objects. Otherwise the collection of elementary particles which are present in the stars forming a given constellation would be identical with this constellation, which is false since one collection consists of elementary particles and the other of stars.

The problem was discussed by Frege (1884) who showed conclusively that no collection is a physical object. Even a collection consisting of just one element is not the same as this element: this is particularly obvious in the case when the unique element of a collection is not a collection.

Stating the thesis that collections are abstract entities and not physical objects we do not take any philosophical stand concerning the 'real' existence of abstract entities. All we want to say is that all names of collections belong to the family of words which do not name physical objects. Of course, there are many such words in everyday language e.g. all adjectives. The mere fact that words denoting collections are nouns like the names of physical objects does not imply that collections exist in the same sense as physical objects. On the contrary, collections are not physical objects and exist only in the same sense as do properties.

1.5 *Collections and properties*

There are close connections between collections and properties. In everyday language we can always define the former in favour of the latter. Each collection is completely determined by a property: the collection of Poles who were 51 in 1969 is completely determined by the property of being a Pole born in 1918. We should note, however, that different properties may sometimes determine the same collection: in the example above we may consider the property of being a Pole born in the year in which the first world war ended.

Let us call two properties extensionally equal if any object which possesses one of them also possesses the other. Two properties determine the same collection if and only if they are extensionally equal. Thus remembering the principle of abstraction we may state that collections are (or can be uniquely correlated with) equivalence classes of the relation of the extensional equality.

The criterion for the identity of collections also helps to make clear why collections are not physical objects. There might be some temptation to think, for example, that a ship is identical with the collection of planks of wood used in its construction. That this suggestion is incorrect can be seen by considering the fact that if a rotten plank is replaced by a new one, the resulting collection of planks is, by the foregoing criterion, a different collection from the original one. The identity of the ship, however, remains the same. The battleship *Victory* which can be seen today by tourists is the same ship as the one which was engaged in the Battle of Trafalgar, although doubtless it is a different collection of planks. Similarly, a building is not the same as the collection of bricks and stones which were used to build it. This observation, though it does not prove conclusively that a collection is not a physical object, does dispense with the most obvious reason for thinking that it might be (see D. Wiggins, 1967, for further discussion of this point).

1.6 *Collections of collections*

The abstract character of collections manifests itself in the possibility of forming collections whose elements are themselves collections. Their use is perfectly sanctioned in everyday language. Thus we speak e.g. of a collection of football teams or of a collection of all constellations or of a collection of all sets of silverware.

Objects which are not collections are said to be of type 0; collections whose elements have type 0 are said to be of type 1; collections whose elements have type 1 are said to be of type 2 etc. In everyday language we use only exceptionally words denoting collections of type higher than 2. Also we never consider collections with mixed types, i.e. ones some of whose elements have types different from the others. However, there are no compelling reasons why we should exclude such collections on principle. They just do not seem to be needed in situations described in everyday speech.

1.7 *Remarks*

The thesis stated above about the abstract character of collections is accepted widely but not universally. One very ardent proponent of the opposite thesis was Leśniewski who maintained that collections are physical bodies and that the relation of an element to a collection has properties similar to that which a part of a body bears to the whole body. See Luschei (1962) for a detailed discussion of Leśniewski's theory; see also Goodman (1951).

2. DEVELOPMENT OF THE CONCEPT OF A SET IN MODERN MATHEMATICS

Henceforth we shall constantly use the word 'set' instead of 'collections'. It became common to use this word in mathematics and no linguistic awkwardness can result from its use. Moreover, various words which in ordinary language are used to denote certain collections acquired in mathematics very specific meanings and sometimes do not denote any sets at all. This is true e.g. for such common words as 'group' and 'class'.

2.1 *The set-theoretic foundation of mathematics*

Sets were used in mathematics long ago as is witnessed by the notion of geometric loci used since times immemorial in the teaching of geometry. They did not play an essential role, however, until the nineteenth century when mathematicians began to use them extensively in their work on the foundations of calculus.

Let us recapitulate briefly some salient historical facts. The great mathematical discoveries made in the seventeenth century were followed during the next century by a stormy development of the new ideas and of their applications. The new mathematics created in this way was very different from the old not only because the content was changed but also because the new mathematics was incomparably less exact. The mathematicians of the eighteenth century strove towards enriching mathematics by new interesting facts and finding new applications. It is well known that the founders of calculus based their theories on utterly unclear notions. When one reads some of the works of the best mathematicians of the eighteenth century one often wonders how it was possible that they were able to find correct results, so unclear and unconvincing (by our present standards) were their methods (*cf.* Polya, 1954, 20–21). The wonderful precision of the old Greek mathematics fell into oblivion. During the nineteenth century a reaction set in. We see many outstanding mathematicians working on re-formulating and correcting the foundations of analysis. The essential task was to formulate exact definitions of such basic concepts as function (or mapping), sequence of numbers, complex number, real number and then to derive their properties from axioms and generally accepted laws of logic.

We cannot present here the details of the long and painful work done by the leading mathematicians of the nineteenth century starting with Cauchy and ending with Frege and Cantor. Their work resulted in what is usually called the set-theoretic foundations of mathematics: all concepts necessary for a rigourous exposition of mathematics proved to be definable by means of very few basic concepts provided that a rather unrestricted use of sets was allowed in the definitions. All theorems formerly accepted on the basis of intuition alone or established in an incomplete and often objectionable way proved to be strictly derivable from a small number of very natural axioms which express the fundamental properties of the basic concepts. The word 'set' occurred in many of these axioms even though at this early stage no axioms for sets existed. If we could ask a nineteenth century mathematician why it was so, he would probably answer that properties of sets are established in logic and are of no concern to mathematicians.

We shall show a few examples of reduction of mathematical notions to more simple ones. The intuitive notion of a mapping, or function, from a set A into a set B, which may or may not be different from A, is that of a fixed rule which associates with each element x of A one, and one only, element y of B. Thus, for example, the function defined by $+\sqrt{x}$ of the set of integers into the set of real numbers associates with each integer x its positive square root. The image of an element x of A under a mapping f from A into B is the element y of B which is associated with x by the mapping f. Thus, in the above example, 2 is the image of 4 under $+\sqrt{x}$. However, the notions of 'fixed rule' and 'associate' are themselves vague. A precise definition of a mapping can be given in terms of sets, using the concept of an ordered pair, that is, of a set constructed from two elements x and y such that the ordered pair (x, y) is the same as the ordered pair (w, z) if and only if $x = w$ and $y = z$. Thus a mapping f of A into B is defined as a set of ordered pairs (x, y), with x in A and y in B, such that y is the image of x under f. Thus instead of mappings (functions) we can speak of certain sets of ordered pairs. Ordered pairs can also be defined by means of sets, but we shall not discuss this reduction here.

Similarly, a sequence $a(0)$, $a(1)$, ... of real numbers is defined as the function which maps the integers 0, 1 ... into reals and correlates with the integer n the value $a(n)$. Thus again a sequence can be replaced by a set of pairs. Complex numbers $a + bi$ can be defined as ordered pairs (a, b) of two real numbers.

Most difficult proved the analysis of real numbers. This was, of course, to be expected because, as is well known to everybody even moderately acquainted with the history of mathematics, these numbers had already caused a great deal of trouble in pre-Euclidean times. In modern mathematics one has two ways of dealing with these numbers. One way is to accept the notion of a real number as primitive and characterize it by means of suitable axioms; the other is to define real numbers by means of rational numbers (i.e. fractions). The first method is called axiomatic, the second genetic. In both methods the concept of a set plays an essential role. Thus if we use the genetic method, we define a real number a as an ordered pair consisting of two sets of rational numbers. Intuitively speaking the first set consists of rationals which are smaller than a and the second of those which are greater than or equal to a. If we use the axiomatic method we adopt among others the axiom of continuity which says that if A and B are two sets of real numbers such that each element of A is smaller than each element of B, then there is a real number x which separates these sets, i.e. has the property that no element of A is greater than x and no element of B is smaller than x.

Rational numbers are easily definable by means of integers but an analysis of this latter notion again proved to be rather difficult. Usually one admits this notion as primitive and characterizes it by axioms. Again sets are of paramount importance because they are used in the basic axiom of induction. (The simplest axiom equivalent to the axiom of induction states that every non-void set of integers contains a least element.) The genetic method of introducing integers was attempted by Frege (1884; 1893–1093) (*cf.* Section 3.3 below). Axioms for integers were first formulated by Peano (1889).

Before we leave the subject discussed in this section we want to make three observations:

A. The use of sets in laying down correct foundations for analysis is an historical fact but does not seem to be a necessity. Other general notions such as functions or relations could be equally well used instead of sets to achieve this purpose. It is not impossible that still other notions can be invented which could replace the notion of sets.

B. In the formulations of the axioms and in the descriptions of the various definitions given above we did not speak of individual sets but of their totalities. This is witnessed by the fact that we use quantifiers 'for every set' in the axioms of continuity and of induction. Thus we behave as if the totality of all sets (of reals or of integers) were a well-defined collection of objects.

C. If the genetic method of constructing real numbers is used, then sets of which we implicitly speak in mathematical theorems have much higher types than the collections about which we are used to speak in everyday language. E.g. a mapping of reals into reals becomes a set of pairs each member of which is an ordered pair consisting of two sets of rationals.

2.2 *The role of sets in further development of mathematics*

We saw above that the notion of an arbitrary subset of a given set became a legitimate mathematical notion (*cf.* remark B above). Very soon mathematicians began to use it extensively and formed with its help new chapters of mathematics which were designed partly to deepen the study of the old 'classical' domains of mathematics and partly to deepen the study of the new notions *per se*.

We cannot, of course, present here the details of the new theories which were created in this way because their subject matter is obviously very 'technical'. We may, however, try to point out certain relevant facts.

In older mathematics the main interest was focused on special functions which mapped either the set of real numbers into the set of real numbers or the set of complex numbers into the set of complex numbers and which had some interesting properties or were useful in mechanics or other parts of physics. The immediate effect of allowing arbitrary subsets of a given set was the rise of interest in quite arbitrary functions of reals into reals; each function is as we mentioned above, nothing else but a set of ordered pairs. In this way was created the new theory of real functions. It turned out that properties which in old theory were deemed essential for the notion of function (like continuity and derivability) were only exceptionally satisfied by arbitrary functions: most real functions are discontinuous and most continuous functions cannot be differentiated. Thus new methods had to be created in order to study such functions. The theory of arbitrary sets was again the basic tool in this theory.

The modern theories of measure and integration were a natural outcome of this development. These theories proved much superior to the older theories of measure and integral created in the nineteenth century. Many classical parts of analysis could develop only because the old theories of integral were replaced by the new one. Today not only mathematicians but even physicists are taught abstract general measure theory.

Similar development took place in geometry where one started to discuss properties of very general sets of points instead of analysing as before only very regular curves and surfaces.

The strive towards generality did not stop here. Having been so successful in the study of arbitrary mappings of reals into reals mathematicians began to consider functionals, i.e. functions whose arguments were themselves functions or sets. An integral or a measure are the simplest such functionals. The systematic study of functionals resulted in the creation of a new mathematical theory called functional analysis. Thus we see that the step which has led from the study of certain specific real functions to the general theory of arbitrary such functions has been repeated but on a higher level. Using the notion of types we can say that the functional analysis discusses objects which in the hierarchy of types lie one step above the objects discussed in the classical analysis.

Processes similar to that outlined above took place not only in the theory of functions but also in geometry and especially in topology. Everywhere the interest shifted, from the study of simple objects to the study of objects of higher types. If we look at this development from the point of view which interests us here, we can express as follows the general principle which underlies these processes: whenever a set is acknowledged as a legitimate object of mathematics, so is the set of all its subsets.

We shall now describe the ultimate step in the strive towards generality which is so characteristic of modern mathematics.

Modern theories like functional analysis, topology and some others were concerned in their early stages almost exclusively with particular examples. Thus e.g. in topology very general sets were discussed but the underlying space in which the sets under discussion were contained was very special. Similarly functional analysis dealt with functionals which were quite abstract and general but which operated in some precisely defined special sets, e.g. the set of real functions or the set of all real sequences etc. The ultimate step consists of replacing these underlying sets by arbitrary ones. Thus in the modern theory one starts with defining axiomatically certain 'spaces', i.e. sets in which some additional structures may be given. The object of the study are subsets of the space or mappings of one space into another. This abstract approach is very economical because it usually allows us to obtain many of the previously developed theories as particular instances of the general theory.

That such an abstract is possible is, of course, due to the development of the theory of abstract sets. We shall outline this development in the next section but before doing this we shall add some more remarks about the importance of the abstract set-theoretic approach in applications of mathematics.

2.3 *Remarks about applicability of the abstract theories*

These remarks must of necessity be very brief because the author does not feel competent enough to discuss the problem at length. Let us therefore only mention that the abstract functional analysis finds applications in quantum theory where it was discovered that physical magnitudes such as energy, momentum, etc. can best be described by operators (functionals) acting in an abstract space.

On a logically more elementary level the study of functions defined on abstract sets has made it possible to create, for example, the theory of games whose practical importance is today generally recognized. If one reads the description of games e.g. in von Neumann and Morgenstern (1947), one sees that no mathematical description of this concept would be possible without abstract mathematics with its emphasis on the study of arbitrary sets and functions. The same can be said of the modern theories of probability with their many applications as well as of the computer science.

3. THE DEVELOPMENT OF ABSTRACT SET THEORY DURING THE NINETEENTH CENTURY

Abstract set theory was created by Cantor, and this section is almost entirely devoted to his work. However, we mention briefly the work of Bolzano who had already discovered many essential facts before Cantor, and Frege whose studies on the logical foundations of arithmetic had a profound although indirect influence on the theory of sets.

3.1 *Bolzano (1781–1848)*

Collections about which we speak in everyday language necessarily consist of finitely many elements. We saw in the previous section that sets which are really important for mathematics are always infinite. The

Czech philosopher B. Bolzano was the first who systematically discussed infinite sets. (Some remarks about this subject can also be found in earlier writings starting from Antiquity: see Becker, 1964, 272.) Bolzano discovered that the properties of infinite sets are very different from finite sets, and he was so puzzled by this difference that he named the book in which he described his discoveries *Paradoxes of Infinity* (1851). Of course, the name is very misleading because there is nothing paradoxical in the theory of infinite sets; they just happen to behave differently than the finite sets and upon reflection one must admit that it would be strange if it were not so.

Let us give an example of a 'paradox' discovered by Bolzano. Two sets *A*, *B* are called equipollent if there is a one-to-one function *F* which maps *A* onto the whole of *B*. The expression 'one-to-one' means that two different elements of *A* are always mapped onto different elements of *B*. Thus e.g. if *A* consists of all letters which occur in the word 'spirit' (there are just 5 such letters because 'i' occurs twice) and *B* consists of all letters occurring in the word 'Catulla' then we obtain a one-to-one mapping of *A* onto *B* if we correlate 'C' with 's', 'a' with 'p', 't' with 'i', 'u' with 'r' and 'l' with 't'. In other words, the function which establishes equipollence of the two sets *A* and *B* is the set of ordered pairs (s,C), (p,a), (i,t), (r,u), (t,l).

For finite sets equipollence means simply that they have the same number of elements, from which it follows that no finite set is equipollent with any of its proper subsets ('proper' means that the subset is not identical with the whole set.)

For an infinite set *A*, one can easily exhibit a function which establishes the equipollence of *A* with one of its proper subsets. Thus if *A* is the set of positive integers 1, 2, 3, .., then the mapping *f* defined by the formula $f(x) = 2x$ establishes the equipollence of *A* and the set of all even integers.

3.2 *Cantor (1845–1918)*

Cantor was the true founder of the abstract theory of sets. Very early he rediscovered most of Bolzano's 'paradoxes' and what is more important showed that the abstract notions of set theory can be used to obtain amazingly simple solutions of some mathematical problems (*cf.* his well-known proof that there exist transcendental numbers).

The basic notion around which centered the whole theory is that of the equipollence of two sets. Instead of saying that A and B are equipollent Cantor used to say that A and B have the same cardinality. If A is equipollent to a part of B but not conversely, then we say that the cardinality of A is smaller than that of B.

The first and most important discovery of Cantor was that there exist infinite sets of different cardinalities; e.g. the cardinality of integers is smaller than that of reals. More generally he showed that the cardinality of any set A is smaller than the cardinality of the set of all subsets of A.

Deeper results concerning cardinalities were established by Cantor by means of a new and most original notion – that of a well-ordered set. Let us briefly explain it.

A set as such has no particular structure. Of each object one can say that it either belongs to the set or not but from a mere definition of a set one cannot draw any inferences about how its elements are related to each other. A set together with certain relations defined for the elements of this set is called a structure. Thus e.g. the set of integers together with the 'less-than' relation is an example of a structure as is the same set together with the relation 'x is divisible by y'. Of course these structures are different because the relations are different.

A relation R is called connected in a set A if for any two (different) elements a, b of A either a bears R to b or b bears R to a. (Thus the 'less than' relation is connected in the set of integers but not the relation of divisibility.) A relation R is well founded in A if there exists no infinite sequence a, b, c, ... of elements of A such that b bears R to a, c bears R to b, etc. A structure consisting of a set A and a relation R which is connected and well founded in A is said to be well ordered by R. In cases when there is no doubt what is the ordering relation R we simply speak of well ordered sets. As an example of a well-ordered set we may quote the set of integers with the 'less than' relation. But the same set with the 'greater than' relation is not well ordered.

The notion of well-ordering which may seem strange at first is as Cantor has shown very important indeed. The well-ordering of a set replaces in the theory of infinite sets the elementary process of counting as we know it from the everyday practice: if we know a well-ordering of A, then we can say which element of A is the first (in the given well-ordering), which is the second, which is the first which follows all elements of a given subset of A, etc.

Using the theory of well-orderings Cantor was able to show that any two sets which can be well ordered are comparable with respect to their cardinalities. Indeed, the cardinalities of any family of well-orderable sets form themselves a set well ordered by the 'less-than' relation between cardinalities. In particular, it follows that for each well-ordered set A, there is another such set whose cardinality immediately follows the cardinality of A.

Other results obtained by Cantor with the help of well-orderings were concerned with proofs and definitions by means of the so-called transfinite induction. We shall not pursue this matter here.

The theory of well-orderings has immediately raised several problems. We mention only a few of them: can every set be well ordered? Is the cardinality of real numbers next to the cardinality of integers? Is the cardinality of the set of all subsets of any infinite set A next to the cardinality of A? These problems are called respectively: the problem of well-ordering, the continuum problem and the generalized continuum problem. Thile we know a great deal about the first, we know next to nothing about the second and third.

We shall give no more details about Cantor's work although of course the above remarks contain only a small portion of results reached by him during the many years which he devoted to set theory. (Modern exposition of Cantor's results are contained in all textbooks of set theory, see e.g. Fraenkel, 1956. The original writings of Cantor are easily accessible in Cantor, 1932.)

3.3 *Frege (1848–1925)*

Frege's contributions to the theory of infinite sets were only indirect. He was mainly occupied by what we would call today the genetic theory of integers (*cf.* Section 2.1). He wanted to found the theory of integers on the set-theoretic notions alone but treated the theory of sets as part of logic. He expressed the laws of logic on which he based his constructions with an unusual precision and clarity which allowed their thorough inspection and discussion. In this way a first serious analysis of the basic assumptions of what essentially was set theory was made possible. The result of this analysis was devastating: Frege's theory proved to be inconsistent and he had to abandon his grandiose plan.

The basic idea of Frege was very simple. He defined similarly as Cantor and Bolzano the relation of equipollence, noticed that it is an equivalence relation and applied to it the principle of abstraction which he himself discovered (*cf.* Section 1.1). The equivalence classes can be called cardinalties; those which consists of finite sets are according to Frege the usual integers.

Frege went beyond Cantor insofar as he explicitly used the set of all sets in his construction. The relation of equipollence is defined for all sets and therefore the principle of abstraction was applied by Frege to the set of all sets. While Cantor would certainly not oppose such a set, yet he never used it explicitly. His excellent mathematical intuition must have warned him that set is somewhat dubious and moreover of no importance for mathematics. But Frege who was a great logician had less interest in pure mathematics and therefore fell easily into the trap. The inconsistencies discovered in his axioms brought about a long crisis in the foundation of set theory.

4. ANTINOMIES OF SET THEORY AND A REVISION OF ITS FOUNDATIONS

4.1 *Examples of antinomies*

The weakest side of the theory created by Cantor were its foundations. Cantor explained sets as collections of objects which together form a new entity. In Cantor's own words: 'Unter einer Menge verstehen wir jede Zusammenfassung M von bestimmten wohlunterschiedenen Objekten m unserer Anschauung oder unseres Denkens (welche die 'Elemente' von M genannt werden) zu einem Ganzen' (*Mathematische Annalen*, 1895).*

If this loose explanation is accepted, then evidently the set of all sets

---

* For the benefit of readers who like the complicated nineteenth century German we quote still Cantor's definition dating back to 1879 (Über unendliche Lineare Punktmannigfaltigkeiten, § 3, *Mathematische Annalen*, 1879): 'Eine Mannigfaltigkeit (ein Inbegriff, eine Menge) von Elementen, die irgendwelcher Begriffssphäre angehören, nenne ich wohldefiniert, wenn auf Grund ihrer Definition und infolge des logischen Prinzips vom ausgeschlossenen dritten es als intern bestimmt angesehen werden muss, sowohl ob irgendein derselben Begriffssphäre angehöriges Objekt zu der gedachten Mannigfaltigkeit als Element gehört oder nicht, wie auch ob zwei zur Menge gehörige Objekte, trotz formaler Unterschiede in der Art des Gegebenseins einander gleich sind oder nicht.'

exists. But then we immediately obtain a contradiction. If we denote the set of all sets by A then according to Cantor's theorem mentioned in Section 3.2 the set B of all subsets of A would have the cardinality larger than the cardinality of A, which is impossible because B is a subset of A.

A more elementary and better known antinomy was invented by Russell who considered sets which are not their own elements and showed that if X is the set of all such sets then the statements 'X is an element of X' and 'X is not an element of X' are equivalent to each other.

Russell's antinomy was published in the appendix to Frege's book (1893–1903) (*cf.* also Heijenoort, 1967, 127 and 126). The first antinomy ever to be published was that of Burali-Forti (*cf.* Heijenoort, 1967, 104). It dealt with slightly less elementary concepts and we shall not reproduce it here.

Cantor's first reaction to the antinomies was that sets should be divided in two classes: the consistent and inconsistent ones. Whereas the former can be 'thought of as an object', this is not true of the latter (*cf.* Cantor, 1932, 443, also Heijenoort, 1967, 113). Thus presumably the usual laws of set theory are valid only for consistent sets.

The following antinomy discovered by Richard (*cf.* Heijenoort, 1967, 142) shows that inconsistencies may appear even if one restricts oneself to sets of integers. We present this antinomy in a slightly modified version. Let us consider infinite sets of integers such that there are infinitely many integers which do not belong to the set. If such a set can be defined by means of an expression consisting of finitely many English words, then we call it a Richardian set.

We observe now that all English expressions consisting of finitely many words can be arranged as they are in a dictionary and one obtains thus an infinite sequence containing all such expressions. We remove from this sequence expressions which do not define infinite sets of integers or define infinite sets of integers which contain all but finitely many integers so that we are left with a subsequence of expressions each of which defines a set containing infinitely integers and such that infinitely many integers lie outside. Let the terms of this sequence be $D(0)$, $D(1)$, ... Now we select a pair (a_0, b_0) of integers such that a_0 is the least integer in the set defined by $D(0)$ and b_0 is the least integer which does not belong to this set. Let (a_1, b_1) be a pair such that a_1 is the least element of the set defined by $D(1)$ which is different from a_0 and from b_0; similarly b_1 is the least integer not in the set defined by $D(1)$ which is different from a_0

and from b_0. The next pair (a_2, b_2) consists of the least element a_2 of the set defined by $D(2)$ which is different from a_0, b_0, a_1, b_1 and of the least integer b_2 which is not an element of the set defined by $D(2)$ and is different from a_0, b_0, a_1, b_1. Continuing in this way we obtain an infinite number of pairs and we see easily that the set R consisting of the numbers $b_0, b_1, ...$ is infinite, and that infinitely many integers do not belong to it (e.g. none of the numbers a_j belongs to this set). The set R has been defined above by means of an English expression because the whole of the present paragraph can be considered as a definition of R. Hence R is a Richardian set and thus is defined by one of the expressions occurring in the sequence $D(0), D(1), ...,$ say, by the expression $D(r)$. But this is a contradiction because b_r is not an element of the set defined by $D(r)$.

Evidently the only possible explanation of these antinomies is that the sets A, X discussed above do not exist. It is not clear however how to pinpoint the place where we violated the rules for forming sets.

The disturbing idea which must have crept into the minds of some mathematicians after they learnt about the antinomies is that perhaps sets used in mathematical theories and defined by means of purely mathematical concepts also lead to contradictions. They have not yet been discovered, but there is no assurance that they will not be discovered in future.

It must be said that most mathematicians did not share these doubts. They developed set-theoretically orientated mathematical theories while remaining unconcerned with what happened in the foundations of set theory itself. They felt confident that if we follow certain rules of constructing sets, no contradictions will appear. The rules accepted by the majority if mathematicians were eventually codified as axioms of set theory. These axioms will be presented below. Yet there remained a small but important group of mathematicians who were not convinced that the mere formulation of the axioms represents the final solution of the problem posed by the antinomies. We mention some of these dissenting views in Section 6.2.

4.2 *Zermelo-Fraenkel axioms of set theory*

The first axiomatic system for set theory was formulated by E. Zermelo in 1908 (*cf.* Heijenoort, 1967, 199); essential amendments were introduced by Fraenkel (1922) and Skolem (see Heijenoort, 1967, 290) in the early twenties. Various modifications of the system were also proposed and we shall mention them later but first we want to describe the Zermelo-Fraenkel system (abbreviated Z-F) itself, which is by far the most widely-used axiomatic system of set theory.

The primitive concepts of Z–F are sets and the relation of being an element of a set. These concepts are not defined but characterized by axioms. The first axiom (axiom of extensionality) states that sets are determined by their elements or more precisely: if A, B are sets and each element of A is an element of B and conversely, then $A = B$. The next three axioms describe operations which yield new sets from sets already given. These are: the axiom of pairs, which says that for every two sets there exists a new set whose unique elements are the given sets; the axiom of power sets says that for each set A there exists a set whose elements are all the subsets of A; the axiom of unions says that for each set A, there exists a set which contains as a subset each set belonging to A.

All these axioms, however, do not yet guarantee that sets exist in the first place and even if they exist, whether there are infinite sets. In order to settle these problems we assume the existence of at least one infinite set. The formulation of this axiom of infinity by means of the primitive concepts is rather involved and we shall omit it.

There remain still three axioms to be enumerated. They are more complicated than the ones we mentioned thus far and require a more detailed description.

The first of them is called axiom of choice and says that for each set of sets A no two different elements of which have common elements, there exists a set C (the choice set) which contains exactly one element from each non-void element of A.

The axiom of choice has a distinctly different character than the previous ones. Unlike the axioms of construction given above, it does not describe an operation which yields a uniquely determined result when applied to a set; it only states the existence of a choice set. In general a set A satisfying the assumptions of the axiom will have many choice sets. For this reason the axiom was met with a degree of mistrust especially by those mathematicians who wanted to consider only sets defined by properties of their elements. We now know that; in general, no such definition is possible: for instance if A is the set of all unordered pairs $\{f, -f\}$ where f is a real function defined on the set of all reals, then no choice set for A can be defined in the form: the set of all those x which satisfy a condition F. Here F may be any condition expressible in the (first-order) language of set theory and not containing parameters. (This example has been communicated to me by Dr W. Marek.)

In spite of this however, much can be said for admitting the axiom of choice. In several special cases it can be proved, e.g. when the set A is finite. Many important results cannot be proved without its help. For instance, we need this axiom in the proof that each set can be well ordered (*cf.* Section 3.2). The choice axiom is equivalent to many theorems which seem to be intuitively obvious. Thus although some consequences of the axiom are very strange, it is almost generally accepted. Most mathematicians like to visualize a set as a bunch of objects and maintain the existence of the choice set C by arguing that if several bunches of objects are given, we can select an element from each bunch and collect these elements together to form a set.

Before we formulate the last axiom (of replacement) we discuss a weaker axiom of comprehension (also called axiom of subsets). This was the axiom originally accepted by Zermelo. Only later Skolem and Fraenkel noticed that a stronger axiom was needed.

Zermelo's formulation of the comprehension axiom was the following: 'whenever the propositional function $E(x)$ is definite for all elements of a set M, M possesses a subset M_E containing as elements precisely those elements x of M for which $E(x)$ is true' (*cf.* Heijenoort, 1967, 262).

The obvious weakness in the formulation of this axiom is that it uses the concept of a 'definite propositional function' which must be made precise if one wants to avoid the recurrence of antinomies of the Richard type. Zermelo's own explanation of this concept was not very clear.

We know at present two ways which allow us to express precisely the axiom of comprehension. One of them proposed by Skolem (*cf.* Heijenoort, 1967, 290) will be presented below. The second method will be dealt with in the next section.

Skolem's idea was to specify the language of set theory and identify definite propositional functions with those which are expressible in this language. Thus instead of a single axiom of comprehension we obtain a scheme of axioms, each particular case of the scheme corresponding to a formula of the language.

The formulae of the language are defined by induction: we select a class of initial (or 'atomic') formulae and construct the compound ones by applying arbitrarily many times the operations of joining two formulae together by a logical connective and of prefixing a formula by a quantifier ranging over objects which are either sets or elements of sets. For the purpose of the general set theory it is sufficient to admit as atomic formulae the following ones: 'x is a set', 'x is an element of y', where letters 'x' and 'y' may be replaced by any other letters.

The axiom scheme of comprehension takes now the form:

'For every set A there is a set B such that an arbitrary object x is an element of B if and only if x is an element of A and $F(x)$'.

We obtain particular cases of the axiom of comprehension replacing in this scheme '$F(x)$' by any formula in which the variable 'B' does not occur.

We now come to the last axiom of the Zermelo-Fraenkel system, the so-called axiom of replacement. Speaking loosely, this axiom states that for an arbitrary operation defined on elements of a set, the images of all the elements of this set form again a set.

Again the concept of an operation requires clarification and we achieve this by allowing only operations defined in the language. Thus we assume the following scheme:

'If A is a set and for every element x of A there is exactly one object y such that $F(x,y)$, then there is a set B such that an arbitrary object y is an element of B if and only if $F(x,y)$ for some element x of A'.

We obtain particular cases of the axiom of replacement replacing in this scheme '$F(x,y)$' by any formula in which the variable 'B' does not occur.

In order to make the content of the scheme more accessible to the reader we notice that the assumption states the existence of an operation defined by the formula $F(x,y)$ for all elements of A: to each x in A corresponds exactly one y such that $F(x,y)$. The conclusion then says that there exists a set B whose elements are all the images of the elements of A under this operation.

The description of the axioms of Z–F is now complete and the axioms of comprehension and of replacement are precise. However, they are not single axioms but infinite collections of axioms determined by schemes.

We notice still that each particular case of the axiom (scheme) of comprehension can be derived from a suitable particular case of the axiom (scheme) of replacement so that the former scheme can be dispensed with. We preferred to keep this scheme, however, because it is much simpler than the axiom scheme of replacement and very often used in set-theoretic proofs.

Skolem's idea of a correct formulation of Z–F axioms is very neat because it reminds us that sets which we mostly use are defined by means of properties of their elements, and properties are expressed in a language. The drawback of his method is that we do not obtain a finite number of axioms but an infinite collection of axioms defined by two schemes.

Of all the methods for founding abstract set theory on a secure basis the system Z–F is most widely used and seems to approximate best the intuitive mathematical idea of sets. A group of French mathematicians who publish under a joint pseudonym 'Bourbaki' were right in calling a slight variant of Z–F 'a system of foundations of mathematics for working mathematicians' (*cf.* Bourbaki, 1949).

More references to sources quoted above can be found in Fraenkel (1956); this book contains a detailed exposition of topics dealt with in this and in the subsequent sections.

4.3 *Von Neumann-Bernays-Gödel axioms of set theory*

In this section, we describe briefly another method of making precise the axioms of comprehension and of replacement.

The basic idea was formulated by von Neumann (*cf.* Heijenoort, 1967, 393) who introduced the concept of an arbitrary operation as a new primitive concept of set theory and gave axioms which characterize it. His idea was taken up by Bernays and Gödel (*cf.* 1939); instead of operations these authors used a concept of a propositional function. It is customary to use the word 'class' instead of 'propositional function'. Thus the von Neumann-Bernays-Gödel set theory (abbreviated B–G) has now three primitive concepts: 'set', 'class' and 'elementhood'. All objects dealt with in the theory are divided into elements, i.e. objects which belong to at least one class, and non-elements (also called proper classes) which are not elements of any class. One assumes that each set is a class: more precisely a set is a class which is an element; proper classes are therefore not sets. A class f is an operation if its elements are exclusively ordered pairs and moreover if it contains no pairs with the same first member but with different second members: if (x,y') and (x,y'') are elements of f, then $y = y'$. The domain of f is defined as a class which consists of all elements x such that, for some element y, the ordered pair (x,y) is an element of f. The range of f is defined similarly: it is the class consisting of all elements y such that, for some element x, the ordered pair (x,y) is an element of f.

With these definitions we can express the axioms of comprehension and of replacement very briefly: the axiom of comprehension says that the intersection of a set and of a class is a set, whereas the axiom of replacement says that if the domain of an operation is a set, then so is its range.

However, we need still several axioms which allow us to prove the existence of various classes. They are called axioms of class formation. We describe them only briefly and do not formulate all of them. First, we assume the existence of two classes: V whose elements are all sets and E whose elements are all pairs (x,y) such that y is a set and x is an element of y. These classes correspond to the atomic formulae used in the method of Skolem. In the remaining axioms we assumed that certain operations corresponding to logical connectives and quantifiers performed on classes again yield classes. We also assume that two classes with the same elements are equal. The reader is referred to Fraenkel (1956) for a complete discussion of these axioms.

In most modern expositions one assumes that *all* elements are sets, but this assumption is not really necessary and is only made in order to simplify certain arguments.

The axiomatic system B–G has many advantages. Unlike Z–F it is axiomatized by means of finitely axioms. Moreover, the use of classes allows us to simplify our mode of speech; we can e.g. state and prove the theorem saying that the class of all sets is not a set and have thus a rational way of expressing a theorem which lies at the bottom of various antinomies. Proper classes would of course be counted by Cantor to 'inconsistent sets' (*cf.* Section 4.1). Thus the system B–G allows us to discuss some at least of these sets.

In spite of these advantages, we believe that it is the system Z–F rather than the B–G which occupies the central place in foundations of set theory. The new primitive concepts (that of a class or of an operation) play in B–G or in the original system of von Neumann a subordinate role. The sole purpose for which these concepts were introduced was to simplify the formulation of the axioms of replacement and comprehension of Z–F. This is witnessed by the rather artificial and complicated form of the axioms of class formation and was the reason why we omitted them above.

Let us finally note that the systems Z–F and B–G are related to each other so that the consistency of one of them implies the consistency of the other (see Fraenkel, 1956).

4.4 *Type theory*

More or less simultaneously with Zermelo, B. Russell formulated another system which allowed him to reconstruct the essential parts of the Cantorian set theory. This system, called the simple theory of types, is interesting because of its close connections with the conception of sets which we admit in everyday language. As the adjective 'simple' indicates, Russell also considered another theory of types (called the ramified theory of types) and oscillated for several years between these two theories as is evident from the introduction to the second edition of his (and Whitehead's) *Principia Mathematica* (1910).

According to the simple theory of types all objects are divided into types. Objects which are not sets have type 0, sets of these objects have type 1, sets consisting of sets of type 1 have type 2, etc. This hierarchy of sets is in complete agreement with our intuitive concepts of sets: we noticed already in Section 1.6 that we always distinguish between collections whose elements are objects and collections whose elements are themselves collections.

The theory of types was expressed by Russell in a very elaborate language in which variables were divided into types and could occur only in certain combinations. Thus antinomies were avoided because they simply could not be formulated in the language of type theory. The theory was based on axioms the most important of which bore close relation to the axiom of comprehension. Most of current mathematic can be expressed already in the theory of types, although not without a certain degree of awkwardness.

We want to discuss relations between the type theory and Z–F. We can easily show that the type theory is interpretable in Z–F. In order to achieve this we select an arbitrary set R_0 of objects which are not sets and define in Z–F an infinite sequence $R_0, R_1, R_2, \ldots$ such that R_{n+1} is the set of all the subsets of R_n. We can now define an interpretation of the type theory in Z–F: objects of type 0 are interpreted as elements of R_0, sets of type 1 as elements of R_1, sets of type 2 as elements of R_2 whose elements have type 1, etc. Sets obtained in this way are definable in Z–F in terms of

R_0. All axioms of the type theory become theorems of Z–F with the possible exception of the axiom of infinity which is satisfied if and only if the R_0 is infinite.

We see from this interpretation that Z–F is a much richer theory than the theory of types. While each set considered in the type theory must have a type, the theory Z–F does not exclude sets consisting of elements of various types. For instance R_3 contains sets some of whose elements have type 0 and some type 1. We say that such sets have mixed types.

The sequence of the sets R_n can be further extended: we denote the union of all the sets R_n by 'R_ω' and start again forming successive power sets: $R_{\omega+1}$, $R_{\omega+2}$, ... where each term consists of all the subsets of the previous one. This process can be extended further: for each well-ordering α we obtain a set R_α. Sets R_0, R_1, ... correspond to the case of well-orderings of a finite set, but if α is a well-ordering of an infinite set we obtain new sets whose types we call transfinite. The elements of R_α have, generally speaking, mixed types.

Assuming in Z–F some additional axioms which we shall not formulate here, one can prove that every set belongs to one of the sets R_α. Thus in this extended theory, one can prove that each set has a (in general mixed and transfinite) type. This shows that the theory Z–F while very different from the theory of types is in effect not so unrelated to this latter theory as might be thought at the beginning. It rather represents a far-reaching extension of the theory of types obtained by allowing sets of mixed types and extending the hierarchy of types far beyond the finite types.

4.5 *Other methods of avoiding antinomies*

In this section we mention briefly still two theories which, like Z–F, B–G and the type theory, attempt to salvage set theory from antinomies while preserving as many classical results as possible.

A. P. Morse (1965) and J. L. Kelley (1955) extended the system B–G by admitting that every formula defines a class consisting of all sets which satisfy this formula. In the Bernays-Gödel system the existence of this class can only be proved for formulae whose bound variables are restricted to sets (*cf.* Section 4.3).

W. V. Quine (1969) has published several versions of a completely different system (see esp. Chap. XIII). His conceptions deviate most from those of Z–F: e.g. one can prove in his theory that for every set A there is a set whose elements are all those sets which do not belong to A (!). Yet no antinomy has appeared in his system because of restrictions imposed on formulae which can be used to construct a set. Although they are efficient, these restrictions seem to lack sufficient intuitive justification, and it seems doubtful to the present author whether any part of Quine's theory will ever gain popularity among mathematicians.

5. INCOMPLETENESS OF SET THEORY

5.1 *Theory and metatheory*

Each mathematical theory is expressed in a language which must not be confused with the language in which we speak about the theory. In order to explain why this distinction is so important we return to antinomies and discuss once again the antinomy of Richard (see 4.1). The concept of definability used in the definition of a Richardian set is clearly a meta-theoretic one and we saw in Section 4.1 that the use of this concept in set theory results in a contradiction. Only the limitation imposed on the language of Z–F (Section 4.2) or of the theory of types eliminates contradictions from these theories.

Once a mathematical theory is formulated with a sufficient degree of precision we can ask (in the metatheory) various general questions concerning this theory. Thus we may ask: is the theory consistent? Is it consistent relative to another better known theory? Is the theory complete? Are its axioms independent?

5.2 *Problem of consistency*

Not very much can be said about this important problem. As is well known Hilbert reacted to the discovery of antinomies by initiating extensive metamathematical studies whose purpose was to show that he whole of mathematics (provided that it be correctly described, e.g. as an axiomatic system) is consistent. However, Gödel has shown (1931), see also (Heijenoort, 1967, 592) that every such proof must use means which go beyond the axioms whose consistency we want to prove. It follows thus from Gödel's result that no consistency proof for set theory exists which would use exclusively methods formalizable in this theory. Now set theory is such a strong system that practically all of the present day mathematics can be interpreted in it (*cf.* Section 3.2). These observations explain why no strictly mathematical consistency proof for set theory has been found. For the same reason there can be no proof of consistency relative to theories which can be interpreted in set theory, like e.g. arithmetic of integers or arithmetic of real numbers.

All mathematicians believe, however, that the system Z–F is consistent and they argue, not without good reason, that if there were contradictions in the system they would certainly have already been found. After all, the system has already existed for almost 60 years and was extensively studied by the best mathematicians of the present century.

5.3 *Incompleteness*

The general results of Gödel (1931) show that if Z–F is consistent, then it is incomplete and that the same is true for other axiomatic systems proposed for set theory. The disquieting fact is that in the case of Z–F as well as in other systems proposed as a possible foundation for set theory it is rather easy to formulate problems which cannot be decided on the basis of the axioms. Roughly speaking, all problems which have not been easily solved within a short time after being formulated turned out to be undecidable. We shall describe below some undecidable problems.

5.4 *Large cardinals*

The axiom of infinity secures the existence of at least one infinite set; using the power set axiom and the axiom of unions we can obtain from this set other sets of surprisingly high cardinalities.

Now we ask about properties of these cardinals. Let us call a cardinal accessible if it is the cardinal of a set R_α and is either the power set of a preceding R_β or is representable as a union of a family of sets A whose cardinality is smaller than R_α and all whose elements have the cardinality smaller than R_α. The idea behind this definition is that a set R_β with an accessible cardinality can be obtained from sets of smaller cardinalities by the use of two operations: forming unions and sets of subsets. The question whether there exist inaccessible cardinals has proved to be undecidable in Z–F. More exactly if Z–F is consistent, then it remains so after adjunction of an axiom stating that all cardinals are accessible. The consistency of an axiom stating that there are inaccessible cardinals cannot be proved but it seems extremely unlikely that this axiom would be inconsistent with Z–F.

Investigation of inaccessible cardinals was started already in 1912 by Mahlo (1912–1913). The present state of the theory of these cardinals is due mostly to Tarski (1963–1964 and the extensive literature quoted therein). We cannot discuss this highly technical subject here and remark only that in the course of these studies a great many axioms were proposed which were all called axioms of infinity because they postulate the existence of extremely high cardinalities. All these axioms are independent of Z–F and probably consistent with Z–F. They are interrelated to each other sometimes in a very complicated way and much work was done in order to establish these relations and to study the effects which the admission of some axioms of infinity would have on the theory of smaller cardinals. Set-theorists do not know at present whether they should admit or reject these axioms.

5.5 *The continuum hypothesis*

This hypothesis states that the answer to the continuum problem which we formulated in Section 3.2 is affirmative. The generalized continuum hypothesis states likewise that the answer to the generalized continuum problem is affirmative. Both these hypotheses belong to a large family of sentences which neither can be proved nor refuted in Z–F. In addition, it has been shown that the strengthening of Z–F by the axioms of infinity securing the existence of inaccessible cardinals does not change the situation. In 1939, Gödel (see also Section 6.2) showed that if Z–F is consistent, then it remains so if we add to it the generalized continuum hypothesis. Gödel's discovery represented the first great breakthrough in the meta-mathematical study of set theory. Another such breakthrough is due to Cohen (1966) who proved in 1964 that continuum hypothesis is independent of Z–F. He achieved this remarkable result by showing that if Z–F is consistent, then there exists a model of Z–F in which there are sets whose cardinalities (calculated in the model) are intermediate between the cardinality of integers and that of reals, i.e. are greater than the former and smaller than the latter. What is still more striking is that Cohen showed that there are many such models. In some of them there is just one intermediate cardinality, in others two or three, or four, etc., still in others there are infinitely many such cardinalities. Thus Cohen showed that axioms of Z–F give us almost no information about the cardinality of the set of reals. We know that this cardinality is different from that of the integers and we also know that the set of reals is not the union of a sequence of sets with increasing cardinalities. But no hypothesis consistent with these two result contradicts the axioms (Solovay, 1965). Similar phenomena are valid for the generalized continuum hypothesis. (See Rosser (1969) and references made there to the work of Easton.)

These results show that, contrary to earlier expectations, Z–F is an utterly incomplete system. How its axioms should be strengthened in order to decide the continuum hypothesis is again an open problem.

5.6 *Other undecidable problems; independence of axioms*

There are many other problems of set theory which proved to be undecidable in Z–F. They are very technical and it would not be possible to present them here. Methods of proving undecidability can also be applied to establish the mutual independence of various axioms. Thus Cohen (see 1966) was able to solve completely the vexing problem of the independence of the axiom of choice, and many more refined problems concerning the mutual dependence of several consequences of this axiom were solved subsequently by him and his followers.

6. OTHER TRENDS IN FOUNDATIONS OF SET-THEORY

6.1 *Philosophical importance of the independence results*

Do the undecidability results described in the previous section prove that there is anything wrong with abstract set theory? The problem is an old one and was discussed long before the recent undecidability results were strictly established. Since the early twenties, nobody has really believed that the continuum hypothesis can be solved on the basis of Z–F and there were distinguished mathematicians like e.g. Lusin (1927) who from the start believed that even very strange hypotheses concerning the cardinalities of the continuum are compatible with Z–F.

The general results of Gödel (1931) have shown that no axiomatic theory containing arithmetic can be complete. Thus the mere incompleteness of Z–F is not an alarming symptom by itself. What is disturbing is our ignorance of where to look for additional information which would permit us to solve problems which seem very simple and natural but which are nevertheless left open by the axioms of Z–F. We come here very close to fundamental problems of the philosophy of mathematics whose basic question is: what is mathematics about? A formalist would say that it is about nothing; that it is just a game played with arbitrarily selected axioms and rules of proof. The incompleteness of Z–F is thus of no concern for a formalist. Platonists on the contrary believe in the 'objective existence' of mathematical objects. A set-theoretical Platonist believes therefore that we should continue to think more about sets and experiment with them until we finally discover new axioms which, added to Z–F, will permit us to solve all outstanding problems (*cf.* Gödel, 1947).

Whatever the final outcome of the fight between these two opposing trends will be, it is obvious that we should concentrate on the study of concepts which seem perfectly clear and perspicuous to us. In Cantor's time the concept of an arbitrary set seemed to be a very clear concept but the antinomies proved that this was not so. Today, this concept has been replaced by that of an arbitrary subset of a given set. In addition, the belief that all subsets of a given set form a set is almost universally accepted. However, it is by no means true that these views are shared by all mathematicians. Even Gödel himself, who as the quotation above indicates should be counted among the Platonists, has once expressed the view that the concept of an arbitrary subset of a given set is in need of clarification (*cf.* Gödel, 1951).

The present writer believes (although he cannot present convincing evidence to support this view) that it is in this direction where the future of set theory lies.

6.2 *Finitism and nominalism*

One of the general mathematical concepts which is accepted without hesitation by all mathematicians is that of the repetition of one and the same operation an arbitrary number of times. It is this concept which lies at the bottom of the arithmetic of integers and also of the theory of computations.

The most radical trend in the foundation of mathematics, which is represented by a Russian school under the leadership of Markov and

Shanin (*cf.* 1958), wants to retain in mathematics exclusively computable sequences $a(0)$, $a(1)$, ... of integers and such other concepts as are immediately reducible to them. All other concepts are to be simply rejected. Let us remind briefly what computable sequences are in order to see how much we lose by adhering to this view.

A sequence $a(0)$, $a(1)$, ... of integers is said to be computable if for each integer n the term $a(n)$ can be computed in accordance with a finite set of absolutely explicit and mechanical instructions requiring no mathematical ingenuity for their application. We can also say that a sequence is computable if its terms can be calculated on a machine programmed with certain finite and explicit sets of instructions and capable of performing certain simple operations such as printing or erasing symbols on an arbitrary long tape, or shifting the tape in accordance with the given instructions. Such machines are called 'Turing machines' (*cf.* Davis, 1958).

The family of computable sequences is thus very small when we compare it with the family of sets, sequences and functions admissible in the classical theory. Of course, most of the results of abstract set theory would be irreparably lost if the approach of this radical school was generally adopted.

Less radical proposals were made by mathematicians and philosophers who insist that sets considered in mathematics should correspond to properties expressible in a language. This is not an unreasonable point of view: most sets one first considered in mathematics and all collections accepted in everyday language are defined either by means of properties of their elements or by the use of the principle of abstraction applied to a definable equivalence relation.

Many ways were proposed in the past of how to limit the concept of a set so as to deal only with sets which are defined in one or other sense of the word. We can subsume them all under the name 'nominalistic trends'.

The earliest attempt in this direction was represented by Russell's ramified theory of types (*cf.* 1910). In this theory sets are not only divided into types but each type is further divided into orders. The order of a set is determined by the form of its definition.

Variables of the language used to express the ramified theory of types are also divided into types and orders. A set of type t is counted to the order n if and only if it can be defined by means of a formula which satisfies the following two requirements: 1) it contains no variables whose types are either of a type higher than t or of the type t but of an order higher than n; 2) it contains no bound variables of type t and of order n. These formal requirements correspond to the famous 'vicious circle principle' by means of which Russell wanted to eliminate all antinomies. The principle says that 'no totality can be defined in terms of totalities to which it belongs'. Notice that according to Russell, each set of type t and order n is involved in the construction of each set of a type higher than t and also of each set of type t and order higher than n. Also this set belongs to the range of quantifiers which bound variables of type t and order n. We thus see that the limitations imposed on formulae which define sets of type t and order n were so selected that the vicious circle principle can not be violated in the ramified theory of types.

Extensions of the ramified theory of types to include certain transfinite types were proposed by Wang (see Fraenkel (1956) for a description of his theory).

Also the concept of a constructable set which Gödel invented (1939 and 1951) in order to prove the consistency of the continuum hypothesis was obtained by extending the concept of sets defined in the ramified theory of types.

However, Gödel allowed arbitrary well-orderings to occur as types and orders, and so his constructable sets do not satisfy the strong requirements of nominalism which insist that all sets have to be defined by formulae. It is this non-nominalistic 'admixture' which is responsible for the fact that all axioms of Z–F are true of constructable sets. On the other hand, the fact that many set-theoretical problems (like the general continuum hypothesis and the Souslin problem) become solvable in the domain of constructable sets is due to the fact that these sets, while not defined in the absolute sense of the word, are definable by induction by means of well-orderings about which we know much more than about arbitrary sets.

The axiom stating that all sets are constructable was once, perhaps not too seriously, proposed by Gödel (1939) but rejected by him as 'false' (1947). Yet the axiom is consistent relative to Z–F (*cf.* 1939 and 1951).

We should still mention calculi invented by Lorenzen (*cf.* Fraenkel, 1956 for their description) which also represent an increasing hierarchy of systems conforming to the nominalistic thesis.

At the other extreme we find proposals to replace the ramified hierarchy by a more narrow family of sets. Thus e.g. Weyl in his influential book (1921) argued that only sets of order 0 should be admitted and the idea of his 'predicative' analysis based on the notion of sets of order 0 was taken up by Grzegorczyk (1954), Kreisel (1960) and others.

The limitations imposed on the concept of a set by all the programs enumerated above go very far indeed. They automatically exclude sets defined by a chance event (e.g. by repeated tosses of a coin) although such an idea is very clear and should not be abandoned without serious reasons. Besides classical mathematics only the intuitionistic mathematics of Brouwer is sufficiently rich to admit this concept. On the other hand, Brouwer's ideas on logic and set theory are so radically different from the usual ones that one can wonder whether even modest parts of Cantorian set theory can be reconstructed in intuitionistic mathematics (see e.g. Fraenkel (1956) for a description of Brouwer's ideas).

CONCLUSION

Let us briefly summarize our discussion of sets and their theory. Sets or whatever other name we give them in everyday language are very useful in describing various situations of life. We use them because we possess a capacity to look at various separate individuals as if they formed together a new object of a higher type.

The concept of sets was taken over by mathematicians who used it to organize and systematize the basic concepts of their field. During this process they considerably extended the concept of sets to include infinite sets and assumed, first subconsciously and later consciously, certain principles of construction of new sets from other sets. The free use of sets in mathematical constructions brought about the creation of new mathematical theories which were more abstract and more general than the ones previously cultivated. The new theories allowed the mathematicians to introduce new concepts which proved useful not only in pure but also in applied mathematics. In addition, studies on foundations of set theory proved to be extremely fruitful: they prompted the development of logic, showed the necessity of a correct use of language and of distinguishing language from meta-language. The appearance of set-theoretical antinomies and the apparent impossibility of solving many simple questions concerning sets on the basis of axioms of set theory raise doubts whether in spite of the tremendous successes of the set-theoretic approach to mathematics the very concept of set is really as clear and perspicuous as is generally believed. Nevertheless, abstract set theory is being constantly developed and the objects of set-theoretical studies become more and more abstract.

The saying of A. N. Whitehead (1933) can very appropriately be applied to set theory – it is like Ophelia: very beautiful, but a little mad.

REFERENCES

BECKER, O., (1964) *Grundlagen der Mathematik in geschichtlicher Entwicklung*, 2nd edition, Freiburg-Munich.

BOLZANO, B., (1851) *Paradoxien des Unendlichen*, Prague.

BOURBAKI, N., (1949) 'Foundations of mathematics for the working mathematician', in *The Journal of Symbolic Logic, 14*, 1–8.

CANTOR, G., (1932) *Gesammelte Abhandlungen mathematischen und philosophischen Inhalts* (edited by E. Zermelo), Berlin.

COHEN, P., (1966) *Set Theory and the Continuum Hypothesis*, New York-Amsterdam.

DAVIS, M., (1958) *Computability and Unsolvability*, New York.

FRAENKEL, A., (1922) 'Zu den Grundlagen der Cantor-Zermeloschen Mengenlehre', in *Mathematische Annalen, 86*, 230–237.

FRAENKEL, A., (1953) *Abstract Set Theory*, Amsterdam.

FRAENKEL, A. and BAR-HILLEL, Y., (1956) *Foundations of Set Theory*, Amsterdam.

FREGE, G., (1884) *Die Grundlagen der Arithmetik. Eine logischmathematische Untersuchung über den Begriff der Zahl*, Breslau (English translation by L. Austin: *The Foundation of Arithmetic*, 2nd edition, New York, 1960).

FREGE, G., (1893–1903) *Grundgesetze der Arithmetik, begriffschriftlich abgeleitet*, vol. I and II, Jena.

GÖDEL, K., (1931) 'Über formal unentscheidbare Sätze der Principia Mathematica und verwandter System I', *Monatshefte für Mathematik und Physik, 37*, 173–198.

GÖDEL, K., (1939) 'Consistency proof for the generalized continuum hypothesis', *Proceedings of the National Academy of Sciences of the U.S.A., 25*, 220–224.

GÖDEL, K., (1951) *The Consistency of the Axiom of Choice and of the Generalized Continuum Hypothesis with the Axioms of Set Theory*, 2nd edition, Princeton.

GÖDEL, K., (1947) 'What is Cantor continuum problem?', *Amer. Math. Monthly, 54*, 515–525.

GOODMAN, N., (1951) *The Structure of Appearance*, Cambridge (Mass.).

GRZEGORCZYK, A., (1954) 'Elementarily definable analysis', *Fundamenta Mathematicae, 41*, 311–338.

HEIJENOORT, J. VAN, (1967) *From Frege to Gödel. A Source Book in Mathematical Logic 1879–1931*, Cambridge (Mass.).

KELLEY, J. L., (1955) *General topology*, New York.

KREISEL, G., (1960) 'La prédicativité', *Bulletin de la Société Mathématique de France, 88,* 371–391.

LUSCHEI, E. C., (1962) *The Logical System of Leśniewski,* Amsterdam.

LUSIN, N., (1927) 'Sur les ensembles analytiques', *Fundamenta Mathematicae, 10,* 1–95.

MAHLO, P., (1912–1913) 'Zur Theorie und Anwendung der ρ-Zahlen', *Berichte über die Verhandlungen der Sächsischen Akademie der Wissenschaften zu Leipzig* (math.-phys. Kl.), *64* (1912), 108–112, and *65* (1912–1913), 268–282.

MORSE, A. P., (1965) *A Theory of Sets,* New York-London.

NEUMANN, J. VON and MORGENSTERN, O., (1947) *Theory of Games and Economic Behavior,* 2nd edition, Princeton (N.J.), Princeton Univ. Press.

PEANO, G., (1889) *Arithmetices principia, novo methodo exposita,* Turin (*cf.* G. Peano, *Opere scelte,* Roma, 1958 and English translation in Heijenoort, 1967).

POLYA, G., (1954) *Induction and Analogy in Mathematics,* Vol. 1, Oxford.

QUINE, W. V., (1969) *Set Theory and its Logic,* 2nd edition, Cambridge (Mass.).

ROSSER, J. B., (1969) *Independence Proofs,* New York.

RUSSELL, B., (1910) See Whitehead and Russell (1910).

SHANIN, N. A. (ed.) (1958) 'Problemy konstruktivnogo napravlenya v mathematike Sbornik rabot', *Trudy Matematičeskogo Instituta im. V. Steklova, 52,* Izd. Ak. Nauk SSSR, Moscow-Leningrad.

SOLOVAY, R., (1965) $2 \aleph$ *can be anything it ought to be. The theory of models* (edited by J. W. Addison), Amsterdam, p. 435.

TARSKI, A. and KEISLER, J. H., (1963–1964) 'From accessible to inaccessible numbers', *Fundamenta Mathematicae, 53,* 268–282.

WEYL, H., (1921) *Das Kontinuum,* Leipzig.

WHITEHEAD, A. N., (1933) *Adventure of Ideas,* New York, Macmillan.

WHITEHEAD, A. N. and RUSSELL, B., (1910) *Principia Mathematica I,* Cambridge; 2nd edition: Cambridge 1925.

WIGGINS, D., (1967) *Identity and Spatio-temporal Continuity,* Oxford.

2 The concept of structure

JEAN PIAGET

INTRODUCTION

In cognition, one of the most spontaneous tendencies is to proceed from the simple to the complex; in principle this is legitimate, provided we agree on what we mean by simplicity – a highly relative concept. Difficulties arise from the fact that there are two kinds of simplicity – objective simplicity (inherent in the objects) and subjective simplicity (i.e. deriving from our own familiar actions). An example of objective simplicity is simple addition – adding one –, which allows us to move from 1 to $1 + 1 = 2$, from 2 to $2 + 1 = 3$, and so on. On the other hand, it would be a matter of subjective simplicity, when the subject, accustomed to fashioning a whole by the assembly of antecedent parts, generalizes this attitude to a case where he is called upon to interpret an organized totality; in this instance, a kind of *a priori* or preconceived idea leads him to begin by looking for the elements of which the totality might be composed, treating it as a simple combination of these elements.

Now, it is at once apparent that although the $+ 1$ operation is elementary, it really expresses a law of formation: the law expressed by H. Poincaré by the symbol $n + 1$, which governs the entire class of natural numbers (or of all whole numbers if, in addition, $+ 1$ is inverted into $- 1$); in this case the shift from the simple to the complex does not destroy the latter's properties and the elementary operation is in no way at odds with the building of a 'structure' in the sense in which we shall shortly define it. On the other hand, when psychologists in the last century (and far on into the present century) originally regarded a 'perception' (a complex reality such as the immediate apprehension of an object, a geometrical figure, a face, etc.) as having to be the product of a set of initial 'sensations' which were simply associated, or again, when linguists before Ferdinand de Saussure saw language primarily as an assemblage of words, and thought that they had exhausted the tasks of linguistics once they had traced the history of each one, in both cases they proceeded uncritically from the simple to the complex, in virtue of a tendency more subjective than objectively substantiated, which impelled them to begin by breaking down the wholes they were studying into individual elements, more or less real (the words), or even partly artificial (the 'sensations' considered as psychological rather than essentially physiological units).

A sort of reversal of this natural tendency of the intellect was, therefore, needed in order to think that a whole might have laws of its own as a totality; and that the method that had at first seemed the only one possible, because it started from pre-existing elements, in fact tended to conceal these laws of totalities or to distort them rather seriously. Structuralism, whose object is to get at precisely these laws of systems, emerged only belatedly, then, in the development of science. For example, geometry, the source, since the end of the nineteenth century, of such splendid examples of structuralist analysis, remained curiously opaque to this line of thought among the Greeks: Euclid's *Elements* never even got to establishing interconfigurational relationships ('space' and its co-ordinates, in contradistinction to the internal properties of the configurations) and the theorems did not approach the question of the transformation group which they implicitly used.

In actual fact, if we take 'structuralism' in its strict sense, without extending it to include all the speculations about forms in the static sense (from Aristotle onwards), or about the organism as a higher unit, animated by a 'vital force', etc., a structuralist method only emerged in science with Galois's discovery of the 'group' structure in algebraic transformations. Yet this first model already presents the essential characteristics which are to be found in the various structuralist methodologies proper to the different scientific disciplines (disregarding, of course, the abuses to which this term has given rise and which are disquietingly rampant in certain contemporary fads). We may, therefore, take Galois's 'group' structure as our starting-point in setting out to define structures.

1. GENERAL FEATURES OF STRUCTURES

1.1 The first property of a structure is that it constitutes a totality, with laws of its own; that is, it has laws as a system, independently of the particular characteristics of its elements. In the case of a group these properties are the following:

a) The introduction of an operation combinable with itself, that we shall call T. To take our earlier example of objective simplicity, this will be the operation $+n$ which figures in the additive group of whole numbers, and enables any integer to be added to any other.

b) To each operation T there corresponds an inverse T^{-1} which in this specific case will be the subtraction $-n$.

c) The product of an operation T and of its inverse T^{-1} is a neutral element 0, whose combination with others does not modify them: $n + 0 = n$ (identical operation).

d) The combinations are associative: $(l + m) + n = l + (m + n)$.

These four properties thus characterize the whole system, considered as a totality, in contradistinction to the particular properties of the elements (odd or even numbers, numbers divisible by 3, etc.). In other structures than the group, the properties of the totality will obviously be different, but there always are such properties, distinct from the properties of the elements.

1.2 The second general characteristic of a structure is that these laws of the totality operate on transformations, in the broadest sense, and not on static characteristics. In other words, the structure consists of a system of operations whose combinations transform one term into another. In our earlier additive group example, the fact of adding or subtracting one number to or from another leads to a third number (except as regards $+ 0$), etc. This characteristic of transformation is particularly striking in the case of the 'fundamental groups' of the various types of geometry, formerly considered models of purely descriptive sciences, dealing only with 'forms' or static figures. To begin with, the constituent group of Euclidian geometry is the transformation group which allows the position of an element to be changed, without changing its form or size. If we vary distances, so that only angles, parallel lines and straight lines remain unchanged, we get the group of transformations of similitude. If we further vary angles, we get the affine transformations group. By modifying parallel lines in addition we get the projective groups and, if we do not retain even straight lines, we come to the group of topological equivalents or homeomorphisms. Each of these groups being a subgroup of the succeeding group, with the possibility of passing from one to the other, we end up with a general system of transformations which has profoundly renovated geometrical studies.

1.3   A third characteristic of structures is less frequently brought to notice, at least with the vocabulary we shall be adopting. This is their self-regulatory property, that is: the internal combinations of the structure never give products outside the structure (a whole number added to another always gives a whole number again), while constantly enriching it, and never involve any extraneous element. In the case of operational structures this self-regulatory property goes without saying and is simply one with the laws of combination. When we come to biological, psychological or social structures, we shall find self-regulation by a whole range of homeostatic mechanisms. But it is possible to conceive of all the transitions from cybernetic loop structures, with regulation proceeding from the result of the actions, to operational systems where pre-corrections and the combination of anticipations and retroactions constitute 'perfect regulations'. The psychogenetic development of the cognitive functions enables us to witness in a concrete form this passage from regulation to operation.

Let us further note wherein this third characteristic of structure would seem to be responsible for the notion's success: whether we take the sort of constructive autonomy that its self-regulatory property gives to a formal structure, or whether we take the organisation inherent in the self-regulating elements of a living system, we arrive in either case at an explanatory principle far superior to the hypothesis of linkages established after the fact between pre-existing elements.

2. MATHEMATICAL STRUCTURES

2.1   The fecundity of mathematics comes from its unlimited power of constructing operations upon other operations and, since any one operation can never be isolated, but always ties in with the others, mathematics can accordingly be looked on as a general theory of structures. Given two sets E and F, it is possible first of all, to 'apply' an x in E on to one (and only one) y in F, resulting in a functional operation that may be one-to-one (if there is only one x) or many-to-one (if there are several x). The 'product' $E \times F$ of the two sets can be got; or alternatively their 'quotient-set', by a partition based on an equivalence relation (e.g. the set 'mankind' divided by the relation 'co-citizens' gives the set 'nations'). Or again, the 'set of subsets' may be extracted from any set by a combinatorial; or, by repeating operations, an overall scale on the base $E-F$ may be obtained. Thus, it is possible to form 'structures', regardless of the nature of the basic sets, by identifying common properties through the operations carried out on these sets, and the various structures can finally be compared. This point marks the start of the unrestrictedly flexible range of 'morphisms'. In particular, there will be said to be isomorphism between two structures where there is one-to-one correspondence both between their elements and between their relations (including directions). Likewise we shall hear of univalent if not multivalent theories linking isomorphic structures.

The Bourbaki school has distinguished itself in this re-thinking of mathematics as a theory of structures, in seeking, in the relations between the structures, to arrive at sorts of formal filiations which, through successive constructions, can comprehend the entire field of mathematics. The principle of this is to begin by getting back, by the determination of the common properties (isomorphisms), to a minimal number of parent structures not reducible to each other but able, by their combinations, to engender all other structures. The problem is then to determine, as though one were dealing with the growth or the evolution of living organisms, the differentiation and co-ordination processes giving rise to these derivative and more particularized structures. The differentiation takes the form of complicating one of the fundamental structures by introducing successive requirements or restrictive axioms, thus defining the possible substructures (by a process analogous to that described in Section 1.2 for the fundamental groups of the various geometries); or, alternatively of reducing a 'strong' structure to 'weaker' structures (e.g. a semi-group, which would be associative, but would lack a neutral element). Co-ordination on the other hand takes the form of imposing two structures at a time on a single set of elements, as, for instance, for algebraic topology.

This vast enterprise was crowned with complete success and has profoundly altered our overall vision of mathematics, in the sense that the multiplicity of sectors or branches hitherto distinguished solely by their content has been superseded by a single edifice, in which everything is comprehended but whose 'architecture' has become purely structural, i.e.

hinging solely on the forms, without regard to the nature of the elements and hence to the contents, with their diversifications and artificial distributions. In this way the authors effect an admirable generalization of the structuralization which had already gained acceptance in certain domains during the nineteenth century, following the discovery of the group structure, but for which it has thus become possible to adduce still other structures in support.

The fundamental structures arrived at by the initial isomorphism-based reduction process turned out, in fact, to be three in number, not on the grounds of *a priori* necessity, but on the grounds of an inductively oriented inventory. The first consists of the 'algebraic structures', whose prototype is the group, and whose distinctive characteristic is that they allow of reversibility through inversion or negation: $T.T^{-1} = 0$. The second fundamental structure is the 'order' structure, whose prototype is the 'lattice', bearing on the succeeding-preceding relations of the elements, any two of which always have a least 'upper bound' (the least of the succeeding elements or *supremum*) and a greatest 'lower bound' (the highest of the preceding elements or *infimum*). Earlier conjectured by Dedekind, this structure was studied mainly by Birkhoff, and its universality is comparable to that of the group. It is this structure, for example, that characterizes the relations operative in the 'sets of sub-sets' (or simplexes) discussed in the early part of this section. As in all systems of relations, its reversibility is based upon reciprocity, the law of duality of lattices transforming '$A.B$ precedes $A+B$' into '$A+B$ succeeds $A.B$' by permutation of the (.) and (+) and of the relations 'preceding' and 'succeeding'. Lastly, the third type of fundamental structure is topological in nature, based on the notions of neighbourhood, continuity and limit.

2.2 To arrive at the epistemological significance of the notion of structure in mathematics, the first thing is to ask oneself if these three fundamental structures, whose differentiations and co-ordinations can then produce all the other structures by a quasi-organic process, are or are not 'natural', in the sense in which we speak for example of 'natural numbers' to indicate that they had already been worked out by pre-scientific thought. Of course, the use of structures by mathematicians involves their formalization, and the axiomatic method employed in so doing does not help us answer the question. It is, however, important to note that this kind of method is in no way incompatible with the existence of 'intuitive' correspondents attesting the entrenchment of the fundamental structures in the mechanisms of the intelligence itself, though in an obviously elementary, if not to say rudimentary, form.

In fact, if we study the spontaneous development of the first logical and mathematical operations in the child, we notice that they are organized from the start in structures such as classifications, seriations, correlations, etc. which certainly are not passed down by adult teaching (as their appreciable limitations are enough to show). (This research was carried out before people had turned, as is now the fashion, to trying to teach Cantor in infant schools, incidentally without the least suspicion of what the child can do on his own and in his own language.) Now an examination of these 'natural' structures shows right away that they belong to three general forms. The first is founded on reversibility through inversion and covers the 'operational groupings'* by formation of classes: $A - A = 0$, etc. The second characterizes the relationship groupings and is founded on reversibility through reciprocity. The third concerns partitions or envelopings bearing upon the continuum and bringing in the notions of neighbourhood and separation, interior or exterior, boundaries, etc. Here, therefore, there is an evident kinship with the three fundamental structures; and comparison remains possible when, at later stages of the subject's development, we find him becoming able to co-ordinate the inversions N and reciprocals R, implicitly using for the purpose a quaternion or Klein group, such that, for example, an implication (which we can write $p \supset q = I$) will include its inverse ($N = p.\bar{q}$), its reciprocal ($R = q \supset p$) and its correlative ($C = \bar{p}.q$), leading to the commutative compositions $NR = C$, $NC = R$, $RC = N$ and $NRC = I$.

If the 'structures' thus have natural roots, then this means that, starting from these elementary forms, the intellect, through a combination of 'reflection-by-abstraction' and of new operations carried out *upon* the previous ones, is able to embark on an unbroken sequence of constructions. Structuralism is thus by no means incompatible with mathematical constructionism, but, on the contrary, implies it. A further indication of this is provided by the fact that, within the Bourbaki school itself, there is a strengthening tendency today to make preponderant use of the 'category' structure described by McLane and Eilenberg, which

---

* For the notion of a 'grouping', the interest of which is genetic rather than formal, see section 4.

bears upon classes of objects plus their functions and morphisms. This structure is built *upon* the very operations that gave rise to the foregoing structures, hence by 'reflection-by-abstraction' and by reorganization on a higher plane (it may, incidentally, be noted that 'categories' are represented in trivial natural forms and at a level earlier than the operational constructions, in the course of the development of the intelligence).

A third indicator of this constructionism inherent in structuralism and extending the 'natural' constructions of the human intellect is that arising from Gödel's well known theorem of the limits of formalization. First let us simply note that formalization *has* limits, and that outside these limits there are operational constructions in action which are not (or not yet) formalized, thus implying some kind of relationship with natural structures. Secondly, if, for the complete formalization of a structure (that is, for everything in it to become 'decidable'), another 'stronger' structure is required, this gradation in the 'strength' of the systems implies unlimited construction. Thirdly, Feferman and Schütte have recently succeeded in demonstrating the existence, within transfinite sets, of a number 'Kappa' (Ko) which marks the limit of 'predicativity'. Beyond this limit there is therefore no further 'effective' constructivity, that is, constructions based on a combinatorial. On the other hand, new possibilities may then be opened by means of what must be called 'relative' recursivity and decidability. Suppose we have a class So in which everything is decidable, excepting a non-decidable proposition $ND1$. If, for reasons exterior to the system, we arrive, by hypothesis, at the belief that it is true (or false), we get the set $S1$ (= So + $ND1$), which is 'relatively decidable' in relation to $ND1$. Suppose we then have a second undecidable proposition $ND2$; if we can treat this in the same way, we then get the set $S2$ (= $S1$ + $ND2$) which is 'relatively decidable' in relation to $ND2$, and so on, by transfinite repetition. We thus get a hierarchy of 'degrees of solubility', in which each stage is increasingly strongly irreducible to that preceding it. It may, therefore, be concluded that the set of possibles is not a closed set and that each discovery (bearing in this instance upon the NDs) 'opens' new possibilities, which further demonstrates the union between structuralism and constructionism taken in the epistemological sense: i.e., operational constructions conceived as constitutive, and not merely as conditions of accession.

3. PHYSICAL AND BIOLOGICAL STRUCTURES

3.1 There are still more compelling reasons for seeking a relationship between logico-mathematical structures and the systems of transformations at work in the knowing subject, and even partly in objects. Namely, the existence of physical structures, and the question of their relations with those of the physicist-subject's structures; and the existence of biological structures which might even be considered the source of a subject's own structures, in his psychological functioning.

The physicist's work long consisted essentially in seeking laws, by 'applying' logico-mathematical operations to objects, and thus determining functional equations which express the dependence between measurable variables. However, partly because of the increasing difficulties of measurement on the different scales involved, and partly due to the overpowering need to understand and explain, rather than simply to note and predict phenomena, physics has turned increasingly to the elaboration of models, whose deductive character satisfies the intellect, but which are also and always expected to be 'attributable' to the objects themselves. But the construction of models leads to the discovery of structures, and contemporary physicists are getting to the point of seeking the structure before they have even got the measurements.

Now the structures thus brought to light in physical phenomena are the same in part as those which the mathematicians have mastered, and this raises the two related problems of the adequation of mathematics to material reality on the one hand and of the degree of objectivity or subjectivy of the structures thus attributed to the real on the other. In a broad sense, physical reality is a vast hierarchy of nested structures, on scales ranging from the most minutely nuclear to the most sweepingly cosmological, and, on all these scales, the experimental results are mathematizable to a point where a great many of them can be reconstructed deductively by theoretical models appreciably surpassing the intuitive representations in finesse and power. However, as a result of the twin facts of the irreversibility of time and the essential rôle of probability considerations – which partly amount to the same thing in fact – the mathematization is not necessarily a matter simply of reducing the models to the major structures discussed in Section 2. This makes it all the more striking how relatively frequently the latter do enter the picture: the group structures in particular occur with surprising persistence at all orders of magnitude, from microphysics to relativity theories, achieving a remarkably accurate correspondence with certain transformations of the real.

This being the case, should we therefore assume that the 'group' appertains to the objects, expressing their properties independently of us, or on the contrary should it be viewed simply as a superior instrument of representation, or again (an intermediate possibility) as translating the experimental actions that we perform on the objects and the co-ordinations between observers tied to different systems of reference? In fact, these three eventualities are all realized, varying with the situation; and the point of interest is precisely the bond which links them, deriving from the nature of causal explanation.

In effect, to the extent that physics thinking seeks the reason for the laws observed, it is obliged to go beyond the frontiers of the observable since its immediate experience embraces only movements or changes of state, whereas the problem of explanation boils down to arriving at necessary links between relations observed. However, any 'reading' of the facts itself presupposes the use of operational recording instruments (instruments in the double sense of logico-mathematical operations and material manipulations, with all the transitional stages possible between the two); when it comes to combining the established data into a system that provides an explanation of them, the solution can only consist in co-ordinating the laws and attempting to understand how the objects give rise to these regularities; but since the latter are inseparable from the operations whereby they may be determined, it is self-evident that the system being sought will consist first and foremost in a co-ordination of these operations, that is, in a structure whose transformations are reckoned to express the actions of the objects themselves. In other words, the transition from law-seeking to cause-seeking will consist in replacing operations which are simply 'applied' to objects by operations which can be 'attributed' to the objects, that is, by the same operations, reinforced by a system of transformations. All the psychogenetic research on the development of the notion of causability has demonstrated this rôle of operational transformations attributed to the real as soon as they are framed by the subject: transitivity in the case of transmissions, additive compositions, multiplicative compositions (proportions and distributivity), reciprocities (actions and reactions), etc.

We thus see that the group structure can indeed be regarded alternately as a property of the objects (when they lend themselves to it), of the experimental manipulations, or of the subject alone limiting himself in this case to anticipatory applications. As regards the more general problem of the adequation of mathematics to the real, a key is no doubt to be found in the analysis of biological structures.

3.2 A living organism comprises laws of a totality, a complex of continuing transformations and systems of self-regulation. It is thus unquestionably a 'structure', in the sense of the definition in Section 1, but one whose secrets are unfortunately still far from entirely revealed. Were they all revealed, that structure or those structures would present the considerable interest of having some of the characteristics of physico-chemical mechanisms while at the same time being at the origin of the structures of behaviour and of cognitive functions; since the organism is thus both an 'object' and the starting point of what constitutes the subject, it is probably in this union that we are likely to find the answer to the problem just posed, of the harmony, not pre-established but intrinsically established, between mathematical and physical structures.

In the meanwhile, the known data of biology already offer some lessons which are highly instructive on the general theory of structures. The first is the manner in which, at all levels of the organism, what might have seemed to be made up of aggregates (with simple associations between independent elements) turns out on analysis to be a system with its laws of the totality and above all its regulatory mechanisms. Thus, at the beginning of this century, the genome was regarded as a collection of genes with no relations between them, each seemingly responsible for the hereditary transmission of a single individual characteristic. For this conception, that Mayr humorously labelled 'beanpile genetics', the facts have led to the substitution of a more 'structural' image: several genes play a part in the transmission of any given characteristic and each gene is involved in the transmission of several characteristics ('polygeny' and 'pleiotropism' or, in other words, several-to-one and one-to-several correspondences) and the whole operates 'as an orchestra and not as a collection of soloists' as Dobzhansky has remarked. From the genome level onwards we get the intervention of regulatory mechanisms, and what Lerner has called a 'genetic homeostasis'. The most striking fact in this connexion is that the natural unit is not so much the individual genome or the genotype as the 'population', or mixture of balanced strains, with its 'genetic pool' in which the genotypical heredities are blended. And the blend itself, instead of forming a simple aggregate, as one might have supposed, is in its turn the seat of stabilizing regulations, as has been shown by the classic experiment by Dobzhansky and Spassky on fourteen strains, mixed artificially, where after a phase of imbalance we get the recurrence of a good proportion of the originals' survival and recombination coefficients.

In a word, the facts just cited illustrate clearly what was said at the start of this article, namely, that in dealing with unfamiliar processes, we begin by following the natural bent of the intellect in trying to work from the simple to the complex by a sort of atomistic compounding process, but sooner or later we discover laws of totality that impose a structural composition, and it is only then that the objective explanations begin.

The second structuralist lesson provided by modern biology is the fundamental importance of self-regulatory mechanisms and feedback circuits. We have just seen this at the level of the genome. Waddington used the name 'homeorhesis' for the kind of dynamic equilibration which, in the course of embryogenesis, brings the embryo back to its 'necessary paths' (or 'creods') whenever deviations occur; now this is not simply an effect of hereditary programming, since ontogenesis derives from an 'epigenetic system' in which the syntheses take place in interaction with the environment. On the physiological plane of the adult organism, we are pretty well acquainted with the multiple homeostases whose description derives from the researches of Claude Bernard and Cannon and whose delicate self-regulations are being revealed by contemporary research. As regards the nervous system, it follows *a fortiori* that the situation is the same: to take only one example, it is known today that the so-called reflex arc is by no means a simple associative 'arc', but itself includes a homeostatic loop system.

All of this is highly important for structuralism, from at least two points of view. Firstly, we find that, alongside the formal structures whose operational self-regulation derives from their closure and the intrinsic necessities which go with closure, the living structures, while remaining relatively open (since they comprise constant exchanges with the outside and not only among their own substructures, as with closed structures) make use of temporal and dynamic systems of self-regulation which represent a kind of outline or an incomplete form of the operational systems. Secondly, these self-regulatory systems, becoming increasingly mobile and active with the multiplication of the organism's exchanges with the external world throughout its learning and development, in fact constitute the source of the cognitive structures which, on the plane of the human intellect, lead to logico-mathematical operational structures.

4. PSYCHOLOGICAL STRUCTURES

Hence it is the psychogenetic study of the formation of these latter structures which provides the means of justifying the hypothesis of a transition from structures of the self-regulation or homeostasis type to structures of the operational or logico-mathematical type.

The Gestalt theory, born in 1912, can already be considered structuralist, its principle being to seek from the start laws of totalities in all areas (perception, motivity, memory, intelligence), and to consider the elements not as primary but as being 'structured' from the first, rather than being 'structuring'. But this school of psychology, while having the great merit of exposing the misconceptions of the associationists, with their atomistic models, made the mistake of trying to reduce everything to a single type of structure, the *Gestalt*, and of formulating this concept on the pattern of the 'fields' of physics, notably the electro-magnetic fields. From the fact that the laws of totalities are other than the laws of their elements, which is true, Wertheimer and Koehler drew the false conclusion that a necessary concomitant of any psychological or cognitive structure is a non-additive composition. But elementary operational structures such as a classification, a seriation, or the series of natural numbers are rigorously additive, even though they involve laws of totalities above and beyond the particular properties of their elements. This shows from the start that the structures of intelligence are not reducible to the structures of perception, these latter being indeed non-additive and fitting the definition of the *Gestalt* (for example, if $A < B < C$, the element B will be perceptually overestimated if compared to A and underestimated if compared to C, through a perceptual exaggeration of the differences, a fact which excludes additivity as it does quantitative conservation itself).

In its research on the development of the cognitive functions, the Geneva school therefore set itself the task of studying the diverse varieties of structure in their formations and above all in their filiations, so as to understand in particular what the logico-mathematical structures spring from in the way of psycho-biological sources.

An instructive initial finding is that, as early in the child's development as the sensori-motor stage, i.e. before language, we note the growth of certain structures such as the group of displacements, although at this stage it is a matter of co-ordination between successive actions (in particular, the reversibility and the associativity of the group, corresponding to returns and detours) and not yet a matter of simultaneous representations. At this sensori-motor stage, incidentally, many other general co-ordinations are to be noted, but as yet without a structuration comparable to that of the spatial group: co-ordinations between action schemes according to order of succession, or by unions, inclusions, correspondences, etc., from which will be derived at later stages by reflective abstraction the relations which constitute the representational structures.

When representation becomes possible, with the acquisition of semiotic tools and language, we first have a phase in which actions are interiorized, followed at age 5 to 7 on average, by the elaboration of what may be called the 'constituent functions' expressing the interconnexions proper to the action schemes and the dependences between the variable characteristics of the objects; for example, understanding that pushing on a flat rectangular block near one of its corners makes it turn instead of moving forward in a straight line, or that if liquid is poured from A into B, the level drops in A if it rises in B etc. The result is the formation of elementary structures of 'categories', in particular in the case of 'several-to-one' applications. But neither inverse correspondences nor reversibility in general, nor above all quantitative conservations are yet grasped, so that we cannot as yet talk of operations.

At the following level (7–10 years of age), we get the crystallization of the operations which will be called concrete in that they bear directly upon objects and not as yet on hypotheses: classification, seriation, correspondence, the sequence of whole numbers by synthesizing inclusion and order, etc. These nascent operations, sources of conservations due to their reversibility and to a previously unrecognized transitivity, thus constitute well-defined operational structures that are, however, essentially limited by their step-by-step composition, as yet lacking the combinatorial and, hence, 'sets of subsets'. These structures, which we have called 'groupings', are half-way between the group proper (though without complete associativity) and the lattice (with *supremum* but without *infimum* or the reverse) and present the psychogenetic interest of preparing the way to both; and, additionally, of providing elementary examples of algebraic structures with their inversions, of ordered structures with their reciprocities, and of topological structures, as we have seen in Section 2.

Lastly, at the level of propositional or formal operations (age 11–12) we get operations carried out on these operations, which then give us a combinatorial (combination operations being classifications of all possible classifications of *n* elements, and permutation operations being seriations of seriations) and the INRC group, which co-ordinates in a single system inversions and reciprocities. A series of substructures then becomes possible and advances in this logico-mathematical structuration are echoed in the domain of causality by the ascription of a series of attributes to the objects, expressing in kinematic and dynamic terms the newly constructed operational transformations (e.g. actions and reactions, vector composition of forces, distributivity in the internal modifications of a system, etc.).

The main lesson of this psychogenesis of structures is its demonstration of the possible and even necessary union between structuralism and constructionism. None of these structures whose development has just been very briefly outlined could be considered an 'innate idea' or an *a priori* necessity, but each is constructed from the structures preceding it by a combination of reflective abstractions, drawing certain co-ordinations from simpler systems, and of reorganizations or reconstructions which in the final analysis consist in carrying out second power operations on the preceding operations until the creation of a coherent new whole. In other words, each structure requires a genesis, but each genesis consists in a formative passage from a simpler structure to a richer one that integrates the simpler in going beyond it.

Further, the formative principle of these successive structures consists in self-regulations or equilibrations which, during the phases of elaboration, manifest themselves in various 'trial and error' approaches, with progressive co-ordination of retroactions and anticipations, as in simple feedback regulations, but which in their final form are operational structures. In this respect, operational reversibility can be taken as the product of the equilibrations, and as the limit term of the semi-reversibilities proper to the regulations. The psychogenesis of the structures thus comes in between the homeostases of various biological levels and the construction of the logico-mathematical structures.

From this point of view, the intrinsic necessity which characterizes these last structures is seen not as the product of antecedent conditions but as a terminal characteristic produced by the closing of systems that remain open during the phases of their formation but which, once completed, become self-contained, and are dependent only on their internal compositions. A particularly clear example is the relationship of transitivity, of the form $A < B$, $B < C$ therefore $A < C$. This is not acknowledged as a necessary relation before the stage of concrete operations, but it becomes evident as soon as the subject becomes capable of constructing a seriation by an exhaustive method without trial and error, working simultaneously on the relations $<$ and $>$.

5. LINGUISTIC AND SOCIAL STRUCTURE

A language is a 'social institution' (in Durkheim's sense), even though individual speech may exploit the possibilities of the language in constantly changing forms; so an examination of linguistic structures is undoubtedly the best and most exact method of grasping at once the mechanism of the social structures and the degree of initiative which, in any instance, they leave to or require of individuals. It is not without reason, therefore, that the structuralism of a Lévi-Strauss should rely on linguistics as much as, if not more than, on algebraic structures.

Linguistic structuralism dates back to F. de Saussure, who described it in terms of 'systems', and introduced two fundamental innovations: first, that a language is a genuine whole whose elements are interdependent in their oppositions no less than in their connexions; and second, that this system, inasmuch as it is a phenomenon of equilibrium (here, De Saussure drew his inspiration from the work of economists), depends essentially on the synchronic conditions, so that the historical, etymological, etc. and even comparative researches of pre-Saussure linguistics did not get at any reasons behind linguistic phenomena.

By their characteristics of totality and self-regulation, as well as by the play of their internal transformations, the linguistic structures discovered by De Saussure are in a sense comparable to the cognitive intellectual structures which we have just been discussing, despite certain obvious differences in the nature of the transformations involved (not that language has not a certain logic of its own, if only in the relationship between subject and predicate). But there is a fundamental distinction between systems of signs, from which language stems, and operational structures, which bear upon notions and operations, that is, upon what is signified rather than the signifiers. Indeed, since signs are conventional and hence partly 'arbitrary' ('absolutely' or 'relatively' so, as the case may be, as De Saussure specifies), the synchronic state of the system may be independent of its previous states in varying degrees (according as needs have changed, as in the history of markets in economics); on the contrary, an operational structure imposes itself with necessity – its state of equilibrium is the end result of its history, that is (as was seen in Section 4), of a process of progressive equilibration. The relationship between diachrony and synchrony is thus wholly different in the structures of language and of the intelligence.

Lévi-Strauss took linguistic structures as a model for structuralism in ethnology, and the primacy of the synchronic factor led him, in particular, to under-appreciate histories and genesis. As regards genesis, however, recent work in linguistics has radically modified its structuralist perspectives. After Harris and Halle had emphasized the continuous creativity distinctive of language, since speech consists in an endless construction of new combinations, N. Chomsky worked out the notion of generative grammars and provided the methods of studying them, positing incidentally, as the starting-point of this constructive process, an 'innate fixed kernel' of a rational kind. Thus, certain positions that had been traditional since De Saussure's linguistics have been ruled out (Bloomfield, etc.): synchrony and genesis cease to be contradictory; reason or logic are no longer products of language, but the reverse, etc. We then see the harmony between this constructionism and the constructionism we found in our research on intelligence (Section 4); the only difference is the linguists' hypothesis of the innateness of the initial fixed kernel, but this hypothesis is unnecessary to the extent that sensorimotor intelligence, ante-dating language, suffices to provide the conditions for the development of this initial kernel, and that this initial form of cognition is itself the product of successive constructions and equilibrations.

Turning now to the properly social structures, a considerable number of forms can be described, with the same spread as in psychology: from simple homeostatic feedback systems, pointed out by the economists; through quasi-operational forms (like the interlocking of legal language norms so profoundly analysed by H. Kelsen's 'normativism'); to true operational structures such as those that we have sought to bring to light in the mechanism of co-operation in cognitive exchanges (when reciprocity occurs without the intervention of constraints or of authority).

It is important, however, not to misuse the term structure – as it is currently fashionable to do: its use is not justified simply because one is discussing totalities. The great virtue of Durkheim's sociology is to have spotlighted these totalities but, by regarding them as simply emerging from a union of individuals, and by attributing their regulations to an overly general process of 'constraints', he missed achieving their structuralist analysis (actually initiated by his disciple, Marcel Mauss). Parsons' 'structural-functional' system on the other hand goes further towards this kind of analysis, particularly as regards the mechanisms of equilibrium and valorization, and has the virtue of not dissociating structure and functions, imperative whenever 'functioning' takes place through time.

The prototype of a structuralism whose intention is quite authentic is the work of Lévi-Strauss, who did not content himself with linguistic inspirations but set himself, with the help of mathematicians, to formulate in algebraic terms structures that he discovered in kinship relations, etc. Two basic aspects of his theory are to be noted in this connexion, the first of which seems to compel assent, whereas the second poses problems. Firstly, Lévi-Strauss concludes that his structures are distinct from laws or general relationships that can be established by simple observation, for such laws do not by themselves provide the *raison d'être* that would explain them in their detail. Just as the physicist, to interpret his phenomena, is obliged to go beyond the observable and to construct models embracing the transformations attributed to the objects as such, so the structures invoked by the ethnologist are both the product of deductions which go beyond the limits of the phenomenon alone and at the same time the expression of a reality conceived of as objective even though not immediately discernible in the facts. In other words, the structures exist or are deemed to exist, but remain unknown to the members of the social group; and this is precisely the writer's own position on the terrain of the cognitive structures, which express what the subject is capable of (operations, etc.) at a given stage of development, but not what he can say or what he is conscious, in his formulated thinking, of being able to do.

But the second tenet of the doctrine goes farther than the first; as a result of his over-emphasis on synchronic considerations and his relative depreciation of history and genesis, Lévi-Strauss is led to the assumption that his unobservable structures express a sort of permanent synchrony, or in other words, that they bear witness to the existence of a human mind continuingly identical with itself, quite overlooking the necessity of psychogenetic or biological considerations. He thus seems to ignore* the problem of what has happened between childhood and adulthood or between the higher primate and Man.

The problem that then inevitably arises is that of the mode of existence of these structures: in what does their 'being' consist if they are immutable? Do they hark back to Platonic or phenomenological 'essences' – a notion that Lévi-Strauss disclaims? Do they originate in an 'innateness' in the sense of Chomsky's 'fixed kernel'? If so, the interpretation of the great ethologist K. Lorenz, who is at once a Kantian and a mutationist, reveals the dangerous limitations of such a hypothesis, and we shall come back to this. Do they not, then, result from the compelling and in fact very general character of equilibration and self-regulation mechanisms? Such appears to be the only remaining and, indeed, *prima facie* reasonable solution, but in this case then the common and stable kernel of such formative mechanisms results solely from their functioning, a conclusion that in no way excludes but, on the contrary, requires the complementary hypothesis of the construction of endlessly new structures that result from the interaction between this functioning and the immediate demands of the moment.

6. CONCLUSION: STRUCTURALISM AND CONSTRUCTIONISM

Structuralism is a method and not a philosophy – a method consisting in identifying the characteristics of a whole regarded as something more than a simple aggregation of antecedent elements, and arriving at these characteristics by processes which may be formal or partly experimental as the case requires, but which are always verifiable. As such, structuralism

* This is actually not the case, as his more recent work reveals (cf. *L'Homme nu*).

is necessarily interdisciplinary; in the domains of logic and mathematics, which are wholly self-sufficient disciplines, the fact remains that, to establish the full epistemology of the structures, and not stop short at their technical aspects, they must be compared with the structures whose psychogenetic construction can be followed. However, the study of this construction sooner or later calls into play our knowledge of physical, biological and social structures, and reciprocally, comprehension of these three sorts of structure requires recourse as much to psychogenetic analysis as to the formal methods of construction. In a word, any structure is always located at the intersection of a multiplicity of disparate disciplines, so that no general theory of structures can possibly escape the requirement that it be not simply multidisciplinary but authentically interdisciplinary.

The first insights afforded by such a general theory, even though it is still an embryo and not a full-fledged discipline, demonstrate that in all fields structuralism goes hand in hand with some sort of constructionism. Whether the latter remains abstract and non-temporal as in mathematics, where it is nevertheless imposed by the limits of formalization, or whether it is an integral part of a real genesis, as in all other disciplines, the fact remains that the *esse* of the structures derives from their structuration, that is, from the self-regulations and operations of which they are the products.

This being granted, if we discount, in hypothesis, the Platonism which never adds anything to our effective knowledge (for the only method of arriving at the eternal Ideas is to reconstruct them, and this construction is self-sufficient) there appear to be only two possible sources, as regards the putative origins of the structures, once they are conceived of as 'natural': either they are innate or else they are the result of self-regulations. Now the advantage of the hypothesis of innateness is that, in the abstract, it can be translated into *a priorism*, ergo into terms of necessary antecedent conditions. In the concrete, this means that the problem is situated in the field of biogenesis, which superficially may appear sounder than that of psychogenesis. An attempt has been made by the ethologist K. Lorenz to effect this synthesis between Kant and neo-Darwinism. According to him, the major categories of knowledge (and one can include the structures here) are the product not of experience or of the environment but of antecedent biological conditions comparable to a hereditary preformation; just as the horse's hooves and the fish's fins develop during ontogenesis well before these creatures use them, simply by hereditary programming, so, says Lorenz, Kant was perfectly correct in regarding our cognitive categories as predetermined structures 'activated' immediately on contact with experience, without this meaning that they result from it. But the trouble is that heredity varies from species to species, and hence, there is nothing general and above all nothing necessary about its content. So, self-consistently but dropping the 'necessity' which is the most fundamental criterion of Kantian *a prioris*, Lorenz ends by regarding the latter as simply 'innate working hypotheses', and as such, therefore, they are imposed on us but they lack intrinsic intelligibility.

These analyses by Lorenz seem to this writer to be of great importance because they demonstrate unmistakably the limitative character of an interpretation in terms of innateness. The constituent self-regulations of organic life are in fact much more general (since they are already in play even at the stage of the transmission of hereditary characteristics, the genome as such having its own self-regulation) and manifest themselves in a far more easily verifiable manner in the evolution of behaviour and during the entire psychogenesis of cognitive functions, including structures. To explain the formation and indeed the very nature of structures, therefore, in the present state of our knowledge, we find ourselves turning to self-regulations and to the constructions that these entail.

From the epistemological point of view, the process inherent in progressive equilibration, with its alternations between disequilibrium or conflicts of coherence and re-equilibrations on new levels, naturally calls to mind dialectical conceptions; and on this point again we need to underscore the necessary union of structuralism and dialectical constructions, notwithstanding that some denigrators of the former, as superficial as any slaves of fashion, have posited a fundamental conflict between these two methods of thinking. In the domain of formal structures, it is well known (and Bachelard stressed the fact in his *Philosophie du non*) that, as soon as a structure or even a 'theory' has been constructed, one tries denying an essential character of it, to get beyond thesis and antithesis and reach a new synthesis; the non-Euclidian or non-Archimedean geometries, the non-commutative algebras, the logics without excluded middle (since Brouwer) and even without negation (Griss), etc., are instances of those dialectical moments peculiar to the history of logico-mathematical structures. In all natural and social sciences, the reconciling of the temporal, historical or genetic perspective with structuralist tendencies imposes, *a fortiori*, a continuous dialectic which is said to be immanent in the real, as well as necessary to the subject seeking to understand the real.

In fact, this is the very point on which we choose to conclude this paper on structuralism, resolutely rejecting the idea, propounded by some, that this fecund method necessarily rules out any considerations of history, genesis, functioning, and even a subject's activities.

REFERENCES

BOUDON, R., (1968) *A quoi sert la notion de structure*, Paris.
BOURBAKI, N., (1948) 'L'architecture des mathématiques', in: F. Le Lionnais (ed.), *Les grands courants de la pensée mathématique*, Paris.
CHOMSKY, N., (1957) *Syntactic Structures*, The Hague.
'Dialectique marxiste et pensée structurale', (1968) *Cahiers du Centre d'Etudes Socialistes, 76–81* (Feb.–May).
Genèse et structure, (1965) Paris.
GRANGER, G. G., *Pensée formelle et sciences de l'homme*.
JOINER, J. H., (1968) *Essentials of the Theory of Structures*, New York.
KUHN, T., (1968) *Structure of Scientific Revolutions*, Chicago (Ill.).
LÉVI-STRAUSS, C., (1958) *Anthropologie structurale*, Paris.
LÉVI-STRAUSS, C., (1962) *La pensée sauvage*, Paris.
LEWIN, K., (1951) *Field Theory in Social Science*, New York.
PARSONS, T., (1960) *Structure and Process in Modern Societies*, Glencoe (Ill.).
PIAGET, J., (1967) *Biologie et connaissance*, Paris, Gallimard (Series 'L'avenir de la science').
PIAGET, J., (1968) *Le structuralisme*, Paris, Presses Universitaires de France.
PIAGET, J. *et al.*, (1967) 'Logique et connaissance scientifique', in: R. Queneau (ed.), *Encyclopédie de la Pléiade*, Paris, Gallimard.
SINCLAIR DE ZWAART, (1967) *Acquisition du langage et développement de la pensée*, Paris.
'Le structuralisme', (1966) *Aletheia, 4*.
'Structuralismes, idéologie et méthode', (1967) *Esprit* (May).
Temps modernes, (1966) *246* (Nov.).
VIET, J., (1965) *Les méthodes structuralistes dans les sciences sociales*, Paris.

3 Systems concepts

1. CONCEPT OF SYSTEM: ORIGIN AND PRESENT ROLE

During the last three decades there has been an ever-increasing interest in the phenomena which can broadly be called information-processing and decision-making. These are of great importance in science engineering and management. Observation data are transformed for specific purposes. A need was felt for a concept to relate results obtained from various subfields, developed in detail but in isolation, i.e. for a system as understood in the new and rather broad sense of systems theory or systems science, and in its applied forms (such as systems engineering or systems management). In general, a system denotes the *existence of relationships between data or variables* or, more specifically, a transformation of a set of data into another set. As different physical theories deal with different kinds of physical phenomena, various aspects of information-processing and decision-making theories can deal with various types of systems, their behaviour, transformations, control, and so on.

Does a formal, mathematical, definition of a system introduce a too severe restriction, especially in dealing with complex biological or social problems? It can readily be shown that the limitation, if any, is only nominal. For example, if a description is expressed only as a set of statements, the formal aspects of the observations can still be expressed as a system. To every set of statements a mathematical model can be assigned, i.e. a system to represent the formal aspects of the theory. If the system has very little structure and in this sense does not reveal much about the functioning of the real-life phenomena, this is due to the limitation of our knowledge about the behaviour of the real-life system rather than due to the application of formal, mathematical, methods.

Consider now some methods for more detailed description of a system. First step in that direction is to recognize cause-effect relationships in the system; this is done by partitioning the family of system objects into two sets: the sets of *inputs* (or stimuli), X, and the set of *outputs* (or responses), Y. The system is then represented as a relation on two sets.

$$S \subset X \times Y \tag{1}$$

where $X = V_1 \times \ldots \times V_k$, $Y = V_{k+1} \times \ldots \times V_n$. The system in general is then considered to transform inputs into outputs.

There are two basic problem areas in the systems field: 1) How to describe the system more specifically, i.e., how the inputs are transformed into outputs? 2) What are the basic properties of a system of a given kind (i.e. with a given type of description)?

Starting from the concept of a general system as a relation on abstract sets there are two approaches by which the system can be described in more detail. In the first approach the system is considered to process certain information flow and a more detailed specification is given in terms of a 'mechanism' by which this is done. This is referred to as terminal approach and the system is considered as a terminal system (or causal system). In the second approach the system is considered to be pursuing a certain goal (or purpose) and the output of the system is described in terms of a goal-seeking process, as a response to a given input (stimulus). These systems are referred to in general as goal-seeking systems or more specifically as control systems, decision-making systems and the like.

2. TERMINAL SYSTEM

If S is a function, i.e. with every input, $x \in X$, there is associated a single output, it is referred to as a functional system

$$S : X \to Y \tag{2}$$

A basis then exists to describe the system by an 'internal mechanism' which is essentially a procedure to specify the right output for any given element of the input set. This is usually done by means of a set of equations or a transformation table in case of systems with lower cardinality. For example, let X be a sequence of real numbers restricted to the interval $T_{10} = \{0,1, \ldots, 10\}$, i.e. any $x \in X$ is a sequence $x = (x_0, x_1, \ldots, x_{10})$ where x_i

is a real number; furthermore let Y be also a sequence on T_{10} but such that the first element is always a given number, say $y_0 = \alpha$. A functional system $S : X \rightarrow Y$ can be then defined by the difference equation

$$y_i = 2y_{i-1} \, x_{i-1} + x_{i-1} \qquad (3)$$

i.e. for any $\hat{x} \in X$, the corresponding output $\hat{y} \in Y$ is a sequence such that its first element is α while all other elements are obtained (generated) by (3). Equation (1) represents a *constructive specification* of the system. The type of the constructive specification which can be used to describe a system depends of course, on the type of sets X and Y. E.g. if X and Y are sets of continuous functions constructive specification can be given by means of differential or partial differential equations.

If S is a proper relation it first has to be transformed into a function before a constructive specification can be given. Two approaches have been developed: state space approach and probabilistic approach.

In the state space approach a new object, Z, is introduced first so that the system, $S \subset X \times Y$, is made a function

$$S : Z \times X \rightarrow Y \qquad (4)$$

If X and Y are time functions Z is also a set of time functions, e.g. z is a sequence of elements from a set Z, $z = (z_0, z_1, \ldots, z_n)$; the first element of z is termed initial state, an arbitrary element is termed the state of the system and the set Z is the state space. The constructive specification is now given in terms of two sets of equations: first giving the elements of z from x and the initial state, e.g.

$$z_i = 4z_{i-1} + 2x_{i-1} \qquad (5)$$

and the second giving the elements of the outputs for the given elements of z, e.g.

$$y_i = 3z_i \qquad (6)$$

If at for any given time, i, the state of the system, z_i, and the remaining input $(x_i, x_{i+1}, \ldots x_n)$ are given, the remaining output sequence of the system is completely specified. In this sense the state of the system completely specifies 'the internal conditions' of the system at any given time.

Instead of introducing new objects (like state space), one can regain functionality in describing a system by considering groups of similar inputs (stimuli) and then describing how such groups of inputs map into groups of outputs. This leads to a probabilistic approach. One first describes the input and output sets in probabilistic terms; i.e. X is partitioned into subsets and with each element of a given subset there is associated a number smaller than unity. If some additional technical conditions are satisfied the interpretation of such a construction is that the number indicates the probability with which a given element occurs. The system itself is then described in reference to these probabilities or some derived statistical characteristics. Apparently one regains a functional description of the system by moving to a different 'level' of description, i.e. relating subsets rather than elements of the system's objects.

Systems which are functional or for which there is given a state space constructive specification are termed *deterministic systems*. Systems which are described via probabilistic approach are termed *probabilistic* or *statistical systems*. Apparently probabilistic systems are but a special class of relational, non-deterministic, systems since the application of probabilistic approach requires the satisfaction of a number of fairly restrictive technical conditions. Of particular interest is the probabilistic description of a system as an *information channel* in which the signals are described in terms of a logarithmic-type probabilistic measure.

Systems can be classified according to the type of their objects. E.g. if X and Y are sets of time functions, one talks about *time systems*. If X and Y are described algebraically, one talks about *algebraic systems*. Similarly, if the state space is a finite set, one talks about *finite state systems*; otherwise, *infinite state systems*. Also one talks about numerical or symbolic type systems in reference to whether X and Y are described in terms of numbers or symbols. If both X and Y have more than one component sets the system is *multivariable*.

Another classification is made in reference to the type of constructive specifications. Thus, one talks about differential (equations) or difference (equations) system, about *static* and *dynamic* systems or systems with memory or delays in reference to the properties of the constructive specification which describes the evolution of the systems' response in time.

There are a number of properties which are defined specifically in the framework of a terminal description of systems, e.g. causality, stability, controllability, reproducibility, etc. Systems are also classified in reference to these properties, e.g. as stable, controllable in a given sense, etc. It should be mentioned that in conjunction with the terminal description one should not use systems properties which are pertinent to the goal-seeking approach such as learning, adaptation, self-organization, etc.

3. GOAL-SEEKING APPROACH

In the goal-seeking approach the response of a system to any stimuli is described in reference to the pursuing of a goal or purpose. A simplest way to formalize the notion of a goal-seeking is to represent it as a decision-making system in a general. Some of the aspects of the goal-seeking however will remain then informal. To describe a system $S \subset X \times Y$ as decision-making there should be assumed two items:

– A family of decision problems, $\bar{\Delta} = \{\Delta(x) : x \in X\}$; apparently the family of decision problems, $\bar{\Delta}$, is parametrized by the input set X, i.e. for each $x \in X$ there is associated a given decision problem $\Delta(x)$. Let M denote a decision set for all $\Delta(x)$, i.e. a solution for $\Delta(x)$ is an element of M, denoted by $\hat{m}(x)$.

– A mapping $Q : M \to Y$ which generates an output corresponding to any solution of the systems decision problem.

Systems behavior is then described in reference to $\bar{\Delta}$ and M: for any stimulus, $x \in X$, the system's response is determined by (obtained by transformation from) a solution $\hat{m}(x)$ of the decision problem $\Delta(x)$, i.e. $y = Q(\hat{m}(x))$.

For illustration consider a simple example of a decision-making system. Let both X and Y be time functions defined on the interval $[0,1]$. Let there be given another set of time functions M defined also on $[0,1]$. For each x let there be given an optimization problem, denoted by $\Delta(x)$ and defined by the statement:

Find $\hat{m}(x) \in M$ so that the definite integral

$$G(m,x,y) = \int_{0}^{1} [(y-x)^2 + c\, m^2]\, dt$$

is minimal under the constraint given by differential equation

$$\frac{dy}{dt} = ay + bm, \quad y(0) = \alpha$$

where a, b and c are constraints.

It can easily be shown that for each x there is a unique solution $\hat{m}(x)$ and therefore a unique $y(x)$ as given by the constraint equation. The decision problems $\bar{\Delta} = \{\Delta(x) : x \in X\}$ and the constraint equation define therefore a functional system $S : X \to Y$ such that for any $x \in X$, the pair (x,y) is in the system S if and only if y is obtained by the constraint equation from a solution of $\Delta(x)$.

Classification of the decision-making systems can be made according to the type of decision-making problem involved; e.g. optimization, statistical decision systems etc.

If X and Y are time functions defined on T and for any $t \in T$ the value of the decision variable $\hat{m}(t)$, i.e. solution at time t, is obtained by a mapping on inputs and outputs one has a *feedback control system* described by a pair of mappings

$$F_1 : X \times Y \to M \tag{7}$$
$$F_2 : M \to Y$$

whose composition is the overall system $S \subset X \times Y$. Constructive specifications of F_1 and F_2 describe actual evolution of the feedback system in time.

Other types of goal-seeking systems are recognized in reference to the problem. E.g. adaptation and learning is defined in reference to the uncertainty involved in the decision process. *Adaptation* is activity of a goal-seeking system aimed at reducing the uncertainty. In more complex situations elements of $\Delta(x)$ itself can change; e.g. the structure of the functions and relations involved can change in order to improve the performance of the system. This activity is referred to as *self-organization*. Many other systems properties pertinent to goal-seeking (such as e.g. learning) can be defined in the same framework.

4. LARGE-SCALE COMPLEX SYSTEMS

It is to an extent a relative question what one would consider a large-scale system. As a rule it is not in the system itself but in the approach taken to represent the system whether one should consider a system as large-scale. For example what is a large-scale system to a psychologist is but 'a component' for a sociologist. It is essential for the large-scale system approach that the complexity or 'largeness' of the system be properly reflected in the model, i.e. description of the system as such. The first prerequisite for this is that the system consist of subsystems and that this partitioning be recognized explicitly. This leads to a multi-level or stratified description of a system. On any particular level one considers a family of subsystems as completely isolated but on the next higher level these are incorporated into larger subsystems. The basic question is how the subsystems, as defined on the preceding lower level, interact. Convincing arguments can be presented that any large-scale system requires a hierarchical, stratified, description.

Another important type of large-scale systems requires both the concepts of hierarchy and goal-seeking. Systems described in the preceding section have a single goal even if the system was multi-variable. In general, of course, a system may contain subsystems which have different goals that can be partially or completely in conflict. In this respect the following classification of goal-seeking systems is of interest:

4.1 *Single-level single-goal systems.* These are the systems described in the preceding section. Their behaviour can be very complicated, of course, involving prediction, non-numerical decision-making, learning etc., but there is at least one simplifying feature: there is no conflict within the boundaries of the system. Control and decision-making theory as developed over the last two decades to a considerable level of sophistication is concerned with this type of systems.

4.2 *Single-level multi-goal.* These are the systems which contain a family of interacting goal-seeking subsystems each with a goal of its own and without any supremacy role assigned to a particular unit. From the conceptual standpoint the complexity of behaviour of this type of system is considerably greater than that of the systems in the preceding category. For this class of systems two theories have been developed: (1) game theory to deal with the situations where the subsystems are in competition; (2) theory of teams to deal with the situation where the subsystems are cooperating toward a common objective. Although these approaches have created a conceptual framework in which to deal with these kinds of systems much as yet has to be learned about how to resolve a conflict in a single-level multi-goal system.

4.3 *Multi-level multi-goal systems.* A system, in this class, contains as before a family of interacting subsystems each one of them having a distinct goal possibly in conflict with others, but also there is a hierarchical, supremality type relation between the subsystems so that some of the subsystems can influence – condition, constraint or even control – the goal-seeking activities of others. This of course is an organizational type of system as found in biological, social situations as well as in the complex technological situations (automation).

Although the concept of hierarchy was recognized as important for quite some time, only recently a mathematical theory of multi-level systems and within this framework a comprehensive theory of coordination, i.e. control relationship between units on different levels, have been developed (Mesarovic, 1970). This type of systems is of immense importance in many scientific areas as well as in engineering and management. It has been stated that the future of biology depends upon the understanding of how to cross biological levels, i.e. how the properties on one level are reflected on adjacent levels. Similarly for a theory of organization, which will deal explicitly with the internal structure of an organization, a multi-level systems theory is indispensable. It is hard to overemphasize the importance of multi-level, multi-goal systems. Indeed, it has been argued quite convincingly that the concept of hierarchy is intimately related with the very notion of a large-scale system and that any large-scale system has hierarchical features.

5. APPLICATIONS

Systems concepts pervade many a field. Like applied mathematics, systems concepts are used in almost any area where the development of a formal theory dealing with structural questions is attempted. Broadly speaking applications of systems ideas can be grouped into three areas according to the role they have in the methodology in the respective fields, namely, sciences, engineering and management.

5.1 *Application in sciences*. In non-physical sciences, such as social and political sciences, psychology, economics, etc. systems theory is providing a framework for any type of formal studies whether purely mathematical or based on computer simulation. Systems theory is increasingly being identified with the application of quantitative methods in general. Furthermore, it is providing a new set of metaphors and paradigms for modeling and conceptualization. In the past, concepts from the physical sciences where predominant; one talked about pressures, forces, energy, etc. in the context of social, political and economic situations. New metaphors from the systems fields involve concepts such as feedback, information flow, game-theoretic relationship, hierarchies, etc. These are opening completely new avenues which can lead to a dramatic improvement of our understanding of the social and economic systems especially when coupled with computer-assisted analysis.

In the physical and biological sciences the systems concepts have also introduced a new dimension. This is best illustrated in biology. Classically, scientific explanation in biology is given either in terms of physical laws or chemical principles. Systems concepts provide a new framework for scientific explanation of biological problems; namely, the biological phenomena are described in information processing and decision-making terms e.g. as information channels, feedback control systems, multi-level systems, etc. Results have already been gratifying in particular in physiology. However, it is only fair to state that many methodological and conceptual questions have yet to be resolved. For example, a systems biological explanation is still questioned on occasion as not being quite as fundamental as a biophysical and biochemical explanation, as being somewhat temporary, merely an expedient in the absence of a 'final' understanding which, by assumption, should be in terms of physical laws or chemical principles. This position is not attainable. Solid arguments can be adduced to show that a systems biological explanation is on a fundamental biological level and is not reducible to lower levels, just as chemistry is not reducible to physics in any practical sense.

5.2 *Engineering.* Systems ideas are applied in engineering in many different ways. First, in the synthesis and design of man-made systems which are to perform information-processing or decision-making functions in particular in the design and application of computers. Second, in the analysis of large technological complexes which involve subsystems of diverse nature, electrical, mechanical, etc. Third, in the evaluation of the economics and social impact of large technological systems. Last, but certainly not least in sociotechnological areas such as transportation, urban planning, pollution control etc. These are man-made systems of enormous social implication although technology-based.

The functioning of these systems is not described on the level of physical components and the study has to be conducted in the systems framework. It is this area which is at the hearth of what is termed *systems engineering*.

5.3 *Management*. Systems ideas are used in management in a number of ways. First of all the application of the so-called modern management techniques, such as programming, operation research, etc. is done in the systems framework. Next, automation of management functions such as e.g. management (computer) information systems is developed and used within a systems view of the management functions and the company as a whole. Finally, the systems models and analysis in business domain, e.g. of organizations, marketing, economy, etc. provide a basis for a significant improvement of the management decision process.

A word on the so-called 'systems approach' as used in engineering and management is in order. In the past many of the complex engineering and management problems where not subject to deductive or quantitative analysis because of the lack of framework and tools for analysis. Systems theory and computer simulation have provided these. In the past one was concerned only with some of the subsystems in isolation (those which can be studied by classical mathematical methods) the entire system being hopelessly complicated for a quantitative analysis. In the new 'systems approach' one starts with the entire system and describes its operation in as realistic terms as possible avoiding the pitfalls of using too specific mathematical model (as e.g. differential equation systems). Systems concepts and computers allow the analysis of such poorly structured and weakly described systems. The emphasis is on a realistic representation of the system in its entirety. The usefulness of such an approach hardly needs to be emphasized.

5.4 Implications of systems concepts in other areas is also of interest. Philosophically systems approach is in the tradition of logical positivism. However, it also represents a major departure of the traditional approach in the sense that it is much more of a relativistic character. There is no commitment to a reductionist idea but rather only to the methodology of using mathematical constructs to study some structural relationship of real-life phenomena. Also, it provides new approach to many problems (such as learning, information, etc.) of central interest to various branches of philosophy, in particular epistemology. Finally, in the era of increased specialization, information explosion and exponential increase in detailed factual knowledge, the systems concepts offer one of the few ways of putting the jig-saw puzzle together, of comprehending the world around us 'as it appears', recognizing the interrelationships between what are traditionally considered as isolated details. Systems concepts promise to be of the utmost importance in organizing knowledge. Structural aspects of whatever phenomena one is concerned with can be described in terms of the kind of systems used in modelling. Systems concepts therefore have a potential to provide a framework for organization and classification of facts in most diverse fields. This is of particular importance in education.

6. THEORETICAL BACKGROUND

It is not easy to give a historical account of the concepts of system and the systems approach in general because the field has developed very broadly and lacks spectacular advances – 'breakthroughs' – that can be associated with single person or group. In engineering it was a natural tendency to be concerned with larger and larger systems consisting of subsystems of diverse nature and of increasing economic and social importance. Take for example electrical engineering. The first step toward greater generality was made by studying a 'general rotating electric machine' which can represent either generators or motors of different varieties. Next was to include transformers and to deal with a general electrical or electromechanical energy transformer. With the advent of electronic circuitry the concept of electrical network developed. This was followed by the concept of a generalized network based only on energy exchange regardless of the form (electrical, mechanical, chemical) in which the exchange is taking place. Finally, the notion of a system which deals only with the exchange with the environment which is defined on an abstract, information type, basis rather than in terms of energy or material exchange. Similar trends can be traced in other fields. Increased complexity required greater generality in description and analysis. On the other hand it was the advent of automation and computers which made some of the systems idea of normative as well as descriptive value since one had the possibility to materialize different information processing and decision-making processes. This was all accelerated by sociotechnological developments of unprecedented scale and complexity (e.g. such as space exploration, increased urbanization, population explosion, etc.).

A slightly better defined task is that of tracing the attempts to provide a general systems theory. In this context the following major developments should be mentioned:

A) Proposal to look for some general laws which are valid in social and biological fields (von Bertalanfy, 1968; Boulding, 1956) the development being non-mathematical, intended as a scientific philosophy.

B) Proposal for the development of a theory of cybernetics or 'steering', control (Wiener, 1948).

C) Proposal to develop a mathematical theory of general systems which on the one hand will be essentially relativistic, i.e. it will not make any commitment as to the existence of some general laws (*cf.* A), while on the other hand it will combine the control (decision-making) and information, signal-processing phenomena (Mesarovic, 1964; 1968).

It is hardly necessary to say which position is favoured here. The field, however, is still not fully developed and only the future will show which of the approaches is most useful. The immense importance of systems concepts, however, has already been established.

REFERENCES

BERTALANFY, L. VON, (1950) 'An outline of general systems theory', *The British Journal of the Philosophy of Science*.

BERTALANFY, L. VON, (1968) *General System Theory*, G. Braziller.

BOULDING, K. E., (1956) 'General systems theory-skeleton of science', *General Systems Yearbook*, Ann Arbor (Mich.), University of Michigan.

MESAROVIC, M. D., (1964) 'Foundations for a general systems theory', in *Views on General Systems Theory*, New York, John Wiley.

MESAROVIC, M. D., (1968) 'Auxiliary functions and constructive specification of general systems', *Journal of Mathematical Systems Theory*, Springer-Verlag.

MESAROVIC, M. D., MACKO, D.; TAKAHARA, Y., (1970) *Theory of Multilevel Systems*, New York, Academic Press.

WIENER, N., (1948) *Cybernetics*, New York, John Wiley.

4 Symmetry concepts and the fundamental theory of matter

ABDUS SALAM

Symmetry, as narrow or as wide as you may define its meaning, is one idea by which man through the ages tried to comprehend and create order, beauty and perfection' (Hermann Weyl)

1

From the dawn of all civilization man has wondered and asked questions – questions about the colour of the sunset, about the luminosity of the stars, about rainfall and cloud-burst, about the trajectory of a bullet and a space satellite, and eventually, about life itself. But in all this questioning there has occurred one recurring theme. Man has always believed that the answers to these questions, when they come, must follow from just a very few general principles. Man has always held to an unreasoning faith in an eventual symmetry, an eventual simplicity, in any basic laws which may govern the universe. The history of science is the history of a search for such all embracing, such unifying concepts. And almost invariably the successful concepts have been the ones distinguished by their aesthetic appeal.

To illustrate most rapidly what I mean and the manner in which I wish to develop my theme, consider a basic symmetry which we believe the universe in which we live in possesses – the translation symmetry of space. Translation symmetry is one of the most familiar types of ornamental symmetries – familiar in art and architecture. When a pattern repeats itself after being 'translated' a finite distance – like the recurrence of the delicate arches of the Palace of the Doges in Venice – we speak of translational symmetry possessed by the structure. Assume now that space in which we live in possesses the symmetry of such exact 'recurrence' – more precisely that the results of an experiment performed here on earth are identical to the results of the same experiment performed on Mars; that the translation of an experimental set-up from earth to Mars does not affect the results of the experiment; that the laws of physics are translation symmetric. Clearly if this was not the case, there would be no reproducibility of natural phenomena. The laws of physics, if they differed from location to location – from earth to Mars – would be infinitely more complicated to infer and science, as we know it, would not exist. Now the astounding thing about this postulate of 'translation symmetry' of space is that it can be tested in our own laboratories on earth without going to any other part of the universe. One can show – and I shall discuss this in greater detail later – that the familiar law of conservation of momentum is a direct consequence of this postulate. Thus to the precision that momentum is conserved in any collision, one may assert that space is 'translation-symmetric' and vice versa. If all space is likened to the Doges' Palace and results of a local experiment likened to one of the arches, the symmetry implied by recurrence of the arches makes not only for the beauty of the structure: it does something still more profound. It gives us an explanation of a fundamental phenomenon (momentum conservation) which one has observed so often happening underneath each arch. In physical science, therefore, symmetry concepts possess not just an aesthetic appeal; they provide profound correlations of postulate and experiment.

Having set the stage for our study of symmetry principles let me briefly summarize the particular aspects I shall concentrate on. I shall discuss specifically the following concepts:

1. Space-time symmetry; the postulate of 'translational' and 'rotational' symmetries of space and time.
2. Symmetries of space and time reflection.
3. Symmetries associated with the intrinsic properties of matter – properties like electric charge, hypercharge and unitary charge.
4. The role of approximate symmetries which combine space-time and intrinsic symmetries mentioned above.

I shall not discuss the symmetries one meets in the study of macro-scopic matter – symmetries of crystals for example, and the ornamental symmetries in architecture, sculpture and art – particularly oriental art. These symmetries are aesthetically important but they are not related to fundamental physical laws in the deep manner the other symmetries I mentioned are.

2. ROLE OF 'GROUP THEORY'

Before we discuss space-time and internal symmetries of matter, it may be mentioned that the direct mathematical construct for describing a symmetry is the 'group' concept. A set of objects (the arches in the Doges' Palace for example) possess a group property if the symmetry operations (like the translation operation of one arch on to the next) when performed on a given member of the set interchanges it into another member of the set. 'Groups' are of two varieties, depending on the type of 'group operation'. They are either *discrete* when the number of group operations is finite (e.g. a crystallographic group), or *continuous* – like the group of rotations which, for example, transform one point on the circumference of a circle on to a neighbouring point.

'Group theory' is one of the best developed disciplines in mathematics. It came to flower towards the end of the last century – particularly the theory of continuous groups (in the work of Sophus Lie). Its systematic use in physics is, however, of recent origin, and dates back no further than the beginnings of quantum theory. To see why this has been so, consider the postulated symmetry of space we discussed before. I said earlier that the postulate of translation symmetry of space leads to the law of conservation of momentum. The argument for this is *classical*; it basically depends on how we define momentum. Consider now the role of quantum theory in further sharpening this result. Quantum theory brought group theory (and, with it, the powerful mathematics invented by group theorists) to bear on the description of physical phenomena. Why did this happen? The reason has been spelt out by Yang and Wigner; it lies in one basic circumstance; it lies in the basic postulate of quantum theory that the quantum states of a physical system form a *linear manifold*.

To illustrate, consider space rotations in the three-dimensional space represented mathematically by the rotation group O(3). Throughout the history of physics we have started with the assumption that laws of physics remain unchanged for space rotations. In the final analysis it is an empirical postulate, to be tested by its consequences. We build this postulate into physics by demanding that all basic equations of motion which represent fundamental physical laws should not change in form when written in terms of co-ordinates rotated in relation to those we started from. In physical terms this means we are asserting that if an experimental set-up and the detecting devices are rotated through a certain angle, the results of the experiment are unaltered. One can show by a classical argument that this postulate leads to the conservation law of angular momentum. An application of this rotation symmetry to *classical* trajectories – planetary orbits for example – also tells us that, given a certain orbit, we may infer by rotation the existence of other physically possible ones.

Now this result in classical physics is important but it is by no means very deep. It does not lead to new insights. Contrast this with the case of quantum mechanics. The same statement can be made about quantum orbits. In quantum theory there is, however, the further postulate that all possible orbits form a linear manifold and that one can select from this manifold a linearly independent *complete* set in terms of which all the orbits can be expressed linearly, i.e.

$$| \Psi > = \sum_j a_j | \Psi_j >$$

Now denote the rotation operator corresponding to a rotation g by $U(g)$. From rotation invariance, if $| \Psi>$ is an orbit $| \Psi'> = U(g) | \Psi>$ is another possible one. Specialize to $| \Psi> = | \Psi_i>$. From completeness, we may infer that

$$U(g) | \Psi_i> = \sum_j a_{ij} | \Psi_j>$$

Clearly the α_{ij} give us at once a *representation* – in the technical sense of matrices representing rotations – of the group g. With the quantum postulate of the orbits forming a linear manifold, we immediately strike a level or richness with the mathematical representation theory of groups, unsuspected, unconceived of at the level of classical dynamics.

Let us pursue this further. In quantum theory we are concerned only with unitary representations. This is connected with the quantum mechanical theory of measurement. I shall not go into the measurement theory of physics in any detail; we shall here merely accept that we shall always deal with unitary representations. Write an infinitesimal unitary rotation operator in the form

$$U(g) \approx 1 + i \, \epsilon_j J_j \, (j = 1, 2, 3)$$

The standard commutation relations for the real operators J_i which represent the three components of the angular momentum vector read:

$$[J_i, J_j] = i \, \epsilon_{ijk} J_k$$

Here

$$\epsilon_{ijk} = 1(-1);$$

(Photo Alexis N. Vorontzoff)

The delicate arches of the Doges' Palace in Venice exhibit 'translation symmetry'.

if $i, j, k = 1, 2, 3$ or any cyclic (anti-cyclic) permutation of these numbers and zero otherwise. These commutation relations express the well-known statement that a rotation by an angle θ around an axis A followed by a rotation through an angle φ around an axis B does not give the same final configuration of the system as these two rotations performed in the reverse order. Now it is well known that the operator for total angular momentum $J^2 = J_1^2 + J_2^2 + J_3^2$ commutes with all the three J_i. $[J^2, J_i] = 0$. From the mathematical theory of the group O(3), it is also well known that the group O(3) possesses matrix representations, labelled by two discrete numbers j and j_3, symbolically

$$J^2 \,|\, j,j_3> \,= j(j + 1) \,|\, j,j_3>$$
$$J_3 \,|\, j,j_3> \,= j_3 \,|\, j,j_3>$$

where j can take integral or half-integral values; $0, \frac{1}{2}, 1, 3/2 \ldots$ and j_3 ranges between $+j$ and $-j$. The symmetry postulate for space rotations combined with the completeness of the basic states of a quatum mechanical system allows us therefore to state that all systems in nature must be a super-position of discrete states, with well-defined values of angular momentum. The quantum number j representing as it does the total angular momentum (or the intrinsic spin) of a basic state as well as j_3 the component of the spin along the z-axis, are both *quantized*; *both are integers or half-integers* (in units of the Planck's constant). We all know that quantization, the discreteness of physical quantities is the essence of quantum mechanics. It is the exploitation of the representation theory of groups of the symmetry group of three dimensional rotations which has automatically guaranteed for us that angular momentum shall always be quantized. There could conceivably be no more beautiful synthesis of symmetries, group theory, quantum theory and experiment.

Summarizing, rotation symmetry was the basic postulate; conservation of angular momentum, its *classical* consequence; quantization and discreteness of angular momentum, its *quantum-mechanical* consequence. The whole is one miraculous blend.

3. ROTATION SYMMETRIES OF TIME AND SPACE

We have so far considered translation and rotation symmetries of the three-dimensional space we inhabit. The great revolution of 1905 for which Einstein was responsible, consisted of the special relativity theory postulate which stated that there is in nature a complete symmetry between space and time so far as translations and rotations are concerned. More specifically, the Einstein postulate was that the results of an experiment are not only space-translation and space-rotation invariant: they are time-translation and space-time (Lorentz) rotation invariant. That laws of physics do not change from yesterday to today, nor do they change when studied in a reference-frame space-time-rotated (more simply, moving with a uniform velocity) relative to a frame which is fixed. The direct classical consequences of space-time rotation symmetry are legion – these, as is well known, include equivalence of mass and energy (i.e. the relation $E = mc^2$) as well as the time dilation of uniformly moving objects (an astronaut lives longer, the faster he moves, provided his lifetime reckoning is done, using a stationary clock). We shall not be concerned here with this (classical) aspect of these symmetries; rather our concern will be with the quantum mechanical aspects. These were first discovered by Dirac and then elaborated group-theoretically by Wigner in a classic paper published in 1939. What Dirac and Wigner showed was the following.

3.1 As a consequence of the space-time rotation symmetry, all molecules, all atoms, all nuclear and subnuclear particles carry an intrinsic angular momentum. The particles are not just chunks of matter; they resemble spinning tops, spinning clockwise or anticlockwise relative to their direction of motion.

3.2 The magnitude of this spin is measured in integer or half-integer units of the Planck's constant. Each massive particle with spin J can exist in $(2J + 1)$ states corresponding to the $(2J + 1)$ different polarizations of this spin. For example, a beam of electrons (or protons, or neutrons), each one of which is endowed with a spin of $J = \frac{1}{2}$, is composed of half the number of particles spinning anti-clockwise (mathematically, with J_3, the component of spin along the direction of motion equal to $+\frac{1}{2}$) and half-spinning clockwise with $J_3 = -\frac{1}{2}$. For a particle of non-zero mass and spin $J = 1$ there are three polarization directions $J_3 = +1$, $J_3 = 0$, $J_3 = -1$ and so on.

3.3 For particles with zero rest-mass (and which on account of this property always travel with the velocity of light) there are just two polarizations whatever be the total spin value. For a spin J and zero rest-mass particle, the magnitude of left-spin is $J_3 = +J$, and of right spin $J_3 = -J$, with no other polarizations available. For massive particles the $(2J + 1)$ distinct spin-polarization states mentioned above are equivalent to each other in the sense that they can be transformed into one another by space rotations. This is not possible for the case of particles of zero mass. Here the two states of spin-polarisation $+J$ and $-J$ are completely inequivalent.

3.4 In addition to translation and rotation symmetries, one may postulate other symmetries. The ones I shall consider most specifically are the discrete symmetries of *space and time reflection.*

Space-reflection is something very familiar in our everyday experience. If we look into a mirror, we see the space-reflected world which, as we well know, is not identical with our world. In a mirror, a right hand reflects into a left hand; clockwise motions go into anti-clockwise motions. To assert that laws of physics are symmetric for space reflection is a tremendous assertion. It is the assertion that if right hands exist, some-where in the Universe there must also be left hands. For elementary particles this is the assertion that if right-polarized, right-spinning electrons exist, so must left-spinning, left-polarized electrons.

Time-reflection is something we are less familiar with. We reflect time if we run a film backwards. In a back-run film a diver can be seen rising from the water and settling on to the diving board – a phenomenon one does not frequently come across in real life. Time reflection symmetry would assert that diving and counter-diving are both possible physical phenomena.

Now in 1928, Dirac postulated (not exactly in the manner I am des-cribing) that laws of physics, even though this may not be the most obvious of all things, are in fact symmetric if we reflect space and time simultaneously – that is, we look into a mirror and at the same time interchange the past and the future. This postulated space-time reflection symmetry, together with the space-time rotation symmetry I spoke of earlier, had an amazing consequence. Dirac was able to show that all particles in nature – all atoms, all molecules, all nuclear particles, and all objects made from them – exist in pairs. To every particle there corres-ponds an anti-particle. An anti-particle is an object with the same spin, same mass but opposite electric or nuclear charge. If Dirac was right the existence of the negatively charged electron would imply the possible existence of one positively charged (the so-called positron). If the proton exists, so must an anti-proton. If the hydrogen atom exists, this must imply the possible existence of an anti-atom of anti-hydrogen with the same energy levels. This work of Dirac is some of the most momentous, the most far-reaching in the history of physics. It was, of course, brilliantly confirmed by the experimental discoveries of anti-electrons and anti-protons. At one stroke Dirac had doubled the number of possible structures in the universe – and all from a pure mathematical deduction following upon a set of postulated symmetries.

3.5 Let us now separately consider the space-reflection symmetry. The human frame is space-reflection symmetric so far as our external appearances are concerned; we possess both right and left hands. Not so, when we consider internal organs. Most of us have hearts on the left only. The weaker form of mirror reflection symmetry principle however merely asserts that there should be the possibility of the existence of some right-hearted individual; the fact that they are rare may simply be a consequence of the contingent genetic factors – a result of asymmetric boundary conditions which happened to have perpetuated. This, as we know, is indeed the case. There do exist individuals with right hearts, though they are rare. Reflection symmetry of space seems to hold in nature.

This at least was the opinion held until 1957, from the time of Leibniz who was the first to reflect on this symmetry. We believed that so far as fundamental physical law was concerned, there was no inner difference between the right and the left. Mathematically, one may say that equations of motion of physics which describe the universe remain unchanged when the co-ordinate x is replaced by $-x$.

In the summer of 1956, T.D. Lee and C.N. Yang, two Chinese physicists working in the United States, by a careful analysis of existing experimental data, came to the conclusion that whereas the principle had been checked in the interactions of protons, neutrons, electrons, it had never been checked where neutrinos were concerned. They suggested that direct checks be made to find out if the principle was all that universal.

I heard Professor C.N. Yang in September 1956 question the space-reflection symmetry postulate in a lecture in Seattle. It seemed sacrilegious to me – as indeed it appeared to most other physicists – that nature should give up a symmetry principle lightly. That night a Military Air Transport plane was very generously placed at the disposal of the conferees to the Seattle Conference by the United States Air Force to fly back to London. The plane was too noisy, too uncomfortable to sleep. Over the dark Atlantic I kept being tormented by what Professor Yang had said. I felt that if nature *must* sacrifice the space-reflection symmetry principle it would do so only if this principle conflicted with some symmetry principle aesthetically even more appealing. One knew at that time that the neutrino's rest-mass was very small; it struck me that if one assumed that this mass was exactly zero – i.e. that the neutrino travelled always with *exactly* the light-velocity – one could show immediately and without any elaborate calculations – that this situation would conflict with mirror-symmetry for neutrinos. Right-spinning neutrinos would exist but left-spinning neutrinos would not. Like Hoffman in Offenbach's opera, when a right-spinning neutrino looked into a mirror, it would see *nothing*. Could nature be sacrificing the mirror symmetry principle for another symmetry (now called the γ_5-symmetry) which must govern the behaviour of all spin $\frac{1}{2}$ particles whenever they possess zero rest-mass and travel light velocity.

In early 1957, the experiments of Wu and Lederman in the United States completely confirmed the ideas stated above. Nature does not possess mirror-symmetry where neutrinos are concerned; right-spinning neutrinos exist but left-neutrinos do not. In 1957 this symmetry appeared a weak substitute for the loss of mirror symmetry. In 1969 when γ_5-symmetry has been seen to pervade all parts of physics, nuclear and electromagnetic as well, we know that the loss has been favourably weighted in the balance of gains. This is a development, however, which I cannot write about in detail, for this new γ_5-symmetry is difficult to explain except in mathematical terms.

I have written of this episode of physics because it illustrates the *idée fixe* which most of us share and with which I started this essay. We have always found that whenever a postulated symmetry principle was appearing to fail in natural phenomena, this must be due to some still deeper symmetry, with which it must be in conflict. We may, at a given time, fail to comprehend the aesthetics of nature. When, however, the full and final picture emerges one has invariably found that the symmetries this exhibits are profounder still.

4. SYMMETRIES OF THE INTERNAL STRUCTURE OF PARTICLES

So far I have discussed the space-time symmetries, the quantization of spin using representations of the space group O(3) and the particle anti-symmetry which arises when one thinks of space-time reflection symmetry as a fundamental postulate. In this section we turn symmetries of internal structure of particles and their classification schemes on this basis. The guiding principle once again will be the use of group theory. To illustrate this I shall go briefly over the experimental situation in particle physics as it has developed from 1926 onwards.

Around 1926, two so-called fundamental particles were known to physics; the proton and the electron. These are tiny chunks of matter – the proton with a mass of around 10^{-24} grams, the electron some 2000 times lighter. Both are electrically charged, the proton positively and the electron negatively. They were elementary and fundamental in the sense that all matter – all the 92 atoms – were then (erroneously) believed to be made from just these two objects.

As I said before, protons and electrons are not just simple chunks of matter. Both these particles carry intrinsic spin, group theoretically the particles corresponded to the spinor representation of the group O(3), with $j = \frac{1}{2}, j_3 = \frac{1}{2}, -\frac{1}{2}$. In the vocabulary I have used earlier the proton (or the electron) formed a twofold $(2j + 1 = 2)$ multiplet.

The astonishing thing about these two particles was – and still is – the numerical equality of the electric charge they carried. The masses of the electron and proton are so different – the ratio is 1 : 2000. Their electric charge, however, is equal. Further, like angular-momentum, all electric charges in nature appear to be quantized – quantized in integral multiples of the charge on the electron. These facts we must incorporate in our description of nature, either by the statement that every system in nature is made of protons and electrons or by a description more embracing which may continue to hold, even if protons and electrons are no longer believed to be elementary.

With the success of the symmetry and group theory ideas in under-standing quantization of spin, the pattern for this more embracing description seemed clear in terms of a group-theoretic idea. The group representations of a rotation group in two-dimensions are labelled by positive or negative integers. Assume that there exists a two-dimensional 'internal' space representing the 'internal' degrees of freedom of structure of matter. Call it the 'charge space', and assume that equations of motion of physics are invariant for rotations in this space. This rotation symmetry will imply (through the quantum mechanical procedure sketched earlier) both charge quantization and charge-conservation. The pattern is the same as that for the three-dimensional rotation group; the logical argument is the same. The difference, however, is that, in contrast to the three-dimensional physical space, the new twin dimensions of 'charge space' apparently cannot be directly apprehended. They are apprehended only through their manifestation – the quantized electric charge.

Until 1930, the only known 'internal' characteristic of an elementary particle was just this one quantized entity – the electric charge. In 1930, with Chadwick's discovery of the neutron, there came a break. The neutron was the third 'elementary particle'; it was almost as massive as the proton but was electrically neutral. The proton and the electron attracted each other when close together through the intermediacy of the classical electrostatic force but this force was clearly irrelevant for neutrons since they were neutral. Two neutrons, or a proton and neutron, however did exhibit a strong attraction when close to each other. This was a new force of nature. At comparable distances one found empirically that it was at least 100 times stronger than the electrical force. Thus to an excellent approximation – to the approximation that one could neglect electrical forces relative to the nuclear – protons and neutrons were two states of just one single entity, the so-called nucleon.

4.1 *Isotopic symmetry*

This situation of a single entity (nucleon) existing in two distinct states (proton and neutron) was a situation one had encountered before. One had seen that a spin $\frac{1}{2}$ particle possesses two polarization states $| j = \frac{1}{2},$ $j_3 = + \frac{1}{2}>$ and $| j = \frac{1}{2}, j_3 = -\frac{1}{2}>$. Could one once again postulate the existence of a new 'internal' three-dimensional space – with three infinitesimal rotation generators $I_1, I_2 I_3$, satisfying the commutation relations

$$[I_i, I_j] = i \in_{ijk} I_k$$

The $I = \frac{1}{2}$ reprsentation of this new group could then be identified with the nucleon with $I_3 = \frac{1}{2}$ representing the proton state and $I_3 = -\frac{1}{2}$ the neutron. This suggestion originated with Kemmer, Heisenberg and Breit around 1934–1938. The new 'internal space' was named the 'isotopic space'; the nuclei, which are composites of nucleons, formed multiplets, corresponding to the irreducible representations of this isotopic-rotation group. All nuclei carried isotopic spin, in addition, of course, to the ordinary spin which henceforth I shall call *Poincaré* spin.

The next development in particle physics came in 1935 with some speculations of Yukawa. Yukawa recalled that all accelerating electric charges emit electromagnetic radiation in accordance with Maxwell's laws. The quantum aspects of the electromagnetic force are the photons. Yukawa raised the question: what is the analogue of a photon for the nuclear force? What type of radiation do nucleons emit when they are accelerated? He conjectured that there exist in nature photon-like objects, the so-called mesons, particles with masses intermediate between electrons and nucleons, which are emitted by accelerating nucleons. From the group-theoretic point of view, these particles, if they did exist, would once again correspond to irreducible representations of the iso-topic group. Further, if like photons these are emitted – shed by nucleons – singly at a time, conservation of isotopic spin would demand that their I-spin be an integer and not half-integer.

Yukawa's ideas were put forward in 1935. These were persuasive ideas. The search for these particles was interrupted by the war, but just after (in 1947) Professor E. C. Powell announced the discovery in cosmic rays of the Yukawa particles – the so-called 'pions'. These were three pions, corresponding to an isotopic spin $I = 1$.

$$\pi^+ \rightarrow \mid I = 1, I_3 = 1>$$
$$\pi^0 \rightarrow \mid I = 1, I_3 = 0>$$
$$\pi^- \rightarrow \mid I = 1, I_3 = 1>$$

The Poincaré spin J of the particles turned out to equal zero ($J = 0$). Summarizing, the classification scheme of particles concerned with the nuclear force proceeds in terms of three types of *symmetries*:
(1) The 'external' space-time symmetry, giving rise to Poincaré spin J.
(2) Two 'internal' rotation symmetries giving rise to
     (a) isotopic spin,
     (b) electric charge Q.

4.2 *The SU(3) symmetry*

After 1947 came further experimental discoveries. A whole host of new objects were discovered; particles with different masses, different charges, different Poincaré and different isotopic spins. By no stretch of the imagination could one call these 'elementary particles' any more. But whether these were or were not composites of any simpler entities one had to find a quantum description for these. In January 1964 the situation could be summarized as follows.

As a result of patient and painstaking experimentation, both with cosmic rays and the giant accelerators at CERN, Brookhaven, Dubna, Berkeley and elsewhere, one could classify the newly-discovered particles into the following multiplets:

(1)   8 particles of Poincaré spin $\frac{1}{2}$ (the nucleon family).
(2)   9 particles of Poincaré spin $\frac{3}{2}$ (excited nucleons).
(3)   8 mesons of Poincaré spin zero.
(4)   9 excited mesons of Poincaré spin one.

It is irrelevant for my purposes to go into details concerning these multiplets; in particular the identifying nomenclature, etc., within a multiplet is completely irrelevant. However, there is one common point I need to illustrate about these multiplets, and for this I shall refer to the 8-fold nucleon multiplet which consisted of the following components:

Table 1

	I	I_3	Q	$Y = 2(Q - I_3)$
p	$\frac{1}{2}$	$\frac{1}{2}$	1	1
n		$-\frac{1}{2}$	0	1
Λ^0	0	0	0	0
Σ^+		1	1	0
Σ^0	1	0	0	0
Σ^-		-1	-1	0
Ξ^0	$\frac{1}{2}$	$\frac{1}{2}$	0	-1
Ξ^-		$-\frac{1}{2}$	-1	-1

This 8-fold of particles – all of nearly equal mass, all of same Poincaré spin – consists of four distinct isotopic multiplets (p,n), (Λ), $(\Sigma^+\Sigma^0\Sigma^-)$ and (Ξ^0, Ξ^-) with their I and I_3 values given in the accompanying table. For each isotopic multiplet the quantum number $Y(=2\lambda Q - I_3)$ (the so-called hypercharge) happens to possess the same (integral) eigenvalue. (See the last column of Table 1. The quantum number Y takes the values 1, 0, 0, −1.) Fixing on I_3 and Y, clearly there must exist a higher symmetry group, perhaps a group of rank 2 since we are dealing with at least two simultaneously diagonalizable operators I_3 and Y, according to the representations of which one might classify these particles. That there was some higher symmetry at work in the physics of the nuclear inter-action was clear quite early, around 1956–1957. That the way to progress lay along a systematic search for a Lie group of rank 2 was only very imperfectly understood until 1961. The major uncertainty in the approach was, of course, always experimental. I have blandly stated that the nucleon multiplet was found to consist of eight members, all of Poincaré spin $\frac{1}{2}$, and I have specified the I-spins and hypercharge Y for each particle as if every experimentally discovered object carried a chain around it with a label on which one could read off its characteristics. In real life things are never like this. Until this day, for example, one does not experimentally know with more than 95 per cent statistical confidence that the Poincaré spin of the Ξ^0 and Ξ^- particles is indeed $\frac{1}{2}$. My colleague, Professor P. T. Matthews, has given an illuminating illustration of the difficulties which beset the work of an experimental physicist. There is only one experiment a particle physicist can perform; he can scatter one set of particles off another and, by counting the numbers which fly off in a collision in a given direction, try to find the spins and isotopic spins, etc. of the different end-products. It's like playing a hose of water on a statue in a dark room and being allowed to collect the water that splashes off from the statue's face. One can appre-ciate the hardships of the experimental physicist if one were posed the problem of delineating the statue's features by measuring only the quantities of water that splashed off per square inch of its surface.

Returning to the classification problem, Sophus Lie had already tabulated all groups of rank two. There are just four of these with the technical nomenclature: A_2, B_2, C_2 and G_2. One had to choose one of these as representing *the* symmetry. The problem of finding the correct group and therefore the correct symmetry could be formulated thus.

Associating I-spin with the group structure U_2 and associating hyper-charge Y with the group structure U_1, find a group of rank two which possesses both U_2 and U_1 as subgroups, and has an 8-dimensional representation with components as indicated in Table 1.

Once again let me stress, no working physicist can ever state a physical

problem in this form, except after the event. There are so many reservations, so many hesitations, so much one must take on trust and, most
difficult of all, so much one must discount.

Stated in the form I have used above, the problem had one solution –
the higher symmetry group must be A_2, which is also known under the
name SU_3. This solution was first proposed by the Japanese physicists
Ohnuki, Ogawa and Sawada in 1959. The SU_3 symmetry was named
'unitary symmetry'. Unfortunately the Japanese authors made a wrong
physical identification of particles; the representations of the group they
happened to choose did not decompose in the manner of Table 1. A later
version suggested in 1961 by Murray Gell'Mann and Yuval Neeman
fitted facts better.

This was encouraging, but not encouraging enough. In addition to the
8-fold multiplet of nucleons, there was also the other multiplet consisting
of nine excited nucleons with the following assignments:

Table 2

	I	Y
N^{*++} N^{*+} N^{*0} N^{*-}	$\frac{3}{2}$	1
Y^{*+} Y^{*0} Y^{*-}	1	0
Ξ^{*0} Ξ^{*-}	$\frac{1}{2}$	-1

Now there is no 9-component irreducible representations of the group
$U(3)$; the nearest whose $(U_2 \times U_1)$ decomposition would yield the eigen-
values shown in Table 2 for the generators I_3 and Y must contain ten
objects. One crucial particle was missing; a particle which from the
group-theoretic structure of the representation concerned must possess
isotopic and hypercharges $I = 0$, $Y = -2$. The empirical formula
$Q = I_3 + Y/2$ would give its electric charge as -1. The particle was
hopefully given the name Ω^- before it was experimentally discovered. The
fate of the $SU(3)$ symmetry hung on its discovery.

This was the situation in January 1964. In February 1964, among a scan of millions of photographic bubble-chamber pictures two Ω^-'s were discovered at Brookhaven. The production and decay of these particles is spectacular; the fact that there are even now a total of a dozen known specimens of this particle makes it highly precious. The higher symmetry scheme SU_3 was vindicated; the 'isotopic-spin' group $O(3) \approx SU(2)$ had been generalized to the 'unitary-spin' group SU_3 as the still higher, the still more embracing symmetry of the family of the nuclear particles.

The following question now arises. The group $SU(3)$ has a representation consisting of three objects. This is the so-called fundamental representation. All other representations can be formed from it. The physicists have begun to call it the Quark representation. Its three components, the three individual quarks can be shown to possess the following values of I-spin and hypercharge:

	I_3	Y
q_1	$\frac{1}{2}$	$\frac{1}{3}$
q_2	$-\frac{1}{2}$	$\frac{1}{3}$
q_3	0	$-\frac{2}{3}$

The electric charges of the three quarks would, from the relation $Q = (I_3 + Y/2)$ equal $\frac{2}{3}$, $-\frac{1}{3}$, $-\frac{1}{3}$ (in units of the electric charge). Any one of the nucleons in Table 1 would be composed of three quarks; any one of the mesons of a quark and anti-quark. Quarks, if they exist, would then be *the* basic matter, *the* elementary particles. So far the experimental search for them has proved fruitless but one must remember we have not gone to very high energies either with our present generation of accelerators. The important point to note really is that inexorably the symmetry concepts, charge, isotopic charge, unitary charge, have led to a series of steps which have guided the quest for the most fundamental constituents of matter. No mean triumph for the symmetry principles.

4.3 *The SU(6) symmetry*

The next developments in applications of symmetry principles to particle physics came soon after, in September 1964. And these were still more spectacular. At this stage, one had a total of four complete multiplets:

Table 3

N	(nucleon) $J = \frac{1}{2}$. Number of particles 8	
N^*	(excited nucleon) $J = \frac{3}{2}$. Number of particles 10	

M	(meson) $J = 0$. Number of particles 8	
M^*	(excited mesons) $J = 1$. Number of particles 9	

One had two varieties of quantum numbers:

(1) External;   Poincaré-spin; group structure $O_3 \approx SU_2$;

(2) Internal; I-spin and hypercharge Y; group structure SU_3.

Now when counting the numbers of particles in any internal $SU(3)$ multiplet, no account had been taken of spin polarizations, of spin multiplicity. Supposing we do treat each Poincaré spin polarization as distinct; the count would then be as follows:

Table 4

N	(nucleons) $J = \frac{1}{2}$	$8 \times (2J + 1) = 16$ distinct particles
N^*	(excited nucleons) $J = \frac{3}{2}$,	$10 \times (2J + 1) = 40$ distinct particles

M	(mesons) $J = 0$,	$8 \times (2J + 1) = 8$ distinct particles
M^*	(excited mesons) $J = 1$,	$9 \times (2J + 1) = 27$ distinct particles

In September 1964, the question was raised: is it conceivable that one did have in nature a symmetry higher than $SU(3)$, a symmetry comprising both 'external' Poincaré spin and the 'internal' unitary spin for which nucleons – both those which we have called excited and those others presenting the ground state of the structure – appear as just one multiplet. Could we possibly obliterate the distinction of external and internal symmetries? Could we think up a symmetry group with both $SU(3)$ and $SU(2)$ as subgroups? One obvious candidate was $SU(6)$. This was tried in September 1964 by F. Gursey, L. Radicati and B. Sakita. Among its irreducible representations $SU(6)$ does possess two representations with dimensionalities $35 = 8 + 27$ and $56 = 16 + 40$. These precisely are the numbers of distinct particles of the mesonic $(M + M^*)$ and nucleonic $(N + N^*)$ variety. $SU(6)$ is perhaps a still higher symmetry of nuclear interactions.

So far, so good. One was making progress but how was one to understand this merging of the 'external' Poincaré and the 'internal' unitary spin? Several answers have been given but none universally accepted. The mystery of this merging remains.

5

This then is a brief account of the role symmetries have played in the evolution of the fundamental theory of matter. I shall end by reiterating once again the fundamental faith of the physicist in the eloquent words of the Holy Book of one of the great religions of this world.

'Thou seest not in the creation of the All Merciful any imperfection. Return thy gaze, seest thou any fissure, then return thy gaze again and again. And thy gaze comes back to thee dazzled, aweary' (A. J. Arberry, *The Koran Interpreted*).

REFERENCES

GELL-MANN, M. and NEEMAN, Y., (1964) *The Eightfold Way*, New York, Benjamin.
LANDAU, L. D., (1957) *Journ. Eksp. Theo. Fiz.*, vol. *32*, p. 405 (in Russian).
LEE, T. D. and YANG, C. N., (1956) *Phys. Rev.*, vol. *104*, page 254, Journal of the American Physical Society.
SALAM, A., (1957) *Il Nuovo Cimento*, vol. *5*, page 299, Journal of the Italian Physical Society.
WEYL, H., (1952) *Symmetry*, Princeton (N.J.), Princeton Univ. Press.
WIGNER, E. P., (1967) *Symmetries and Reflections*, Bloomingdale (Ind.), Indiana Univ. Press.

5 Sign

LADISLAV TONDL

1. SEMIOTICS AS THE THEORY OF SIGNS

The traditional definitions of man as a 'tool-making animal', 'rational animal' or the like are sometimes further qualified, to make man into a 'sign-using animal', *animal symbolicum* (E. Cassirer, 1923–1931). In considering two types of social activities – cognitive processes and communication processes – much attention is paid to the role of signs, and systems of signs, in man's activities. Cognitive processes and communication processes are linked, reciprocal and interlocking, and semiotics, the general theory of signs and systems of signs, has been developed primarily to deepen our knowledge of them. The interest of signs is obviously not confined to them alone: sign processes are also of great importance elsewhere to culture and behaviour – in art, religion or politics for instance. Here, however, their characteristics and relations as a rule derive from those exhibited by sign-processes in cognition and communication.

The term 'semiotics' was originally used by John Locke to designate the general theory of signs, following ideas about the function of signs and sign-situations that date back to the Stoics. The first more systematic attempt to develop semiotics into a theory of signs was made by Charles S. Peirce (1931–1935; 1940), who introduced the concept of 'sign process' or 'semiosis', which he conceived as a triadic relation between signs, objects and interpretants. This means that any object, event or property of an object, etc. may become the sign of an arbitrary object, assuming that it can be interpreted by someone, i.e. if an interpretant of the sign exists. It is immaterial whether such an object is represented by material things, events or their properties, behaviour, states of the mind, objects that are products of our thought, imagination, and so forth; Peirce also worked out several sign classification schemes and traced connecting links between semiotics and logic.

The concepts of Peirce were followed up in particular by Charles S. Morris (1938, 1946, 1964), who in addition, connected in his works the influences of Peirce's pragmatism and the influences of logical positivism. An interest in the problems of signs was also characteristic of other philosophical trends. From neo-Kantian positions analogous problems were tackled by Ernst Cassirer (1923–1931), who especially underlined the innate human quality of symbolization and 'creation of the reality' by means of this symbolic creativity. Attempts at developing theories and a typology of signs can be found in the writings of the representative of phenomenology E. Husserl (1913–1921), who stressed, in particular, the special position of word signs (*Ausdrücke*), in contradistinction to signs of other kinds (*Anzeichen*).

The sources of interest in signs, their role in the cognitive and communication processes and in semiotics in general can obviously on no account be reduced to philosophical schools or works inspired by the investigation of philosophical problems alone. For the development of an analysis of signs and sign systems, as well as the elementary problems of semiotics, other fields of science or scientific topics have also been of great importance, especially those relating to linguistics, logic, psychology and aesthetics, to mention but some of them.

Semiotics has long been linked with linguistics. Starting from the classical work of Michel Bréal (1904), its problems have been regarded as a legitimate part of the science of language. In traditional, linguistically-oriented semiotics, it was the word (word sign) and its meaning or the changes occurring in this meaning that were the main point of attention, but its scope has now been substantially extended (particularly in connection with machine translation) through the application of new logical and mathematical methods to the study of natural languages, the analysis of the relations between natural and formalized languages, and so on.

Logic, in ancient and mediaeval times, was much concerned with signs and meanings, the relationship between word and concept, the connotation and denotation of concepts, and the like. This interest has quickened since the end of the nineteenth century, since no satisfactory solution of fundamental questions in logic, the elucidation of problems connected with certain paradoxes, with the concepts of identity, logical consequence, model, and so on, is possible without due regard being paid to relationships with which semiotics is also concerned. The pioneers here include Frege, Russell, Kotarbiński, Carnap, Church, Quine and Martin.

General semantics will, it is hoped, be an autonomous discipline for the study of the functions and meaning of signs. Philosophically, its proponents hold an eclectic mixture of opinions drawn from various schools and disciplines. On the whole, the most fruitful stimuli have come from general psychology, social psychology, psychiatry, neurology, psycholinguistics and aesthetics. *The meaning of meaning* by Ogden and Richards (1923) for example, analyzes the emotive and aesthetic effect of words, distinguishes between the emotive and the intellectual uses of language, and formulates a basic scheme of relationships between sign, object and thought (the 'Richards triangle of reference'). For Korzybski, Hayakawa, Chase and some other authors, general semantics provides a means of 'psychical and social therapy', of 'mental or social hygiene', making for the conciliation of social conflicts; it is concerned with the 'magic' effect of words, fights the so-called Aristotelian language system (identified primarily with two-valued logical systems). Some of these writings incorporate elements of Freud's psychoanalysis, Pavlov's theory of conditioned reflexes and certain discoveries of logic and linguistics.

A somewhat different light is thrown on the function of signs and sign systems, especially in communication processes, by research in cultural anthropology, comparative and historical ethnography, historico-comparative linguistics and psychology – especially by research on primitive mentality and the relations between thought and language among primitive peoples. The hypothesis of linguistic relativism (Sapir and Whorf) sees language as a whole and individual word signs as not only a certain image of the socio-pragmatically determined reality but at the same time its guide. Psychological research concerned with signs and meanings, and with the measurement of meanings, in art and in general, has been extensive and varied.

Semiotics (semasiology, semantics), accordingly, as the general theory of signs, does not provide a homogeneous or well-ordered pattern of scientific results; differences in conceptions, terminology, and approach are so enormous as to preclude a neat summary of results that would embrace them all.

2. THE NATURE OF SIGNS

In everyday language, the term 'sign' (and others with allied meaning, e.g. 'symbol', signal', 'token') is used in a very broad sense. Smoke is a sign of a fire, a colour or animal is a symbol of a political party, a coloured rocket is a particular signal, a nod is a sign of agreement, and so on. This heterogeneity of signs and of the contexts in which we encounter them, and accordingly the differences also, suggest that the approach in considering them must be equally broad. Bertrand Russell for example pointed out that for an organism O any element of the class of stimuli A is the sign of some element of class B, if the realization of this stimulus calls forth, in organism O, a response corresponding with the element of class B. This sign scheme working with the concepts of stimulus and response is actually close to the concept of the conditioned reflex in the context of Pavlov's physiology. The mechanism of the conditioned reflex apparently also supplies the physiological basis of what Peirce and Morris call the 'sign process' or 'semiosis'. Morris discerns five components of the sign process: 1) the sign, 2) the object to which the sign refers (*designatum*), 3) the interpreter, 4) the interpretants, i.e. the response on the part of the interpreter or the disposition of the interpreter to respond in a definite manner to a given sign, and possibly 5) the contexts in which the signs occur. In view of their decisive importance the first three components and their mutual relations are discussed below.

The above conception of sign is extremely broad. It could be applied to any response of an organism (or of a cybernetic equipment modelling the behaviour of the organism) which has the character of a conditioned reflex. Hence, a distinction must be made between sign processes in the broadest sense, and sign processes related to social communication. In the Pavlov reaction of the dog to the bell, all the components of semiosis can be distinguished. It is not tied to social communication and its components are not socially conditioned. Accordingly, we do not encounter signs in the proper sense, i.e. social artefacts that are only *ex post* interpreted as signs of something. No more exact distinction can be drawn between the two types of sign processes, or between 'natural' signs and signs of 'proper' (this distinction roughly corresponding to the traditional differentiation between the *signum naturale* and the *signum ad placitum*). This explains why, in semiotic literature, we meet with such a variety of sign typologies and classifications. Here we shall be mainly concerned with signs proper, but we cannot wholly exclude the intrusion of certain characteristic traits of natural signs and sign processes based on natural signs.

We may find, acting as a sign, any material object, its property, an event, the property of an event, or the like, which in the communication process can serve the purpose of communicating information, i.e. any material object, etc. that can be interpreted. By the interpretation of signs we understand a process which enables the interpreter, on the basis of the sign, to make a decision as to the objects to which the sign is assigned. We usually say that for the interpreter the sign has a certain meaning, irrespective of the fact that the concept of 'meaning' is interpreted in different ways. This means that there can be no signs which would be devoid of meaning, and conversely whatever can be subsumed under the concept of 'meaning' can only be isolated by means of a sign linked with the given meaning. From the above characteristic it is clear that a sign must, necessarily, have the following properties: (A) Communicability, i.e. the ability to communicate information in space and time; (B) Interpretability.

In cognitive and communication processes signs of most diverse types are brought into play. The differences in the outward appearance, uses and functions of signs in cognition and communication are so great as to make it difficult to work out a single typology of signs. Normally word signs or terms are distinguished from signs of other types. In the cognitive and communication processes word signs enjoy a specific position: by means of word signs we interpret signs of other kinds, and by means of the properties and relations peculiar to word signs we reconstruct properties and relations belonging to other signs.

Among signs that do not possess the character of word signs we include, for instance, diverse signals and agreed signs. For a worker, the sound of a hooter means it is time to finish his work, a light signal at a crossroads plays the part of a direction addressed to those operating the means of transport. Also certain kinds of behaviour can have the function of a sign e.g. nodding the head is a sign of agreement, waving the hand is a sign of farewell.

A special group of signs is formed by those when the relationship between the sign and the denoted object is obvious, because of sensory similarity, as in the case of pictures, sketches, drawings or photographs. In such instances we speak of iconographic signs, which represent material, sensorily perceptible objects. In the process of social com munication through the medium of signs we also represent objects that are not sensorily perceptible, such as human virtues, feelings, religious ideas, political views. Usually we say that the cross symbolizes Christendom, the crescent Islam, the owl symbolizes wisdom, the lion bravery, and so forth. Many of these signs are linked with thousand-year old traditions of individual cultures, and the mechanism of their impacts need not be intellectual only, but also emotional.

The above outlined distinction of some elementary types of signs naturally represents but one of the plurality of possible variants of the typology of signs, with the different links and transitions (between individual types of signs). Besides the typologies of the said or similar kinds, which point primarily to exterior differences and links between individual kinds of signs, account should also be taken of other distinctions, differentiating the signs in a more abstract manner, on the basis of their function in the communication process. The sign is perceived, registered and distinguished always as a whole, as a shape, as an element of a certain class of signs. A faithful Christian interprets the cross, i.e. the symbol of his faith, to a certain effect – regardless of whether he is faced with a miniature object he carries around his neck, or a giant structure erected at the peak of a church steeple or of a mountain. This means that in the course of a sign-process it is always a certain sign-event that is perceived, but which is interpreted in terms of the membership of this sign-event in a certain sign class. A written word of a definite language is understood in the same way, irrespective of the type of lettering it has been written in. For these reasons it is useful to discern the sign as a sign-event and the sign as a sign design. (The terminological distinction of the two types of signs differs with individual authors, but the fundamentals of the differentiation essentially agree. In the same sense S. C. Peirce (1931– 1935; 1940) made a distinction between 'token' and 'type', R. Carnap between 'sign-event' and 'sign-design', H. Reichenbach (1947) between 'token' and 'symbol', K. Dürr (1954) between 'signs *in concreto*' and 'sign *in abstracto*', A. A. Markov (1954) between 'concrete letters' and 'abstract letters.' Inasmuch as we discern and interpret signs in their entirety, in the analysis of semiotic problems in logic, linguistics, information theory and other fields it is more customary to consider the 'sign-designs' as the point of departure for the investigation of problems of this kind. However, there are also serious attempts of an extremely nominalistic viewpoint, which regard the sign-events as the starting point of semiotic analysis.

3. LEVELS OF SEMIOTIC ANALYSIS

Semiotic analysis is primarily based on three components of the sign process: 1) signs, 2) objects to which the sign refers, 3) interpreters. (For the individual components the literature employs different terms, for example for 3): communicant, user of the sign, user of the language, speaker, etc.) In this connexion the interpreter is assumed to be able to understand the given signs: this means that a response by the interpreter, or the disposition of the interpreter to respond to the given sign in an adequate manner, are both possible. Taking into consideration the three basic components of the sign process and assuming that we are faced with a sign-system having a linguistic structure, we can distinguish three levels of semiotic analysis:

– In so far as we take into account only the signs and their mutual relations, abstracting from the relationship betweeen the signs and the remaining components of the sign-process, we operate at the *syntactic level of semiotic analysis.*

– If, in addition, we take account of the relations between the signs (or the texts consisting of these signs) and the objects to which they refer, abstracting from the relationship to the interpreters of the signs, we operate at the *level of semantic analysis.*

– If we were also to include the relationship to the interpreters, and possibly their motives, goals, reactions, dispositions and so forth, we would be operating at the *level of pragmatic analysis.*

It is clear that this differentiation of the three levels of semiotic analysis represents a certain abstraction. Every actual sign-process naturally presupposes that all of the relationships mentioned are brought into play. From this angle the syntactic level of semiotic analysis is actually the most abstract, and the pragmatic level the most concrete of the three.

The relations among the three components may assume the form of rules, which according to the nature of these relations are characterized as syntactic, semantic and pragmatic rules.

The sign-systems comprising syntactic and semantic rules are also characterized as *sign systems with a linguistic structure* or languages (in the general sense of the word). From this standpoint we may make a distinction between signs that are elements of a sign-system with a linguistic structure (for instance written or uttered words, symbolical means of mathematics or logic, etc.), and signs that do not form linguistic structures (for example, the hammer and sickle, flags, coats-of-arms, etc.). The actual basis of social communication as well as the elementary means of expression and preservation of the results of cognitive activity are sign-systems with linguistic structure.

Among sign-systems with linguistic structure rank, in the first place, natural languages e.g. English, Chinese, Swedish. From natural languages we sometimes distinguish the so-called artificial languages, such as Esperanto, the structure of which does not however substantially differ from those of the natural languages. A special group is formed by the so-called formalized sign-systems or formalized languages which work with constructive symbolical means and whose structure is fixed by exactly and uniquely formulated rules.

Also the formalized sign-systems use means serving to express certain objects, events or operations. These means, which have been constructed in mathematics and logic, can have either a constant or a variable meaning, the scope of the variability being always determined. From this point of view the signs of a formalized sign-system can be divided into constants and variables. When developing a formalized sign-system certain mandatory steps must be taken: firstly a complete list of signs must be drawn up, and the various kinds of signs must be distinguished. The next step consists in determining the mode in which these signs are to be used, i.e. how they can be made up into expressions qualified in a certain manner, for example well-formed formulae, sentences. In this respect it is usual to speak of the rules of formation of a formalized sign-system. The rules of formation determine exactly which connections and which sequences of signs have a certain qualified character, i.e. which are sentences, well-formed formulae, etc., and which sequences of signs are lacking such a character. The next step in the development of a formalized sign-system is the determination of inference rules which would enable us to derive one set of expressions from other expressions. These steps, which constitute the syntactic component of the development of a formalized sign-system, enable us to undertake certain operations involving signs as well as expressions formed therefrom, without knowing the meaning of the signs and expressions. If however, we are to determine the meaning, what we need are the semantic rules, the sum of which constitutes the semantic component of the construction of a formalized sign-system. If any of the terms (correctly formed according to the rules of formation) are characterized as axioms (i.e. their validity is postulated, other expressions admitted as valid only in so far as they can be deduced from the axioms), the given formalized sign-system is an axiomatized system.

The development of semiotic analysis at all the mentioned levels presupposes that the signs and their mutual relations as well as their relations to other objects have become objects of investigation, the results of which we naturally always express through the intermediary of other signs. It is therefore expedient to make a distinction between object-signs and analogously object-sign systems etc., object-languages and the like, in respect of which we formulate statements – and metasigns, metasystems, metalanguages, by means of which we formulate our statements. Such a distinction has been carried out, in particular, in logic, because mixing object-signs and metasigns may result in paradoxes.

By analogy with this distinction we must discern exactly when the sign has been used to denote an object, and when a sign is on the contrary mentioned as something that denotes itself. This should be clear from the following example:

London is the capital of the United Kingdom.

'London' has 6 letters.

Although the signs 'London' and 'capital of the United Kingdom' denote the same object, namely the city situated on the Thames, we cannot mutually interchange London and 'London', because in the former instance the sign is used to denote another object, whereas in the the latter case it is meant to express the sign itself.

4. SIGN AND MEANING

If in the communication process we come across signs, we are in a position to comprehend them provided we can answer the following or similar questions: 'what does ... mean', 'what is the meaning of ...', 'what does ... refer to', and so on. In all these and similar questions it is presumed that we have assigned the given sign to other extralinguistic objects. (It is only natural that the distinction of linguistic and extralinguistic objects is relative, i.e. is only feasible with regard to the given object-language.) Such an assumption is valid, however, only conditionally: in sign-systems with linguistic structure no such objects can be assigned to certain signs; the function of this special kind of signs is linked with the syntactic structure of the sign system. For these reasons it is essential to amplify the introductory note also to cover the question as to what assumptions must be made for us to be capable of comprehending the signs: we are able to comprehend them if we are familiar with their extralinguistic meaning – or if we know the function of these signs in the syntactic structure of the sign system.

In natural languages, according to an old tradition we keep apart the so-called *syncategorematic words* which have no extralinguistic meaning by themselves, but only in conjunction with words having an independent extralinguistic meaning of their own. In other words: syncategorematic signs are by themselves not able to make any statements on the given universe of discourse – they can only make such statements in conjunction with categorematic words.

In formalized languages we distinguish *logical signs from extralogical signs*. If the function of the signs remains invariant with respect to any universe of discourse, we are confronted with logical signs. Logical signs as such do not refer to any extralinguistic objects: in cognitive processes and communication processes alike, they can be used only in conjunction with extralogical signs. An exact and unequivocal distinction between logical and extralogical signs in sign-systems with linguistic structure is not simple and as a result there is no uniform conception of such a distinction. Sign-systems with linguistic structure are hierarchically arranged. For example, words can be made up into a clause, clauses can be made up into complex sentences: all these expressions we are able to interpret, namely make decisions regarding the objects or states of the given universe of discourse to which we assign the expressions. By analogy this is also valid for formalized sign systems. Of all these signs and expressions in respect of which such an assignment is possible we say that they are capable of being semantically analyzed or semantized.

The semantization of signs and of semantizable expressions in general does not proceed in accordance with a general scheme. What is essential in this connexion is the character of the given universe of discourse, the syntactic structure of the selected sign-system and the level of the semantizable expressions. (It is for example evident that the process of semantization will differ in the case of words representing names of objects, in the case of clauses, complex sentences, sentential contexts, etc.)

While it is not possible to point out a uniform scheme of semantization, it is expedient to sketch some elementary trends in which semantization can be oriented, especially in consideration of the fact that sign-systems come into play in cognitive processes and communication processes. The linkages between cognitive processes and communication processes, and hence also the links between the basic trends of semantization can be outlined in the following diagram:

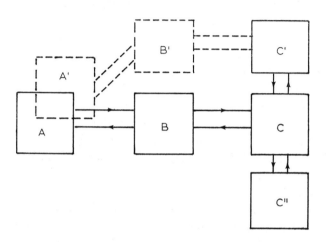

Block *A* which we may characterize as a source of information, is the object area under investigation: block *B* can be a human observer, or an observer fitted with equipment extending his sensory ability to discern, or finally any measuring or experimental equipment able to register stimuli coming from block *A*. Block *C* is a system of expressions. The relations between *A*, *B* and *C* schematically represent the cognitive process, relations between *C*, *C'* and *C''* etc. the communicative process. Knowledge concerning *A*, enabling us to achieve the semantization of the elements *C*, is then acquired by two ways: on the basis of what B. Russell characterized as knowledge by acquaintance, and on the basis of the communication process (Russell spoke in this connexion of knowledge by description. In the former case extralinguistic means can also be used for the semantization of signs or expressions made up of signs – in the latter case other signs or other expressions are always employed for semantization. The procedures of the semantization of signs which are based on extralinguistic means, such as pointing to the object to be denoted, or pointing out the event to be denoted, or carrying out the operation in question and the like, are characterized as ostensive procedures. In process of mastering the meaning of the signs, ostensive procedures represent but the most elementary levels of semantization. Higher levels of semantization are based on the application of other signs, for example definitions, explications, interpretations etc. The same applies to the ways in which children learn languages, the ways and methods of studying other languages, learning of the meaning of unfamiliar signs, and so forth.

Leaving aside the logical signs, the semantization of signs and expressions forming the elements of block C can be understood as *assignment*. The concept 'assignment' is encountered in a simple, and somewhat naive question: 'what corresponds to ...'. This question postulates the assignment to block C of elements of block A, and possibly of block B (in this event we speak of the expressive function of the sign-system, in contradistinction to other functions), or ultimately elements of block C', C'', etc. This question actually presupposes structural similarity of blocks A, B and C, which is a most problematic supposition. Only in the simplest case has the assignment the character of a one-to-one relation, for example with proper nouns of individual objects. In most cases the assignment has a much more complex form, for example with general expressions, signs denoting theoretical concepts, and so on.

Semantization of sign-systems presents a serious problem: the problem of levels for the assignment. Assuming that blocks A, B and C are formed by certain elements, we must not lose sight of the fact that these elements may be categorized in certain ways, that they form certain wholes and establish certain relations, that they are hierarchically arranged in certain levels, etc. If in block C we use natural languages, such as English, German, Russian and the like, we shall find that the expressions appearing in C are made up of words, clauses, complex sentences etc. If, however, we make use of a formalized language the logical basis of which is the predicate calculus, we must distinguish individuals, predicates, sentences and formulae. In this manner we can reach a question that could be formulated in the following way: with regard to which category of discernible elements and at which level are we entitled to think about assignment? Analogously similar questions can also be formulated with respect to the structure of the other blocks.

If it is possible – in view of the given universe of discourse and in view of the given sign-system – to formulate a satisfactory answer to the given question, i.e. select suitable levels for assignment, then it is feasible to isolate, in the sign-system, those signs and expressions formed therefrom which can be regarded as *names* of the objects denoted. The analysis of the meaning of signs based on the name-relation is, however, not the only imaginable approach to the problems of meaning. Besides various variants of the theory of the name-relation a number of other conceptions have been developed: in contemporary semiotics there does not exist a single, universally accepted conception of meaning. Also the scope of signs that can be regarded as names is, as a rule, not uniformly determined.

If we regard certain signs as names of the objects to be denoted, we shall not be able to avoid certain difficulties. Difficulties arise, in particular, if we are confronted with the task of determining which signs are identical, what are the conditions of the interchangeability of signs, what means that two signs have the same meaning, and the like.

The first attempt at a more systematic conception of the name-relation is represented by the conception of Frege who distinguishes between the *denotation* of a name and its sense. (The authors who developed and modified Frege's conception have sometimes employed a different terminology.) Frege starts with the following question: are the names 'evening star' and 'morning star' identical? And if so, then in what respect? His answer is simple: it is convenient to assign to the name not only the denoted object, but also its sense. Semantic analysis can therefore be carried out in two ways: names have denotation and sense. The establishment that the names 'evening star' and 'morning star' have different senses, but the same denotation is not entirely trivial, for such an establishment assumes a certain amount of knowledge. The same can be demonstrated on the oft-quoted example by Russell: 'Walter Scott' and 'the author of Waverley' denote the same person – this fact not being however always known – whereas the sense of the two signs differs.

In logic as well as in logical semantics, the approaches so far most thoroughly developed are those which are based on the concepts of denotation (or extension).

Approaches of this kind have been worked out, in particular, by A. Tarski, R. Carnap and A. Church. Much more difficult is the development of the semantic approaches based on the concept of sense (intension). The critics of detonational – or extensional – semantics would rightly point out that the reason why we understand a sign is not that we can point out its denotation, but because we know its sense. We also understand signs and expressions with respect to which we are absolutely unable to make reference to their denotation, such as the 'round square' or the *perpetuum mobile* and the like. The ways of understanding the sense or intension of signs differ greatly: the sense can be understood as a postulated abstract entity, as a concept, as a set of all logically equivalent expressions or all synonymous expressions, as what is invariant in any correct translation of the sign, etc. Whereas the criteria for the establishment of an identical denotation are considerably simpler, such criteria for the establishment of an identical sense are much more complicated, and as yet subject to extensive discussions.

The semantic analysis of signs, which is based on the concepts of denotation and sense, actually abstracts from the fact that there always is an interpreter of a sign. With the sign the interpreter always associates certain psychical states or beliefs of his own, connects certain external or internal reactions or dispositions to such reactions, certain decisions of his own. Hence we do not debar – especially in the semantic analysis of the signs in the communication process – such assignments as are based upon the attitude of the interpreter as the subject of thought, action, decision, and so on.

If we now revert to our scheme, the previously sketched ways of the semantization of signs representing elements of block C can be understood as various manners of assignment, and in this respect we can operate with both the elements of block A and elements of block B, or elements of blocks C, C', C'', etc. With the modern cybernetic approach to the mutual connexions of these blocks, feedbacks between the different blocks must always be presumed. This implies for example that because of the discrete character of elements C we often tend to regard as discrete also the elements A, or elements B. It should be stressed here that a sign-system usually only affords the possibility of a discrete representation of objects, events, experiences, and so forth, which in themselves may be either discrete or continuous.

5. SIGNS AND CYBERNETIC MACHINES

If we characterize a sign as any material object, its property, an event, a property of an event etc., that in the communication process can serve to communicate information or that can be interpreted, it should be underlined that the interpreter does not have to be, of necessity, man. By means of cybernetic equipment present-day man can imitate the ability to interpret signs, and hence also the ability to process information. Therefore, contemporary computers can also be characterized as sign-using machines. Man as the interpreter of signs is capable of responding to signs in a certain way, whether this response will manifest itself in making certain decisions, in the form of outward behaviour or in the form of mental processes. The cybernetic machine also reacts to signs of a certain kind by making decisions in favour of certain operations. By means of these operations the machine solves the tasks entrusted to it. To 'solve a task' means to convert the given task into a sequence of elementary operations that the machine is able to carry out. The instruction to carry out a sequence of operations with a view of tackling a certain class of tasks on the basis of initial data – is termed an *algorithm*. An algorithm must fulfil the following requirements:

– it must be determined, i.e. at no stage of the operations must it permit doubts as to how to proceed further;

– it must be able to depart from variable initial data, i.e. it must provide an instruction for the solution of a certain class of related tasks;

– it must be capable of leading to the solution required.

A task can be considered algorithmically solvable if it is feasible to construct an algorithm for the investigation of the task. The sign-system through the medium of which an algorithmic solution and hence also individual elementary operations as well as their sequence can be expressed is characterized as an *algorithmic language*. An algorithmic language must be capable of recording the set of elementary operations, their mutual relations, their sequences, and so forth. This means, for example, that it must be laid down what relations and sequences are permissible and what are not. If the sum of the elementary operations is represented by an operational code of a cybernetic machine, then the algorithmic language for this set of operations can be referred to as the 'language of the machine'.

Algorithmical languages, in which data and instructions can be put into a cybernetic machine with the aim of solving a certain task, can be regarded as a special kind of formalized sign-systems.

The initial data needed for the solution of a given task as well as the respective instructions must therefore be put into the machine in the 'language of the machine'. This however necessarily implies that such data and instructions must be translated, i.e. for the data and instructions expressed in the original sign-system we must substitute data and instructions expressed in the 'language of the machine'. The rule governing this translation is usually referred to as a *code*. In the general sense we call coding any representation of a definite object or event by means of other objects or events, i.e. a substitution of one set of sign for another set of signs, while maintaining the semantic characteristics of the signs. (The question as to what semantic characteristics are actually preserved is a subject of discussions, and may be answered in various ways.)

6. METHODOLOGICAL SIGNIFICANCE OF SEMIOTICS

The problems with which semiotics is concerned do not form a closed and homogeneous domain, but touch upon and transcend a series of scientific disciplines: wherever we handle data that can always be expressed by means of signs and expressions formed therefrom, it is necessary to take into account semiotic problems. This is in the first place true of those disciplines in which accuracy of expression has been brought to the highest degree of perfection: mathematics and logic. In the justification of the foundations of mathematics we shall come up against problems that are closely tied to semiotics. Also in logic we shall find it impossible to tackle certain key problems without taking into consideration the results of semiotic analysis, especially the results of the so-called logical semantics dealing with the semantic analysis of formalized languages. The justification of certain elementary concepts in logic, such as the concepts of 'logical consequence' and the concept of 'model', is based on logical semantics.

Also in the language of the empirical sciences problems linked with semiotic occupy an important position. In science we always work with various signs and expressions which must be interpreted. In this connexion it is essential to make a distinction between those procedures by means of which we make decisions on the objects of the province under investigation (in this connexion we sometimes speak of ontic decision-making), and those procedures by means of which we take decisions about signs and expressions formed therefrom (in this connexion we commonly speak of semantic decision-making). In the former case the position is that the objects of the given universe of discourse can be, for example, described, measured, explained, forecast, and the like. In the latter case the position is that the signs and expressions made therefrom can be explicated, interpreted, some expressions can be validated, confirmed, etc. Cognitive scientific activity, of course, involves procedures of both types, mutually interlocking and complementing each other.

Contemporary semiotics has subjected to a thorough study also the problems of the ontic commitments of individual signs and expressions made up of them. The problem we are confronted with is whether the use of signs or expressions of a certain category which represent the names of assumed extralinguistic objects does not commit us to a recognition of the existence of these objects, or possibly in what context and under what conditions such ontic commitments can be accepted. Without taking into consideration the relationships subjected to study in semiotics we cannot achieve the distinction between the ontic character of individual extralinguistic objects, and the semantic character of the signs and expressions formed from them. The problems of ontic commitments in formalized languages are essential to making the decisions as to what entities are permissible as values of free variables.

For the languages of the empirical sciences great importance must be attached to the study of the criteria for the meaning of signs and expressions, as well as a study of the methods which enable us to distinguish meaningless and meaningful expressions. While we have not succeeded in working out a uniform, absolutely valid criterion of meaning, binding for all signs and all expressions of the language of the empirical sciences (attempts to elaborate a uniform criterion for validation, operations, or other empirical criteria having failed) – with respect to a given sign-system, a given universe of discourse and a given class of tasks it is always mandatory to define relatively dependable criteria of the sense of signs and expressions.

REFERENCES

BRÉAL, M., (1904) *Essai de sémantique, science des significations*, Paris.
CARNAP, R., (1942) 'Introduction to semantics', *Studies in Semantics*, Vol. *I*, Cambridge (Mass.).
CASSIRER, E., (1923–1931) *Philosophie der symbolischen Formen*, Berlin.
CHASE, S., (1938) *The Tyranny of Words*, New York, Harcourt, Brace and Company.
CHASE, S., (1954) *The Power of Words*, New York, Harcourt, Brace and Company.

CHURCH, A., (1956) *Introduction to Mathematical Logic*, Princeton (N.J.), Princeton Univ. Press.

DÜRR, K., (1954) *Lehrbuch der Logistik*, Basel-Stuttgart.

FODOR, J. A. and KATZ, J. J., (eds.) (1964) *The Structure of Language*, New York, Prentice-Hall.

FREGE, G. (1892) 'Über Sinn und Bedeutung', *Zeitschrift für Philosophie und philosophische Kritik*, *100*, 25–50.

HAYAKAWA, S. I. (1941) *Language in Action*, New York, Harcourt, Brace and Company.

HUSSERL, E., (1913–1921) *Logische Untersuchungen*, Vol. I and II, Halle, M. Niemeyer.

KLEENE, S. C., (1950) *Introduction to Meta-mathematics*, New York, Van Nostrand Company.

KORZYBSKI, A., (1933) *Science and Sanity. An Introduction to non-Aristotelian Systems and General Semantics*, Lancaster, The Science Press.

KOTARBIŃSKI, T., (1961) *Elementy teorii poznania, logiki formalnej i metodologii nauk*, Wróclaw and Warsaw, Ossolineum. (First edition in 1929.)

LOCKE, J., *Essay concerning Human Understanding*, Book IV, Chap. XXI.

MARKOV, A. A., (1954) *Teorija algoritmov*, Moscow, T.M.I.

MARTIN, R. M., (1958) *Truth and Denotation. A Study of Semantical Theory*, Chicago (Ill.), Univ. of Chicago Press.

MORRIS, C. W., (1938) 'Foundations of the theory of signs', in *International Encyclopaedia of Unified Science*, *I*, *2*, Chicago (Ill.), Univ. of Chicago Press.

MORRIS, C. W., (1946) *Signs, Language and Behaviour*, New York, Prentice-Hall.

MORRIS, C. W. (1964) *Signification and Significance*, M.I.T. Press.

NARSKIJ, I. S., (1969) *Problema znaka i znatchneya Izd*, Moscow, Moskovskogo Universiteta.

OGDEN, C. K. and RICHARDS, I. A., (1923) *The Meaning of Meaning*, K. Paul, Trench, Trubner Ltd.

PEIRCE, C. S., (1931–1935) *Collected Papers*, 6 Vol., C. Hartshorne and P. Weiss (eds.), Harvard Univ. Press.

PEIRCE, C. S. (1940) 'The Theory of Signs', in J. Buchler (ed.), *The Philosophy of C. S. Peirce*, New York, Harcourt, Brace and Company.

QUINE, W. V. O., (1953) *From a Logical Point of View*, Harvard Univ. Press.

QUINE, W. V. O., (1960) *Word and Object*, Harvard Univ. Press.

REICHENBACH, H., (1947) *Elements of Symbolic Logic*, New York, Macmillan.

RUSSELL, B., (1905) 'On denoting', *Mind*, *14*, 479–493.

RUSSELL, B., (1910–1912–1913) *Principia Mathematica*, Vol. I–III (together with Whitehead, A. N.), Cambridge (Mass.), Cambridge Univ. Press.

RUSSELL, B., (1912) *The Problems of Philosophy*, New York.

RUSSELL, B., (1940) *An Inquiry into Meaning and Truth*, New York-London, Allen and Unwin.

RUSSELL, B., (1947) *Human Knowledge, its Scope and Limits*, London-New York, Allen and Unwin.

TONDL, L., (1966) *Problémy sémantiky*, Prague.

TRACHTENBROT, B. A., (1960) *Algoritmi i maschinnoe reschenye zadatch*, Moscow.

6 Language

YEHOSHUA BAR-HILLEL

During the last fifteen years, since the appearance of Noam Chomsky's first book (1957), conceptions of language have undergone a radical change, so that some time can reasonably be spent on bringing them into focus. Interestingly enough, these revised conceptions in part deliberately hark back to views that were prevalent during the rationalist Cartesian period of the seventeenth and eighteenth centuries and might be called neo-Cartesian linguistics, paraphrasing the title of another more recent book by Chomsky (1966), in which these connexions are clearly delineated.

I regard this Chomskyan revolution to be of such decisive importance that I intend to devote most of the present survey to its description, fully aware of the injustice that may thereby be caused to some, perhaps not much less original and fruitful, contributions by others. But the space allotted to me is limited, and I therefore feel that my decision is justifiable.

Let us then see what are the major tenets and consequences of this revolution. I shall not discuss them in anything like chronological order, nor rank them according to their objective importance (since I would not know how to make such a ranking), but according to a scheme which might look rather arbitrary but behind which, I believe, there is some rational justification.

1. NATURAL LANGUAGES ARE SPECIES-SPECIFIC

The ways in which humans, animals, and certain artefacts such as computers communicate with other members of their species and, on occasion, even with members of other species, are many and varied. It is of no particular importance for our present purposes to go at any depth into the terminological question as to whether the term 'communication' is or is not appropriate for the many things that happen, say, between the programmer and the computer, though I will say a few words about this question later.

However, what has become clear during the last years is that natural languages, as we know them, are species-specific and that to the best of our empirical knowledge – and I stress 'empirical' – nothing of the kind exists in beast or machine. There is no 'continuity' in any serious sense between the communication systems in use amongst them and the particular communication system that relies essentially on natural languages in use among humans (see Chomsky, 1966, 1968; Lenneberg, 1964).

This immediately raises the age-old question of the origin of human languages, which has probably given rise to no fewer myths or less speculation than any other of the questions with which mankind has been grappling since the dawn of history.

In view of this antiquity, it seems strange that so many serious thinkers have come to the conclusion that it might still be premature to take it up. They believe that there are a large number of other questions to be solved first; and, if these do not find at least a tentative solution, there is little chance of making much progress in tracing the origin of the human *faculté de langage*, to use the well-known Saussurian phrase.

While this problem of the origins has lost much of its appeal and is nowadays dealt with only in popular or, at best, semi-popular publications but hardly at all in the scientific literature, a related problem has come to the fore, viz. that of the acquisition of language. It, too, is old, in either of its two main forms: the acquisition of a mother tongue in early childhood, and the acquisition of a second language, at any age.

The second variation is usually regarded as being primarily pedagogical and, as such, has attracted countless studies by linguists and educators. The acquisition of one's mother tongue seems to be of deeper importance, perhaps the deepest problem of psycholinguistics altogether, yet still simple enough for almost anybody who has ever had children of his own to raise to be able to make useful and relevant observations. Indeed, the literature abounds in stories told by psycholinguists about their personal experiences with their children. (Notice that most of this material is observational and anecdotal, since, for obvious reasons, one would hardly perform controlled experiments in language acquisition with young children.)

Though there is no dearth of observational material on first language acquisition and of both observational and experimental material on second language acquisition, the theory, in both cases, is still in its infancy – in fact, it is doubtful whether the term 'theory' should be used at all for whatever is available. This is not meant to belittle the work of such pioneers as Wilhelm Stern (1907), Jean Piaget (1926), or Lev Semonovich Vygotsky (1962), or the more recent work reported upon (with bibliography) in Part One of R. C. Oldfield and J. C. Marshall (1968); rather it reflects the objective state of affairs.

The major drawback seems again to lie in the fact that theoretical linguistics as such is still at a very rudimentary stage. Notice that the first textbook to carry the phrase 'theoretical linguistics' in its title (John Lyons, 1968) was published only four years ago; related phrases appear in two earlier books by Noam Chomsky (1965a,b). I myself used this phrase (Bar-Hillel, 1962).

The Chomskyan revolution accordingly postulates that a serious treatment of the problem of language acquisition and, in particular, first language acquisition, must be based on theoretical constructions from a general theory of language.

2. PRIORITY OF LINGUISTIC COMPETENCE OVER LINGUISTIC PERFORMANCE

Acquiring a language is equated with acquiring the knowledge of a language, a certain linguistic competence, i.e. mastering a particular system of rules that relate sound and meaning (to use the standard, somewhat old-fashioned terminology). Having acquired this competence, an ideal speaker-hearer (it is perhaps not superfluous to remark that in the current lingo, one means by the term 'speaker' any producer of some linguistic units, whether by speech, writing, typing or by any other appropriate mode of communication; the same holds, of course, for 'hearer') can express any meaning he wishes to communicate by an appropriate sequence of sounds (perhaps in more than one way) and assign to sound sequences he has heard uttered within certain contexts the meaning (or meanings) that is (are) usually expressed by such sequences (in these contexts), despite the fact – and here lies the crux of the matter – that he might never before have heard this particular sequence in any context, nor have been in a position to want to express this particular meaning.

Real speakers-hearers (as opposed to ideal ones) have limitations that affect their linguistic performance, both in communicating and in understanding. Probably the most important are the limitations of the short-term memory, which, among other things, will affect the degree of syntactic complexity of the sentences which speakers can utter or hearers can understand without having to guess. The production or perception of sentences of great syntactic complexity requires memory aids that are not normally available. However, these sentences still belong to the language known by any speaker of this language; he knows, in principle, how to deal with them, and can do so successfully in practice as soon as he manages to extend his limited short-term memory by some artificial device.

Other factors that impair success in communicating or understanding are, for instance, defects in the articulatory or auditory mechanisms, or in the central nervous system, but also such simple and frequent factors as gaps in the background knowledge of speaker and hearer or even lack of good-will on the part of the hearer. A speaker, when addressing a certain hearer, will often expect him to use his background knowledge and his comprehension of the context as well as of the linguistic co-text to understand the uttered sentence in a unique way, to disambiguate it, if necessary, on this basis, and this in spite of the fact that he might be fully aware that the sentence as such is syntactically and/or semantically ambiguous. The expected disambiguation might fail, however, for the simple reason that the presupposed background knowledge is just not there or that the hearer refuses, for whatever reason, to use the relevant knowledge in his possession for this purpose. This is only one illustration of the countless situations in which communication will fail because the actual performance will fall short of what could have been achieved with the available competence.

Though all this may sound rather simple, even trite, it should be stressed that neither rhetorics nor the theory of argumentation, nor their modern counterparts, psycholinguistics, sociolinguistics and communication theory, the sciences that should study, among other things, the conditions under which communication will succeed or fail, have been able to develop a really satisfactory theory, in spite of countless sporadic observations and occasional laboratory experiments. (Let me call the reader's attention, almost at random, to the following relevant publications: Perelman and Olbrechts-Tyteca (1958), Saporta (1961), Bright (1966), Gumpertz and Hymes (1969) and Cherry (1957).)

This is usually explained, at least in part, by saying that these observations and experiments had no underlying sound theory of linguistic competence to back them up. Now that we seem to be well on the way towards such a theory, it is perhaps no longer premature to expect greater progress in the foreseeable future.

3. SYNTAX – THE LINK BETWEEN SOUND AND MEANING

Linguistics is often divided into grammar and semantics, and grammar is subdivided into phonology and syntax. Among these disciplines, phonology, the study of linguistic sound, already has a more or less satisfactory theory, though discussions between the proponents of the various competing phonological theories will doubtless continue for a long time to come (Chomsky and Halle, 1968). Semantics, the study of meaning, is still in its very earliest theoretical stages (semantics being a catch-all term, it might be useful to distinguish between linguistic semantics, logical semantics and philosophical semantics: for the first discipline, see Ullman (1962), Katz (1966); for the second, see Tarski (1956), Carnap (1946), Hintikka (1969); for the third, see Schilpp (1963), Wittgenstein (1953), Ziff (1960), Quine (1960), Katz (1966), and Bar-Hillel (1970b)), despite two thousand years of study and, on occasion, considerable sophistication. (For an excellent short history of semantics, see the article 'Semantics, History of' in *The Encyclopaedia of Philosophy*, VII, 358–406.) It is in the theoretization of syntax, the system of rules that provide a bridge between the two, that the Chomskyan school has made its most significant contribution so far, one that amounts to a real breakthrough.

The study of syntactic structure as such is as old as the study of language in general, but only very recently has it reached a degree of rigour and precision comparable to that of the better-developed natural sciences. Formulations such as the one which charges the syntax of a language with the task of 'generating' all and only the sentences of this language as well as of assigning them the intuitively correct structure(s) attractive as this formulation may sound, if only we are not frightened away by the hyper-modern term 'generate' (this term has been taken over from an admittedly rather obstruse subfield of mathematical logic, but in our context it has nevertheless an extremely simple meaning) borrowed from mathematical logic, are of very recent origin, but they tend to drive home the fact that syntax has, within a very short period, attained a degree of theoretization which other humanistic studies are still working hard to achieve. It has already reached the stage where one feels oneself entitled to speak of mathematical linguistics. Incidentally, this term is not without its dangers and is indeed often misunderstood. Most people, including some linguists, when they hear this term, almost automatically think of application of statistical methods to linguistic material, of frequency counts and the like. Statistics, however, applies primarily to speech and not to language, though the possibility of applying advanced statistical methods certainly endows the study of speech with a good amount of well-deserved respectability. But this possibility is not sufficient by itself to turn linguistics into a theoretical science. This decisive development happens only when a degree of formalization has been achieved sufficient for algebraic methods to become applicable. It is therefore only the rise of algebraic linguistics, the use of logico-algebraic methods in the study and description of language, which serves testimony to the fact that linguistics has come of age and is now competing with the best of the theoretical sciences for a place in the sun. (For some early papers in objective linguistics, see Luce, Bush and Galanter, 1965, Part II, Vol. II, and Bar-Hillel, 1964, Part II.)

Now that grammars are formulated, to an increasing degree, in a way that allows for a rigorous evaluation of their strength and complexity, it is possible, for the first time in the history of linguistics, to seriously compare competing grammars, and to provide something like proofs for the intuitive inadequacy of certain grammars, and even of whole classes of grammars. Only now, when the so-called immediate-constituent grammars, regarded by many linguists of the last generation as the most adequate types of grammars for the description of natural languages (Lyons, 1968, p. 209f), can be rigorously formalized in the form of phrase-structure grammars (p. 215f) or, alternatively, of categorial grammars (p. 227f), can one discuss the question of their adequacy with sufficient rigour. This rigour forced and enabled the linguists to distinguish between weak and strong adequacy, where a grammar is called weakly adequate when it generates all and only the intuitively well-formed sentences of the language in question, but strongly adequate, if, in addition, it assigns to each of the generated sentences its appropriate structure(s). It is only now that one can at last claim to be able to prove that certain types of grammars, such as the so-called context-free phrase-structure grammars, are inadequate for the generation of all natural languages (and it is irrelevant, for our purposes, whether one can say that these claims have been definitely substantiated). Many linguists are convinced that such grammars are inadequate for assigning to all sentences their correct structures and insufficient to serve as a basis for establishing the various semantic relationships that intuitively hold between sentences of superficially quite different forms such as

(1) John loves Mary

and

(2) Mary is loved by John

whose semantic relation is clearly a very strong one indeed, viz. nothing less than that of expressing the same cognitive content, while assigning the same syntactic structure to sentences whose intuitive semantic structure is, in some important sense, quite different, such as

(3) John is eager to please

and

(4) John is easy to please

thereby leaving vitally important semantic relations unexplained in the first case, while intimating spurious semantic relations, in the second case. These and similar facts made many linguists realize that generative grammars of the phrase-structure type, in spite of their superiority in rigour and degree of formalization over the older immediate-constituent grammars, or perhaps just because of this superiority which made possible a rigorous treatment of issues that before could be discussed only on an informal, non-committal level, are strongly inadequate, though some linguists may regard them as being weakly inadequate.

4. DEEP STRUCTURE AND SURFACE STRUCTURE

The particular way in which the Chomskyan school formulated the shortcomings of phrase structure grammars in explaining the exact relationship between the two pairs of sentences mentioned in the preceding section turned out to be extremely helpful, and might well be

Surface structure of (3)

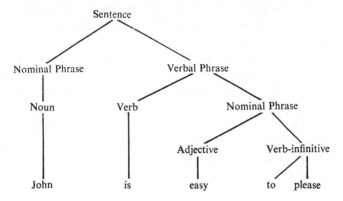

Surface structure of (4)

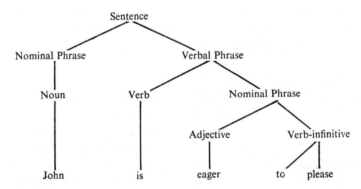

regarded as the most important specific contribution so far of this school to linguistics altogether. The formulation chosen was to say that the sentences (1) and (2), though exhibiting quite different surface (or superficial) structures – notice, e.g., that they have different subjects, that the verb in the one sentence is in the active mood and in the other in the passive mood – have the same deep (or depth) structure (or, perhaps, only very closely related deep structures; it would take us too far to go here into the fine, though highly interesting, details), while the opposite is the case for the other pair of sentences: (3) and (4) have the same surface

Deep structure of (3)

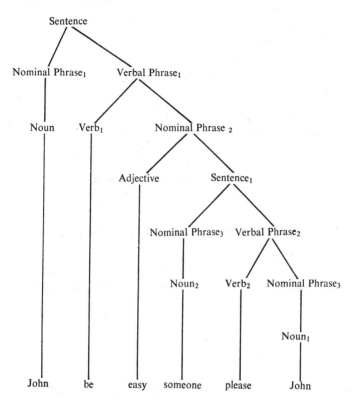

structure (up to the lexical items), and this even for the most detailed 'parsing', but very different deep structures.

Just for the sake of illustration and for whatever its worth in the absence of detailed explanations for which we have no space, let me present here one of the most often used methods of depicting the surface and deep structures of the sentences (3) and (4), the so-called 'tree form' (see above).

The transition from the deep structure to the surface structure is performed by so-called rules of transformation, a term Chomsky took over from his teacher Harris (1957), though not without considerable changes in its meaning, and which should be carefully distinguished from the homonymous one that played such an important role in Carnap's

Deep structure of (4)

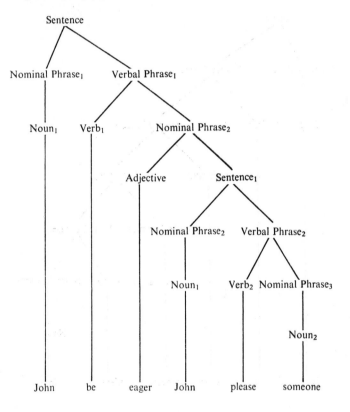

Logical Syntax (1937), where it meant what he later called rules of deduction. This is not the only function of the rules of transformation but the most important one. The terms 'deep structure' and 'surface structure' themselves are also not original with Chomsky since they had been used previously, with approximately the same meaning, though not with the same degree of rigour, by the philosopher L. Wittgenstein (1922) and the linguist C. Hockett (1958; the title of Chap. 29 is 'Surface and deep grammar').

The conceptions of 'deep structure', 'surface structure' and 'rules of transformation' have lately undergone considerable changes, sometimes of a very fundamental character. Since these changes are still very much in process and it is by no means clear at present in which direction they are going, I shall continue presenting here the 'classical' conception of their function. According to this conception, it is the deep structure of a given sentence (or its various deep structures, in case the sentence is syntactically ambiguous) which receives its meaning by the rules of semantic interpretation, while the surface structure receives its phonetic interpretation through phonological rules. The function of the transformation rules is, as said before, to map deep structures onto surface structures. According to the generative-transformational approach, a person who knows a specific language has control of a grammar that generates (or characterizes) the infinite set of potential deep structures, maps them (by appropriate rules of transformation) onto associated surface structures and determines the semantic and phonetic interpretations of these abstract structures by the appropriate semantic and phonetic rules, respectively.

Let it be said, once again, that the term 'generate' carries no psychological connotations. Generative grammars do not tell us how speakers produce the sentences they utter on some given occasion nor why they produce these utterances and not others. 'Generate' is not a psycholinguistic or sociolinguistic term, but a purely theoretical linguistic one; it has nothing to do with performance but belongs wholly with competence.

5. LINGUISTICS – A BRANCH OF COGNITIVE PSYCHOLOGY?

Probably the most daring and therefore also most controversial thesis of the Chomskyan school is the claim that both the theory of linguistic performance and the theory of linguistic competence, that is, linguistic theory in general, constitute a branch of psychology, and more specifically, of cognitive psychology (Chomsky, 1968, p. 1).

Such blunt formulations, needless to say, tread on many people's toes, thus infringe on many vested interests and therefore alienate many linguists for whom the autonomy and independence of linguistics is a matter of deep conviction. It is important, however, to realize that the Chomskyan claims have nothing in common with but, on the contrary, stand in the strongest possible opposition to, other claims which might sound superficially similar, namely claims to the effect that linguistics is reducible to behavioristic S–R (Stimulus-Response) psychology, and which identify linguistics with the study of verbal behaviour. Such claims were made most forcefully in B.F. Skinner (1957) and equally forcefully criticized in a review by Noam Chomsky (1959). Chomsky himself is strongly opposed to any conception that sees language as a 'habit structure', a network of associative connections, a skill expressible as a system of dispositions to respond (Chomsky, 1968, p. 22). He prefers to explore the possibilities for developing explanatory theories, and their implications with regard to the complexity and abstractness of the underlying mechanisms. For him, the search for explanatory theories must begin with an attempt to determine the systems of rules that constitute knowledge of a language and form a correct grammar of that language. As soon as one considers the problem of the confirmation of proposed grammars on the basis of empirical evidence, the actual performance of the speakers-hearers plays, of course, a decisive role. However, Chomsky regards it as a vital methodological principle that since actual speech behaviour is the result of the interaction of several factors, it is necessary, for an understanding of the precise character of this interaction, that each of these separate factors be first fairly well understood by itself.

Chomsky is ready to go one step further and look for explanatory theories of a deeper sort. When a native speaker acquires in his youth the grammar of his mother tongue, he has mastered a certain explanatory theory, on the basis of very restricted and degenerate data, i.e. from whatever he might have heard from members of his family and playmates, from corrections of his own babblings by adults and the reinforcements of his first successes at verbal communication, etc. But the grammar he constructs for himself goes far beyond this restricted evidence. There must be innate in him certain principles that successfully guide him in determining the form of the grammar he arrives at in such a short time. Chomsky proposes to call the set of these principles 'universal grammar' (1968, p. 57, n. 30), following what he believes to be traditional usage. (Though he is probably wrong on this historical count, this is a minor issue in our context.) Now the question at stake is whether the study of this 'universal grammar' can indeed be interpreted as part of the study of the structure of human intellectual capacities. For if we grant this – and we are still a long way from it, the arguments presented by Chomsky in favour of this view being so far not sufficient to convince all doubters – then the study of the structure of grammars of natural languages as well as the explorations of the various systems of meta-rules that explain how the child arrives at a correct grammar of his native language should lead us to a better understanding of cognition in general. Chomsky is fully aware of the fact that, as of today, any suggestions one can make along these lines are tentative and restricted in their coverage. Judging from the short history of these attempts, it seems fair to predict that no presently existing theory will survive for even a few years. But Chomsky and his followers are ready to stick their necks out and are convinced that the science of linguistics, as any other science, will advance only by 'conjectures and refutations', to invoke Popper's memorable phrase (1962).

Since the revival of the term 'universal grammar' has created a lot of misunderstandings, let me stress here that in this new, somewhat idiosyncratic usage, universal grammar is primarily a set of conditions that any human language must meet, almost a 'transcendental grammar' in a quasi-Kantian sense, and only secondarily a skeletal substructure of rules that any such language must contain. I tend to believe that Chomsky is here underestimating the degree of validity of the second more traditional view; on one occasion (Bar-Hillel, 1969), I myself proposed a view according to which logic should be identified with universal semantics and therefore with part of universal linguistics, in the 'secondary' sense, though there is no difficulty in reinterpreting this identification in the 'primary' sense, perhaps even more helpfully so.

6. THE CHOMSKYAN APPROACH VERSUS THE SEMIOTIC APPROACH

The Chomskyan dichotomy, theory of competence vs. theory of performance, is related to the well-known Saussurian distinction between *langue* and *parole* (de Saussure, 1955) and to distinctions drawn by others between language and speech, though it would take us too far to go into the communalities and diversities of the various conceptions.

However, let me point out that this view diverts, on purpose, from another classification which harks back to Peirce (1931–1935) and had been revived in our century by Morris (1938) and Carnap (1946). Peirce divided semiotic, the general theory of signs, into three layers of increasing abstraction. The lowest level, in which not only the relations between the signs among themselves and between the signs and the things denoted by these signs in the 'outside' world are considered, but also the uses of these signs in the various communicative acts are explicitly taken into account, he called pragmatics. At the next level of abstraction in which the uses of the signs are left out of consideration, one moves up into semantics. Finally, when even the relations between the signs and the world are put aside, one arrives in syntax (or syntactics, as it was sometimes called in this connection). (It should be noticed that the terms 'pragmatics', 'semantics' and 'syntax' are sometimes used in an exclusive sense, so that pragmatics is understood to deal only with the relations of the signs to the sign users, semantics only with the relations of the signs to the things signified, and syntax only with the relations of the signs among themselves. The term 'semiotic' is then used in the sense which 'pragmatics' has in its inclusive usage.)

Linguistics was considered by Peirce and his followers to be the theory of a certain specific subclass of signs, the linguistic signs, or symbols, and the tripartite division into pragmatics, semantics, and syntax, was carried over to it.

According to this scheme, then, semantics and syntax are arrived at from pragmatics by successive abstractions. Carnap, however, drew the extremely important distinction between descriptive semantics and syntax, on the one hand, and pure semantics and syntax, on the other, stressing that while descriptive semantics and syntax are indeed obtained by abstraction from (descriptive) pragmatics, so that in this sense pragmatics is the basis for all linguistics, this is not the case for pure semantics and syntax which are independent of pragmatics (Carnap, 1946, § 5).

It is interesting to note that, from the very beginning, the Chomskyan school, though using freely, as everybody else did, the semantics-syntax terminology (though wondering, on occasion, where to draw the borderline between the two and sometimes even doubting whether such a borderline can be usefully drawn at all; see, e.g., Noam Chomsky (1965b, Chap. 4, Section 1; the issue is still very much in active discussion), shied away from using the term 'pragmatics' and sometimes claimed in effect that the study of the impact of the 'socio-physical setting' (the term they used on occasion – Katz and Fodor, 1963 – as an approximate counterpart of 'pragmatic aspects') should be left out of linguistics altogether, the main reason for this decision being that a complete theory of the impact of the socio-physical setting is out of reach (remaining somewhat vague about the question whether this is so at present or whether this will remain so as a matter of principle). They were quite happy to let anybody interested pick up these left-overs from a complete linguistic description, which ideally contains exactly three components, phonological, syntactic and semantic, perhaps hoping that psycholinguists, sociolinguists, ethnolinguists, communication theoreticians, and their likes would declare interest in this mess.

I do not think that we can possibly leave it at that. The relation between linguistic theory and speech behavior must surely be a much closer one, and an efficient division of labor (and there is nothing wrong with division of labor as such) should run on different lines. As a matter of fact, by combining some of the views of Carnap and Chomsky, already described, with some new ideas of Hintikka (1968), it seems that a much more satisfactory picture can be arrived at. First, let us recall that Carnap's use of the term 'pure' preceded his decisive re-evaluation of the status of theoretical concepts and of theories in general. Let us, then, in accordance with this re-evaluation, talk about 'theoretical' semantics and syntax, or better, about semantic and syntactic theory, in preference to 'pure' semantics and syntax, or, better still, about 'linguistic theory', without prejudging the issue whether some classification of the rules of such a theory into phonological, syntactic, and semantic rules will turn out to be appropriate and useful. Whoever has acquired, mastered, internalized, the rules of the linguistic theory of some natural language, has become competent in that language. (There is, of course, no reason not to talk about degrees of competence just as we have no qualms talking about degrees of mastery of some language.) The actual speech behavior of a given speaker will then be regarded as the result of the interaction of his linguistic competence with his intentions and with various other factors and pressures, social or individual, general (such as the already mentioned small size of the human short-time memory) or special (such as pressures resulting from the particular situational context of utterance).

If we adopt this view, we can explain the way by which linguistic theory may throw light on what happens in ordinary discourse as follows: the meaning which an expression receives in the explanatory model provided by the theory is its basic meaning. The actual meaning of an utterance of this expression is obtained through modification of its basic meaning by the various mentioned factors. In principle, it could well happen that for some expression the actual meaning of all its utterances is never the same as its basic meaning, because for this particular expression the social pressures are always so high as to completely mask the basic meaning.

Looking at it from this point of view, certain well-known vexing problems appear in a new light. Though there is nothing wrong in saying that the basic meaning of a symbol for (inclusive) disjunction is such-and-such, it is definitely conceivable that the English word 'or' will seldom have this meaning in an actual utterance. To generalize, what formal logic does, under this conception, is to bring out the basic (or depth) meaning of the so-called 'logical' terms. Formal logic turns out to be the 'depth logic' of ordinary discourse. Using formal logic does not entail modifying or regimenting ordinary speech but is rather an effort to understand it more deeply and fully. Logic, *qua* theoretical, explanatory model, is not discovered but invented. Its rules are used as norms with which to compare and by which to evaluate actual discourse as to its logical force, in particular by which to judge the validity of arguments presented in natural language. Looking at the rules of logic as norms does not, of course, turn logic into a system of conventions, nor into a system of prescriptions. It is not the task of the logician to legislate about validity of arguments, just as it is not the task of the grammarian to legislate about well-formedness of linguistic expressions or their 'acceptability'. Theoretical grammar does not oppose descriptive grammar as being prescriptive, but contrasts with it as being explanatory, just as theoretical physics stands in no opposition to descriptive physics but is its explanatory supplement which no physicist would want to do without. The whole 'prescriptivism' issue disappears in thin air as soon as the theoretical character of a grammar is recognized for what it is (Chomsky, 1968, p. 13), and so do the equally spurious complaints about the 'fictitiousness' of some of the new grammars that go beyond description (Bar-Hillel, 1966).

7. LANGUAGE, DIALECT, IDIOLECT; COLLOQUIAL AND SCIENTIFIC LANGUAGE

Few issues in the study of language have raised so many controversies – and, to many onlookers, rather futile ones – as those centered around the distinctions between language, dialect and idiolect (Hockett, 1958, p. 321f). Everybody knows in his heart that some distinction must be drawn between the system of linguistic rules that govern the speech behavior of a given individual and the systems of linguistic rules that govern the speech behaviour of the various groups to which this individual belongs and that in part turn these groups into linguistic communities. It is only when one begins to theorize about these well-known facts that one quickly runs into seemingly unending differences of opinion and formulation.

I have no intention to enter these discussions here. The only comment I would like to make is to insist that these differences of opinion are no more severe than one should expect and pose no particular methodological problems the like of which do not occur in many other situations.

It is to be expected that the system of linguistic rules a person has acquired at a given age will be somewhat different from that of any other person with whom he comes in communicative contact. Nevertheless, these persons will often understand each other to various degrees, and sometimes perfectly, with the misunderstandings that would still arise to be traced exclusively to extra-linguistic causes. Each individual system is an idiolect, each common system is called a dialect or a language, depending on various other factors into which it would be too complicated to go here. As usual with such theoretical terms, there will be disputes about boundaries, whose acrimoniousness has nothing to do with any special methodological niceties but rather with the fact that certain dialects tend to acquire, for whatever historical reasons, certain prestige values which are absent from others, thereby introducing issues of prescriptiveness which have nothing to do with the scientific status of the problem.

One might also want to deplore the widespread custom of talking about 'scientific language', i.e. the language used by scientists, in opposition to 'colloquial (or everyday) language', i.e. the language used by the man-in-the-street, presumably including the scientists themselves, when 'off duty'. This custom is potentially misleading, though I am not sure whether any actual harm is often caused by it. The system of linguistic rules which governs a scientist's speech when he talks (or writes) shop is in no serious sense different from the one that governs his speech when he talks about everyday affairs. The difference certainly does not lie in that these modes of speech are governed by different rules but that in the scientific mode of speech, the scientist uses additional theoretical terms (and sometimes uses ordinary terms in a special, theoretical sense) whose meanings are theory-dependent, and hence fully comprehensible only to those who master the relevant theory, but the axioms and rules of interpretation of such a theory should be carefully distinguished from the rules of the language in which this theory is embedded. So, why not use 'scientific (or theoretical) mode of speech' rather than 'scientific language', and, if necessary, 'colloquial (or everyday) mode of speech' rather than 'colloquial language'.

8. CYBERNETICS AND LINGUISTICS

From its very beginning, cybernetics, as already indicated in the subtitle of Norbert Wiener's pioneering book (1948), was vitally interested in natural languages, as the main vehicle of communication between humans as well as in computer languages as the main vehicle of control which humans exercise over computers. Shortly after the publication of this book, another classic dealing with the mathematical theory of communication (Shannon and Weaver, 1949) was published, and there was at the time an ubiquitous feeling that with these two works a new era had begun and that a breakthrough had been achieved towards a full understanding of the complexities of communication 'in the animal and the machine' and, in particular, of human language. Among the many applications of this breakthrough, and as a result of a better understanding of the intrinsic properties of those marvelous symbol-manipulating mechanisms, the electronic digital computers, that expressed itself in the credo, 'if a human being can do it, a suitably programmed computer can do it too', one expected to make quick progress towards the full automation of high-quality translation, of document retrieval, of information retrieval, and even of deriving grammars from finite corpuses. Certain initial successes in all these directions were indeed quickly achieved, but one tended greatly to overestimate the reach of these limited achievements and to believe, or rather to hope, that the shortcomings would be overcome through an increase of the learning abilities of suitably programmed computers by the bootstrapping techniques of what became soon known as 'artificial intelligence' and 'self-organization'.

The expected breakthrough never arrived. It is vital, at this point, to shed all illusions in this respect. The high expectations were based in part on a deep misunderstanding of the relation between language and speech, as a result of which one failed to realize that the revolutionary insights of cybernetics and the powerful techniques of information theory, though indeed of decisive importance to the study of speech, were irrelevant to the study of language. In language, there is no place (beyond trivialities) for probability and statistics. Computational linguistics, unless it is based on theoretical linguistics, is, and in all likelihood will remain, of limited impact. But the role of the computer, and of cybernetic types of thinking, in the development of linguistic theories, as of all other theories, is at present extremely restricted. The more we understand the nature of scientific theories, the dimmer becomes the prospect of making increased use of computer facilities in developing such theories, though there seem to be good prospects for a much larger use of computers in the future in the testing of theories developed by humans and in forcing human scientists to increase the formalization of their theories, in order to allow for their testing by computers.

The situation might change if a language could be constructed in which humans and computers could converse, in a more or less literal sense of this word. But, unfortunately, here again, the better we understand the nature of human languages, the slimmer becomes the outlook for the possibility of developing an effective quasi-universal man-computer conversational language. Whatever some of the more speculative minds in the artificial intelligence field might think or say, for the time being at least, such a conversational language will have to look very much like a natural language, if it is expected to have the power and universality of such a language. This has often been realized but until recently the full implications of this realization were not really taken into account, probably just due to wishful thinking. One knew that natural languages are full of ambiguities, and much ingenious thinking was employed to program computers to discover the syntactic ambiguities and perhaps, on the basis of various tricks, to disambiguate given utterances of syntactically ambiguous sentences by taking into consideration the linguistic co-text, for instance, though this was done only after one came to realize that the occurrence of syntactic ambiguities, for all its annoying character, is one of the major sources of the powerfulness of natural languages.

A similar development, involving still more agonizing re-thinking, took place with regard to semantic ambiguities. In spite of some minor successes in the development of semantic disambiguation procedures, based upon partial sketches of semantic theories for natural languages and again on taking into consideration larger and larger co-texts and information solicited from the human partner during the 'conversation', it became soon clear that the successes were definitely of an isolated character, with small chances for significant generalizations. But the situation began to look almost hopeless when the essentially pragmatic character of human languages was fully realized and when one began to look at the relevant facts straight in the face (Bar-Hillel, 1970a). Human communication in natural languages is, in general, so successful and powerful, just because it relies to such a high degree on extra-linguistic channels, on the fact that speakers and hearers have certain background knowledge, have eyes, ears, and hands, and make use of them during conversation, as well as on countless other factors. The fact that in normal communication, utterances of syntactically and semantically ambiguous sentences are most of the time understood by the hearer in the exact sense intended by the speaker, is due mostly to the circumstance that all concerned make efficient use of these additional channels. The dilemma which the planner of a man-machine conversational language has to face is now clear: either the computer has to be equipped with the equivalents of the additional channels, turning it into a quasi-human entity, or else some way has to be found to expand the powers of the only channel available so far, its huge memory capacity and ability to understand certain programming languages, so as to turn it into a medium that will be able to take over the capacities of the other channels. Though attempts in those directions are being made at present by research groups all over the world, it should be unequivocally stated that so far both horns of the dilemma are in a largely programmatic stage and that only the perennial optimists still believe to be on their way towards a satisfactory solution.

Just because natural language has recently ceased to be a mystery, just because we now understand its nature so much better than ever before, we are in a position to appreciate its uniqueness as a system of communication and to get a realistic view of the difficulties that stand in the way of any attempt to replace it by some artifical device.

REFERENCES

BAR-HILLEL, Y., (1962) 'Some recent results in theoretical linguistics', in E. Nagel, P. Suppes and A. Tarski (eds.), *Logic, Methodology, and Philosophy of Science;*

Proceedings of the 1960 International Congress, Stanford (Calif.), Stanford Univ. Press, 551–557.

BAR-HILLEL, Y., (1964) *Language and Information*, Reading (Mass.), Addison-Wesley.

BAR-HILLEL, Y. (1966) 'On a misapprehension of the status of theories in linguistics', *Foundations of Linguistics*, 2, 39–399, reprinted in *Aspects of Language*.

BAR-HILLEL, Y., (1968) 'Cybernetics and linguistics', in S. Moser (ed.), *Information und Kommunikation*, Munich-Vienna, R. Oldenbourg, 29–38. Reprinted in *Aspects of Language*.

BAR-HILLEL, Y. (1969) 'Universal semantics of the philosophy of language', in J. Puhvel (ed.), *Substance and Structure of Language*, Univ. of California Press, 1–21. Reprinted in *Aspects of Language*.

BAR-HILLEL, Y., (1970a) 'Communication and argumentation in pragmatic languages', *Linguaggi Nella Società e Nella Tecnica* (Convegno Internazionale Olivetti, Milan, 1968), Milan, Edizioni di Communità.

BAR-HILLEL, Y., (1970b) *Aspects of Language*, Jerusalem, Magnes Press.

BRIGHT, W., (ed.) (1966) *Sociolinguistics*, The Hague, Mouton.

CARNAP, R., (1937) *The Logical Syntax of Language*, London, Kegan Paul, Trench, Trubner and Co.

CARNAP, R., (1946) *Introduction to Semantics*, Harvard Univ. Press.

CHERRY, C., (1957) *On Human Communication*, New York, John Wiley.

CHOMSKY, N., (1957) *Syntactic Structures*, The Hague, Mouton.

CHOMSKY, N., (1959) *Language*, 35, 26–58 (reprinted in J. A. Fodor and J. J. Katz, *The Structure of Language*, 547–578.)

CHOMSKY, N., (1965a) *Current Issues in Linguistic Theory*, The Hague, Mouton.

CHOMSKY, N., (1965b) *Aspects of the Theory of Syntax*, Cambridge (Mass.), M.I.T. Press.

CHOMSKY, N. (1966) *Cartesian Linguistics*, New York, Harper and Row.

CHOMSKY, N., (1968) *Language and Mind*, New York, Harcourt, Brace and World.

CHOMSKY, N. and HALLE, M., (1968) *The Sound Pattern of English*, New York, Harper and Row.

Encyclopaedia of Philosophy, vol. VII, New York, Macmillan, 358–406.

FODOR, J. A. and KATZ, J. J. (eds.), (1964) *The Structure of Language*, Englewood Cliffs (N.J.), Prentice-Hall.

GUMPERTZ, J. J. and HYMES, D., (eds) (1969) *Directions in Sociolinguistics. The Ethnography of Communication*, New York, Holt, Rinehart and Winston.

HARRIS, Z., (1957) 'Co-occurrence and transformation in linguistic structure', *Language*, 33, 283–340; reprinted in J. A. Fodor and J. J. Katz (eds.) *The Structure of Language*, Englewood Cliffs (N.J.) Prentice-Hall, 1964, 115–210.

HINTIKKA, J., (1968) 'Epistemic logic and the methods of philosophical analysis', *Australasian Journal of Philosophy*, 46, 37–51 (reprinted in J. Hintikka, 1969, *Models for Modalities*, Dordrecht/Holland, Reidel).

HOCKETT, C., (1958) *A Course in Modern Linguistics*, New York, Macmillan.

KATZ, J. J., (1966) *The Philosophy of Language*, New York, Harper and Row.

KATZ, J. J. and FODOR, J. A., (1963) 'The structure of a semantic theory', *Language*, 40, 170–210 (reprinted as Chap. 19 of *The Structure of Language*).

LENNEBERG, E. H. (1964) 'The capacity for language acquisition', in J. A. Fodor and J. J. Katz (eds.), *The Structure of Language*, 579–603.

LUCE, R. D., BUSH, R. R. and GALANTER, E., (eds.) (1965) *Readings in Mathematical Psychology*, New York, John Wiley.

LYONS, J., (1968) *Introduction to Theoretical Linguistics*, Cambridge (Mass.), Cambridge Univ. Press.

MORRIS, C. (1938) *Foundations of the Theory of Signs*, Chicago (Ill.), Univ. of Chicago Press.

OLDFIELD, R. C. and MARSHALL, J. C., (eds.) (1968) *Language*, Penguin Books.

PEIRCE, C. S., (1931–1935) *Collected Papers*, Harvard Univ. Press.

PERELMAN, C. and OLBRECHTS-TYTECA (1958) *Traité de l'argumentation*, Paris, Presses Universitaires de France.

POPPER, K. R., (1962) *Conjectures and Refutations*, New York, Basic Books.

QUINE, W. V., (1960) *Word and Object*, Cambridge (Mass.), M.I.T. Press.

SAPORTA, S. (ed.) (1961) *Psycholinguistics*, New York, Holt, Rinehart and Winston.

SAUSSURE, F. DE, (1955) *Cours de linguistique générale*, Paris, Payot, fifth edition.

SCHILPP, P. (ed.), (1963) *The Philosophy of Rudolph Carnap*, La Salle (Ill.), Open Court.

SHANNON, C. E. and WEAVER, W. (1949) *The Mathematical Theory of Communication*, Urbana (Ill.), Univ. of Illinois Press.

SKINNER, B. F., (1957) *Verbal Behavior*, New York, Appleton-Century-Crofts.

TARSKI, A., (1956) *Logic, Semantics, Mathematics*, Oxford, Clarendon.

ULLMAN, S., (1962) *Semantics: an Introduction to the Science of Meaning*, Oxford, Blackwell.

WIENER, N., (1948) *Cybernetics or Control and Communication in the Animal and the Machine*, New York, John Wiley.

WITTGENSTEIN, L., (1922) *Tractatus Logico-Philosophicus*, London, Routledge and Kegan Paul.

WITTGENSTEIN, L., (1953) *Philosophical Investigations*, Oxford, Blackwell.

ZIFF, P. (1960) *Semantic Analysis*, Ithaca (N.Y.), Cornell Univ. Press.

7 Information

SATOSI WATANABE

1. INFORMATION CONVEYED BY SENTENCE

What is the difference between the following two sentences from the point of view of the information conveyed by them?

(1) John reads the book.

(2) John reads a book.

A meaningful answer to the question can be given if one notices that (1) may be an answer to one of the three questions:

(1.1) Who reads the book?

(1.2) What does John do with the book?

(1.3) Who does what with the book?

Sentence (2) may be an answer to one of the four questions:

(2.1) What does John read?

(2.2) What does John do with what?

(2.3) Who reads what?

(2.4) Who does what with what?

Of course, the question may be actual, tacit, potential or anticipatory depending on the circumstances.

If (1.1) is the question, statement (1) can be re-phrased as

(1)* It is John (among others) who reads the book.

It could be John, Mary, Dick or Linda, but it is John who reads the book.

If (2.1) is the question, statement (2) can be re-phrased as

(2)* It is a book (among other things) that John reads.

It could be a book, a newspaper, a letter, but it is a book that John reads.

The function of the definite and indefinite articles here is to suggest what the possible alternatives are and to tell what the actual choice is. The noun with a definite article is irrelevant to this choice-making, while the one with an indefinite article is relevant. In other words, it helps indicate what the message is, what the information is, i.e. what the underlying question is and what its answer is. This is precisely what the language – at least in its cognitive aspect – is used for. It should answer a question actual or imaginary.

Seen from this point of view, the formal language used in symbolic logic, $P(a)$, meaning that object a affirms predicate P is defective. Does it mean: 1) it is (a) predicate P that (the) object a affirms, or 2) it is (an) object a that affirms (the) predicate P? The idea of information as a choice among possible alternatives is so important that each language has developed its own device to express it. It is surprising to note the same function is performed by entirely different grammatical entities in different languages. Compare two Japanese sentences:

(3) Watakushi ga yuku,

(4) Watakushi wa yuku,

where 'watakushi' means I or me, and 'yuku' means go. The two small particles 'ga' and 'wa' both indicate that the noun or pronoun preceding them is in the nominative case. Hence, both (3) and (4) can be translated as 'I go'.

If you aks a Japanese grammarian the difference between the two, the answer would perhaps be that the emphasis is slightly different. A much clearer answer can be given from our point of view of information. Sentences (3) and (4) answer respectively the following questions:

(5) Who goes?

(6) What do you do?

Hence, the meanings of (3) and (4) can be clarified (though a bit awkward) if we translate them respectively as

(3)* It is I who go.

(4)* What I do is going.

For this reason, (3) and (4) respectively imply also:

(3)** Others do not go.

(4)** Others may remain or go.

Those who know Japanese well enough will agree that (3) and (4) are often used to mean (3)** and (4)**.

(3)* means that there exists a possibility that somebody else, such as John, Sam or Mary, should go but the actual choice is I. (4)* means that I could remain or go or perhaps do something else but the decision is that I go.

2. QUANTITATIVE CONCEPT OF INFORMATION

The short analysis of the preceding section will, it is hoped, have shown clearly that the essence of cognitive language is conveyance of information and the essence of information is choice-making. If that is the case, and if science should aim at an abstract – and if possible, quantitative – formalization of concrete instances, then the science of language, and in particular the science of information, has to take up as its major task a mathematical formulation of the process of choice-making. The term 'choice' has sometimes a connotation of personal preference or aversion, but it is used here of course in a more neutral sense ot which one of the potential alternatives is selected.

The first thing we should ask ourselves is: what should we understand by a large amount of information and a small amount of information? Let us take the case of question (1.1) and its answer (1). If there is only John in the room, then the answer (1) is not conveying any information. For the question tacitly acknowledges already that somebody in the room is reading the book, and if John is the only person in the room, then the logical conclusion already is that 'John' is the answer. On the other hand, suppose that there are many people in the room, then the singling-out of John among many other 'competitors' has 'news value'. This suggests that the larger the choice, the larger the amount of information. So, if n is the number of alternatives and if we denote the amount of information by I, we should assume that I is an increasing function of n, that is to say, I is determined by n in such a way that the larger the n the larger the I. We know that the logarithmic function is an increasing function. So it may be all right to define I by:

$$I = \log n. \tag{1}$$

The reason why we choose the logarithmic function among all other increasing functions is as follows. Suppose there are three boys, John, Sam, and Fred, in the room. Then the sentence (1) as an answer to question (1.1) conveys an amount of information equal to log 3. Next, let us regard sentence (1) as an answer to question (1.2). Let us assume that John can do two things. Either he reads the book or he falls asleep with the book. Then the number of alternatives is 2, and sentence (1) as the answer to question (1.2) conveys information log 2. Next let us come to question (1.3) assuming that each of the three boys can either read or fall asleep with the book. The number of possible answers is obviously $6 = 2 \times 3$: John reads the book, John sleeps, Sam reads the book, Sam sleeps, etc. Therefore, the information carried by sentence (1) as the answer to question (1.3) is $\log 6 = \log 2 + \log 3$. This is exactly equal to the amount of information carried by (1) as the answer of (1.1) plus the amount of information carried by (1) as the answer of (1.2). Since question (1.3) is the juxtaposition of two questions (1.1) and (1.2), this equality is extremely convenient. This convenient additive property stems from the fact that we chose a logarithmic function in (1).

3. GENERALIZATION OF THE QUANTITATIVE CONCEPT OF INFORMATION

Suppose you are planning an excursion tomorrow and you are worried about the weather. Suppose the Weather Bureau tells you that you should expect (1) fair, (2) rain, and (3) snow, with respective probabilities (1) $p_1 = 0.9$, (2) $p_2 = 0.09$, and (3) $p_3 = 0.01$. Next morning, your child opens the window and tells you: it is snowing. You are surprised because there was a very small probability of snow and yet it happened. On the other hand, if your child tells you that it is fair, you are not surprised because that is what you had expected (large probability). This means, the smaller the probability you attach to an event, the larger your surprise if the event actually occurs. ('Events' can be translated in terms of sentences too.) We may then express the amount of 'surprise' of event i by $S_i = -\log p_i$, where i may be 1, 2, ..., n; if there are in total n alternative events. Since the probability is between 0 and 1, this quantity S_i becomes non-negative. The choice of the negative of the logarithmic function rather than any other decreasing, non-negative function has its reason. It is similar to the one given in the last section, but will not be repeated here.

The probabilities, such as p_1, p_2 and p_3 in the above example, represent collectively your state of ignorance about the outcome which necessarily must be one of the possible alternatives. For, if you were omniscient, you would attach probability unity (i.e. certainty of occurrence) to one of the alternatives and probability zero (i.e. certainty of non-occurrence) to other alternatives. If you are not omniscient, you have probabilities which are neither one nor zero. After the child has reported the actual weather, however, the probabilities change and one of them becomes unity. If he says snow, then p_1 and p_2 become zero and p_3 becomes one.

How could we express mathematically the degree of our ignorance? We may say that the larger the ignorance, the larger will be the surprise when the actual choice is made known. Indeed an omniscient person will not be surprised, because he knows the answer beforehand. We said that event i will cause surprise $S_i = -\log p_i$ if it happens. Since event i happens, according to our expectation, with probability p_i, we can make the average or expected value of surprise by calculating $S = \sum\limits_{i=1}^{n} S_i\, p_i$. We may use this quantity

$$S = -\sum_{i=1}^{n} p_i \log p_i \tag{2}$$

as the expression of the degree of ignorance when our state of ignorance is given by probabilities, $p_1, p_2, ..., p_n$. We agree that $0 \log 0$ is zero, although $\log 0$ is $-\infty$. If we interpret the p's not just as our expectation but as a relative frequency in an ensemble defined by certain conditions, we may consider S of (2) also as the expression of uncertainty.

Now suppose we make an observation (like the report of the child) and find out the actual choice, then one of the probabilities becomes one and all the rest become zero. Then the degree of ignorance S becomes zero. The ignorance S given in (2) changes to zero. The decrease in ignorance (by observation or report) can be interpreted as information obtained. For this reason S can also be considered as the amount of information provided by its observation or report. This will explain why the apparent opposite concepts of ignorance and information are expressed by the same formula.

This definition (2) is actually a generalization of our earlier definition (1). Indeed, if we have n alternatives and if we do not know which alternatives are more probable than others, we may put $p_i = 1/n$ for all i. Then (2) becomes $\log n$ as in (1). Engineers like to attribute (1) to Hartley (1928) and (2) to Shannon (1948), but of course both expressions were used already in the last century by Boltzmann (1896–1898) as the expressions of physical entropy. The idea that the physical entropy corresponds, in a certain sense, to the uncertainty about the precise state of the object must have been known to Boltzmann, but it was Szilard (1929) who pointed out with emphasis that a decrease of the physical entropy should imply the obtaining of information by the observer.

4. PART AND WHOLE — THEORY OF STRUCTURE

If the birth of information theory should be marked by its independence from thermodynamics, the present author's paper of 1939 may be regarded as the first paper in the new discipline. Usually, information theory is considered to have been born in 1949 (Shanon, 1949). The paper of 1939 had two messages to convey: (A) the quantity expressed by the function (2) can be used as a measure of uncertainty in any area disconnected from thermodynamics; (B) the same function can be used as a measure of structure in an assembly of individual objects. The theory used in the paper of 1939 was formulated in the framework of the non-Boolean logic (quantum logic) and therefore was much more general than (hence included as a special case) the usual information theory, but we shall not discuss this last point in the present paper. Point (A) may have been made clear by the explanation given in the first three sections of the present paper. We shall now explain point (B) briefly in this and the next sections. The idea of redundancy discovered in the 1950's by the communication engineers is a simple case of what is meant by structure here.

As the 'assembly of individual objects', you can imagine, for instance, a human society or a piece of matter consisting of molecules. Nobody can predict the exact behaviour of individual persons in society or the exact positions and velocities of molecules. The state of each individual can therefore be considered as a chance phenomenon. The assembly, being a collection of these stochastic individuals, also behaves stochastically. When would we then say that an assembly is structured or organized? If the behaviours of individuals are correlated, and interdependent, we would say that there is some structure. The result of such correlation would be that in spite of individual disorder or uncertainty, the behaviour as a whole will show some regularity or predictability and less disorder or uncertainty. It this is the case, the degree of structure may be measured by the balance between the uncertainty of individuals and the uncertainty of the whole. For, the larger the individual disorder and the smaller the total disorder, the larger the structure.

The above consideration leads us to the following idea. The degree of structure K is expressed by the sum of the entropies (the S-function given in (2)) of individuals minus the entropy of the whole.

$$K = \Sigma \; S(\text{part}) - S(\text{whole}) \tag{3}$$

Let us test this idea with a very simple example. Let us consider two girls *a* and *b* in a dormitory. We observe the lounge and if *a* is there, we put 1 in the row corresponding to *a* and if *a* is not there we put 0. Similarly for girl *b*. Suppose we have obtained the following list as the result of eight observations:

$$
\begin{array}{ccccccccc}
 & 1 & 2 & 3 & 4 & 5 & 6 & 7 & 8 \\
a & 1 & 1 & 0 & 0 & 1 & 1 & 0 & 0 \\
b & 0 & 1 & 1 & 0 & 1 & 0 & 0 & 1
\end{array}
$$

This shows that girl *a* has probability $\frac{1}{2}$ of being there and probability $\frac{1}{2}$ of not being there. Hence, her entropy is $S(a) = \log 2$. This can be obtained from (1), as there are two cases (presence and absence) with an equal probability. Similarly, the entropy of girl *b* is $S(b) = \log 2$. Now how about the state of the assembly of two girls together? The are four cases: both there (1,1), both not there (0,0), *a* is there and *b* is not there (1,0), and *a* is not there and *b* is there (0,1). Each of the four cases appears with equal probability in the above list, hence the entropy of the whole is $S(\text{whole}) = \log 4$. Hence, the strength of structure is $K = 2 \log 2 - \log 4 = 0$, i.e. there is no structure.

This result agrees well with our intuitive understanding of the situation. The above list will be obtained indeed if two girls come to the lounge randomly and independently with probability $\frac{1}{2}$.

Now consider the list:

$$
\begin{array}{ccccccccc}
 & 1 & 2 & 3 & 4 & 5 & 6 & 7 & 8 \\
a & 1 & 0 & 1 & 1 & 0 & 0 & 1 & 0 \\
b & 1 & 0 & 1 & 1 & 0 & 0 & 1 & 0
\end{array}
$$

This list shows that each girl comes to the lounge with probability $\frac{1}{2}$ as before, but they are such good friends that they come always together. $S(a)$ and $S(b)$ remain the same, but $S(\text{whole})$ is different. In fact there are only two cases, both there (1,1) and both not there (0,0), with equal probability $\frac{1}{2}$. Hence $S(\text{whole}) = \log 2$. The result is that the strength of structure is $K = 2 \log 2 - \log 2 = \log 2$. The point is that, individually seen, the girls came to the lounge randomly with probability $\frac{1}{2}$, but seen collectively they show some predictable regularity, namely, they come always together.

5. EMERGENT STRUCTURE

The use of entropy functions as a measure of structure was started in the paper of 1939, but a more systematic study along these lines had to wait another twenty years (Watanabe, 1959; 1960; Garner, 1962). These later papers of the present author showed among other things that the entropic measure of structure had a power to reveal 'emergent' properties of an assembly. By an emergent property is meant here a property which does not exist when individuals are taken singly or in pairs but appears when individuals are taken as constituting a group of three or more.

Let us take an example. There are four girls living in a dormitory, and we observe as before their presence and absence in the lounge. The result of eight observations was as follows:

	1	2	3	4	5	6	7	8
a	1	1	1	1	0	0	0	0
b	1	1	0	0	1	1	0	0
c	0	0	1	1	1	1	0	0
d	0	1	0	1	0	1	0	1

The probability of each girl being in the lounge is $\frac{1}{2}$. Therefore their individual entropy is log 2. Take, next, a pair of girls, say, a and b. We find the situation exactly the same as the first list of the last section, i.e. there are four cases (0,0), (0,1), (1,0), and (1,1) with equal probability. Hence, their pairwise entropy $S(a,b) = \log 4$. If we consider the pair as the 'whole' and the individual girls as the 'parts', the structure K for these two is $K(a,b) = S(a) + S(b) - S(a,b) = 0$. There is no structure. This situation is the same for any of the six possible pairs you may take among them. The pairwise structure does not exist among these four girls.

Next, take three girls together, say, a,b,c. We discover from the above list, they show four different patterns (1,1,0), (1,0,1), (0,1,1), (0,0,0) with equal probability. Therefore, the entropy for the three as a group is $S(a,b,c) = \log 4 = 2 \log 2$. Applying our formula to this group of three we get $K(a,b,c) = S(a) + S(b) + S(c) - S(a,b,c) = 3 \log 2 - \log 4 = \log 2$. So, there is some structure in the group of (a,b,c).

Next, take another group of three, say, (a,b,d). We discover that they show eight different patterns. (1,1,0), (1,1,1), (1,0,0), (1,0,1), (0,1,0), (0,1,1), (0,0,0), and (0,0,1) with equal probability. Hence $S(a,b,d) = \log 8 = 3 \log 2$. The structure for these three is $K(a,b,d) = S(a) +$

$S(b) + S(d) - S(a,b,d) = 3 \log 2 - \log 8 = 0$. This means that the group of (a,b,d) shows no structure. There are two more ways of taking a group of three girls, and they do not show any structure either. $K(b,c,d) = K(a,c,d) = 0$.

Why does the group of (a,b,c) have structure while the other three do not? The reason is because the group of (a,b,c) lacks the patterns $(1,0,0)$, $(0,1,0)$, $(0,0,1)$ and $(1,1,1)$ which exist in the other groups of three. Such a situation can very well happen if the three girls a,b,c are emotionally linked by friendship and jealousy in such a way that each of them does not want to be alone in the lounge but does not want to see the other two together at the same time. Such a property disappears if we take girls pairwise but emerges if we take them in a group of three. The groups of three other than (a,b,c) do not have such an emotional tie, hence they come into and leave the lounge in a random fashion.

To simplify the explanation, we took simple and concrete examples, but the method of structure analysis based on the idea of information is applicable also to more abstract items such as grammatical entities, propositions, etc., to reveal structures underlying them. We may discern two different streams of thought in the analysis of structure. One is the now popular 'grammatical' approach and the other is the 'statistical' approach. The first tries to formulate the generative rules from which all individual cases are supposedly derived by deductive instanciation, while the second tries to discover the underlying common generality or regularity inductively from a large number of individual cases. If the former is 'rationalistic' the latter is 'empiricistic'. These two, however, would not consider themselves as mutually exclusive but they should complement each other. Our method of structural analysis belongs of course to the latter stream.

6. 'NOISELESS' CODING

In the United States, the term information theory is understood generally in the sense of its technological applications in telecommunication and, in particular, in the problems of 'coding'. After the second world war, research produced a certain small number of really outstanding discoveries and a large number of scientific heroes, and inevitably, innumerable dissertations, mostly lacking scientific originality and technical utility. The famous classic is a book published in 1949 by Shannon and Weaver entitled *The Mathematical Theory of Communication*.

Coding is usually divided into two categories: 1) coding for 'noiseless' channels, and 2) coding for 'noisy' channels. The first aims at the most economical, i.e. statistically shortest way of encoding the message for transmission through a communication channel, disregarding the problem of distortion caused by possible errors during the transmission. The second aims at the most economical way of encoding the message in such a way that we can retrieve the correct message when it arrives, with certain errors at the receiving end of the channel. The latter is sometimes called 'error-correcting code'. There is of course a third area of coding which has the oldest history, namely, cryptography whose aim is to make decoding feasible only by those who are provided with a certain secret and very specific information. There may have been a considerable progress made in this area in recent years, but not much has been made known to the general scientific public.

The idea of 'noiseless' coding, or of the statistically shortest coding in the absence of errors is not new either. Everybody knows that the most frequently used letter in English is 'e', and that the Morse code assigns the shortest code to it, namely, a single dot. To infrequent letters such as 'q' and 'x', are assigned longer codes. This ingenious idea seems to be attributable to Alfred Vail who worked for Samuel Morse in the first half of the nineteenth century. Of course, the natural languages have already this tendency. More frequent words have usually shorter temporal duration when spoken and shorter spelling when written out.

The contribution of information theory to this problem is a quantitative rule that should exist in the ideal coding between the length of the code for a letter and the probability of its occurrence. Suppose we want to express (encode) four letters L_1, L_2, L_3, and L_4 as series of zeros and ones. One way of doing that may be to assign (00), (01), (10), and (11) respectively to L_1, L_2, L_3, and L_4. There are many other ways, but one of them may be to assign (000), (001), (01), and (1) respectively to L_1, L_2, L_3, and L_4. These two coding schemes can also be expressed as dichotomic trees as given on the opposite page.

We can think of these trees as if they were real trees, and assume that the thickness of the branch becomes one half every time a branch splits off into two branches. This way, we can assign to letters their 'thickness' q_1, q_2, q_3, q_4, assuming the trunk of the tree to have thickness unity. For

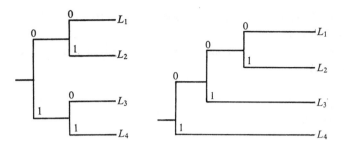

instance in the first coding mentioned above, each q will be $\frac{1}{4}$, for each branch has to go through two branching points. In the second coding, we have $q_1 = \frac{1}{8}$, $q_2 = \frac{1}{8}$, $q_3 = \frac{1}{4}$, and $q_4 = \frac{1}{2}$.

We note two important properties about the thickness. One thing is that if we sum up the q's, it becomes unity. $\Sigma q_i = q_1 + q_2 + q_3 + q_4 = 1$, as if each q were a probability. To assume this, we should not leave any branch unused. The second thing is that the length of each code is proportional to $l_i = -\log q_i$. This must be so because q_i is the r-th power of $(\frac{1}{2})$ where r is the number of branching points. Hence, if we take the negative of the logarithm of q_i, we should get r times log 2. For instance, in the second coding we have $l_1 = l_2 = -\log(\frac{1}{8}) = 3 \log 2$, $l_3 = -\log(\frac{1}{4}) = 2 \log 2$, $l_4 = -\log(\frac{1}{2}) = \log 2$. If we use log 2 as the unit of length, l_1, l_2, l_3, l_4 become respectively 3, 3, 2, 1 as they should.

Let us assume that each letter L_i appears with probability p_i in the language. Then the expected (average) length of the encoded message will become, per letter, $\Sigma p_i l_i = -\Sigma p_i \log q_i$. What are the best values of q's to make this expected length as short as possible? There is an old mathematical theorem attributed to W. Gibbs used often by physicists from the turn of the century, which says that the above expression becomes minimum if $p_i = q_i$ for all i. Thus, the strategy is very simple: make the length of the code of a letter proportional to $-\log p_i$. This is the basic idea of the 'noiseless' coding. For instance, if $p_1 = p_2 = p_3 = p_4 = \frac{1}{4}$, the first coding above will be the ideal. If $p_1 = p_2 = \frac{1}{8}$, $p_3 = \frac{1}{4}$, and $p_4 = \frac{1}{2}$, then the second coding will be ideal. In other words, the length should be $-\log p_i$ divided by log 2.

But what should we do if $-\log p_i$ does not become a multiple of log 2? A possible strategy in such a case would be to take an integer close to $-\log p_i/\log 2$, but there is no guarantee that such a coding is feasible or successful. A general algorithm for the optimal coding for an arbitrary number of symbols in the code language and for an arbitrary set of probabilities was given by Huffman (1952) and later rediscovered independently by Zimmermann (1959) in connection with the problem of 'searching'.

7. ERROR-CORRECTING CODING

Telecommunication implies transmission of encoded messages through some kind of physical medium called a 'channel' (such as copper wire), plus emitting, receiving and amplifying apparata such as those used in telegraphy. It is inevitable that the symbol emitted at the 'input' and the symbol received at the 'output' of the channel are not always identical, because of disturbances, malfunctions, etc. That is, there are non-zero error probabilities. The idea of an error-correcting code is that by cleverly encoding the message we can retrieve the original message correctly in spite of the errors which occur in the channel.

This might mystify the layman, but he will understand how this can be done from the following simple example. Assume that we have 12 possible symbols available for transmission. Assume further that the errors that occur are such that the number received may be the original number, or the original number plus one, or the original number minus one. To make the problem easier, let us imagine that the numbers are arranged like the dial of a clock, so that 12 plus 1 means 1 and 1 minus 1 means 12. Under such circumstances, we may give up sending 12 different numbers and instead send only 12, 3, 6 and 9. Then, if 11, 12 or 1 is received it must have been originally 12 and if 8, 9 or 10 is received it must have been originally 9. In this way we can reconstruct the original message without error in spite of the errors in the transmission channel.

Now, we have to note that this error-correcting operation in the above example was not possible without paying for it, i.e., we have restricted the number of symbols available from 12 to only 4. If we used all the 12 symbols with an equal probability we could transmit information in the amount log 12 according to formula (1) of Section 3. But now by using only 4 symbols, we can send only information in the amount of log 4. We have lost log 3 = log 12 − log 4 of the capacity of information transmission.

The reader must have now seen that in spite of the errors inherent in the channel, a correct deciphering of the received message is possible at the expense of loss of information capacity of the channel. Lengthening of an encoded message implies also a loss of capacity (per unit time). Shannon's famous theory determines in a great generality the amount of the minimum loss of channel capacity for ideal error-free deciphering in terms of the error probabilities of the channel.

There are practically innumerable ways of constructing error-correcting codes, depending on the types of channel, the error types, and other practical constraints. Each, however, wants to come as close as possible to the upper limit of channel capacity set by Shannon's theorem. An elementary precaution in constructing an error-correcting code is not to use a symbol often if it is very likely to incur an error. But not to use such a symbol at all may result in unduly limiting the channel capacity. Many complicated quantitative considerations are involved. Actual codes usually do not correct all possible errors. They correct only the more frequent types of errors and leave some small probability of remaining errors. Usually the error-correcting operation is done on a block of a certain number of transmitted symbols. A longer block tends to decrease the loss of capacity, but becomes more and more awkward for practical handling. The deciphering becomes more and more complicated and we have to wait long before we can start deciphering. Thus, each coding scheme is characterized by the loss of capacity, the length of a block and the remaining error probability. Usually the time required in deciphering is not indicated as one of the characteristics of a coding scheme, but if the scheme is large, the very best error-correcting code will not do much good in practice.

So far we have limited ourselves to a few narrow topics of conspicuous importance related to the quantity called 'information'. This notion is a special explication of the broader notion of information in the general field of 'information sciences'. In the remainder of this paper, we shall glance quickly at the general background from which this new group of scientific developments in information sciences has emerged.

8. INFORMATION IN BROADER CONTEXT

The historical development of science has its own internal causal chain, or at least it can so be described. But at the same time, we should remember that industrial problems have always given incentives to starting a new wave of scientific developments, and a new scientific discovery has often immediately caused new industrial progress. Industrial changes, on the other hand, are inseparable from social and ideological changes, which in turn have interactions with scientific thought. In this respect, the information sciences are no exception.

The nineteenth century was characterized by 'energy-converting machines' which converted chemical energy into heat energy and heat energy into mechanical energy. This caused an industrial revolution in society in general and gave birth to thermodynamics on the theoretical side. The twentieth century has seen the appearance of an entirely new breed of machines whose functions had nothing to do with conversion of energy – telephone, radios, films, gramophones, tape recorders, television, computers, etc. They are concerned with the conveyance, storage and processing of information. There had been predecessors (megaphone, printing, telegraphy), but the 'information machines' are products and symbols of this century. They are causing an information revolution in society in general and gave birth to the information sciences on the theoretical side. If the energy-converting machines can be compared to human muscles, the information machines are comparable to the human nervous system.

Some apologists of the information revolution claim that, because of the efficient and close information transfer that is made possible by new communication media, society is regaining the characteristics of a tribe of a village. But this is a grossly misleading interpretation of the present century. The biggest novelty of this century is obviously the mass media, and the mass media are not a means of person-to-person contact. They provide a tremendous instrument for person-to-mass contact, an instrument most suitable for totalitarian governments, industrial monopolies, and mass advertisement. The village is characterized by person-to-person contact and does not interfere with individualistic differences. The person-to-mass contact on the other hand leads to a uniformization of the masses, and kills individualist differences or individual opinions. This leads to a society of alienation, where each person is just a gear in a transmission box or a diode in a television set (Watanabe, 1968a).

We should now face the problem of what the science of information should be. It may be recalled that information machines are playing the role of the nervous system in the human body. The nervous system receives information from the receptors, conveys it through nervous fibres, stores it in the memory, processes it in the brain, makes decisions, transmits the decision to the effectors. Conversion of physical stimuli into perception, pattern recognition, formation of concepts, deductive and inductive processes, theory-making are all parts of information processes. The importance of selecting what is useful out of an immense sea of worthless information can never be over-emphasized. There must be a theoretical study of all these processes and also of their mechanical substitutes. The formation of thoughts and their communication are genetically inseparable. In that sense, communication and high-level linguistics have still to play an important part, and a large part of the old territory of psychology, covering cognitive processes, must be annexed. Epistemology, which was part of philosophy, has to be reformulated in a quantitative and scientific frame and also handed over. This re-formulated future version of epistemology is what the present author called epistemometrics and should become the centre of the information sciences (Watanabe, 1969).

It is a misunderstanding to believe that a physical object or physical process carries a definite piece of information. Information is definable only by the non-physical interpretation of the physical interaction between such a physical system and an external system. A falling leaf may give an observer information about the tree from which it has come, or about the wind condition of the atmosphere, or about the chemical condition of the soil, or the fact that it is autumn, or that every living organism and its parts are doomed to decay.

The nervous system in an animal does not pick up all the information that is available, but only those pieces that are relevant to the survival and growth of the organism. More generally, we may say that the entire information system in an animal is an instrument helping to adapt to and control the environment. For this reason, information has meaning only in the cybernetic context of life. Life will live, and for this it has to adjust itself and control the milieu. This can be made possible only by collecting pertinent information about the outside world and processing it to obtain appropriate decisions. Cybernetics is a science of controlling the milieu for the survival and development of life. As such, cybernetics implies information and information implies a cybernetical system. The mechanical simulation of information processing is done by computers, and for this reason, it is natural that the computer should occupy an important place in cybernetics and the information sciences. But it must be remembered that the computer without appropriate interpretation is merely a physical system, and by itself cannot be a subject of cybernetical or informatic study. What is important is the purpose for which human beings use it (Watanabe, 1968a).

What is called information in this paper, even in its broadest interpretation, concerns only the cognitive aspect of our thought and communication. It is a common daily experience that a mere glance at a person's face is sufficient to evoke in our mind an emotional empathy for the person. We are receiving some kind of information in this process, but it is not cognitive in nature. Language can convey a great deal of affective information by intonation, style, speed, loudness, choice of vocubulary, etc. It may even be suspected that what we usually call a cognitive process involves the participation of certain non-cognitive information (Watanabe, 1968b). It is doubtful whether such non-cognitive information can be represented by abstract symbols and treated with the help of logic and mathematics. Taken in so wide a sense, the notion of information is at the present day entirely outside the reach of scientific inquiry.

REFERENCES

BOLTZMANN, L., (1896–1898) *Vorlesungen über Gastheorie*, Leipzig.
GARNER, W. R., (1962) *Uncertainty and Structure as Psychological Concepts*, New York, John Wiley.
HARTLEY, R. L. V., (1928) *Bell System Technical Journal*, 7, 535.
HUFFMAN, D. A., (1952) *Proceedings of the Institute of Radio Engineers*, 40, 1098.
SHANNON, C. N. and WEAVER, W., (1948) *Bell System Technical Journal*, 27, 279, 623.
SHANNON, C. N. and WEAVER, W., (1949) *The Mathematical Theory of Communication*, Urbana (Ill.), Univ. of Illinois Press.
SZILARD, L. (1929) in: *Zeitschrift für Physik*, 53, 840.
WATANABE, S. (1939) in: *Zeitschrift für Physik*, 113, 482.
WATANABE, S., (1959), in: *Nuovo Cimento*, Ser. X, 13, Suppl., 576.
WATANABE, S., (1960), in: *IBM Journal of Research and Development*, 4, 66.
WATANABE, S., (1968a) in S. Dockx (ed.), *Civilisation technique et humanisme*, Brussels, Office International de Librairie.
WATANABE, S., (1968b) 'Mind-body problems', in *Proceedings of the Hawaii Conference on Philosophical Problems in Psychology, 1968*, Hawaii, Univ. of Hawaii Press, (1972).
WATANABE, S., (1969) *Knowing and Guessing*, New York, John Wiley.
ZIMMERMANN, S. (1959), in: *American Mathematical Monthly*, 66, 690.

8 Models

HERBERT STACHOWIAK

1. FUNDAMENTALS

1.1 *Attributes and predicates*

By attributes strictly speaking are meant properties (characteristics, qualities) of individuals, relations between individuals, properties of properties, etc. The distinction between individuals and attributes is not based upon any 'metaphysics of substance'. According to suitability, any object-constituting elements can, in one context, stand for attributes, in another, for individuals.

The individuals of an object may also be called zero-order attributes or improper attributes. By contrast, proper attributes would be first-, second-, etc. order attributes. First-order attributes are properties (of the individuals in question) and relations (between the individuals in question), second-order attributes are properties of properties, properties of relations, relations between properties, relations between relations, etc. (according to the type-theoretical distinctions of logic). No attribute (proper or improper) can be said to belong to an object as such. All its attributes are 'attributed' to the object. We may say: The object is constituted, or produced, by attribution.

In the general theory of models only such attributes are admitted for which there is at least one sufficiently conventionalized method according to which the existence or non-existence of these attributes can be decided upon.

Attributes are primarily products of perception and cogitation. Hence they must be carefully distinguished from their linguistic and semiotic articulations – spoken, written, or otherwise symbolized. It must be said, however, that those internal formations are not meant to be a world of 'spiritual entities', isolated 'meanings', or of *Wesenheiten, Sinngehalte,* and the like, existing by itself beside or beyond the world of publicly perceptible signs. The attributes represented by signs are considered rather as being pragmatically constitutive in the sense of expressing psychical processes, inferable only from the different connections of the uses of signs, the latter being stated by external observers.

The symbolizations joined to the attributes and representing them linguistically are called predicates. Accordingly, we are entitled to speak of first-, second-, etc. order predicates.

The formal characterization, as given here, is mainly one by logic of classes; only occasionally, for the sake of conciseness, it makes use of terms and descriptions proper to the logic of predicates.

The following expositions require a type-theoretically structured object language $\mathfrak{T}$ (as well as, for the description of its syntax, a syntactic meta-language $\mathfrak{M}$ of $\mathfrak{T}$). A predicate, considered extensionally, is a class. The elements of such a predicative class are called arguments of the predicate. If the arguments of a predicate are individuals, the predicative class shall be called a one-place predicate, if they are ordered pairs, a two-place predicate, etc. Individuals shall be considered zero-order predicates. Each predicate whose arguments are i-order predicates then is an $(i + 1)$-order predicate for $i = 0,1,2, \dots , n$. As from a consistently extensional formalization of the concept of predicate there would soon result heavy formulations for many-place relations, we may temporarily use terms proper to the (intensional) logic of predicates.

Let then be x and y any predicates (intensionally interpreted) of the type of predicative sentential formulas $x(\cdot)$, $y(\cdot,\cdot)$, etc. with one, two, etc. arguments. Then by $x \in y$ shall be designated, now class-logically again, the fact that the predicate (predicative class) x belongs to the predicate (predicative class) y, x being of a lower order than y. Accordingly, by $x = y$ shall be designated the identity of the predicates x and y; in this case x and y are of the same order. It will be remembered that a predicate with i-order arguments belongs to the $(i + 1)$ order, independently of its number of places (and that individuals are zero-order predicates).

In $\mathfrak{T}$ an i-place κ-order predicate a shall be designated by κa^i. All the attributes of 'attributed' objects shall be formally characterized by means of such predicates. If necessary, distinctive marks (index numbers) are to be used.

1.2 *Attribute classes and predicate classes*

For the various constitutions of objects each cognitive subject disposes of a repertoire, however pre-structured, of possible attributes (attributable qualities). The subject picks out of this repertoire the elements seeming suitable to him respectively, and in an order seeming suitable to him respectively.

Suppose for each attribute class O there is a predicate class P describing O. Let O be taken from the repertoire of attributes $\langle O \rangle$, and P from the respective repertoire of predicates $\langle P \rangle$. All the attribute and predicate classes considered here are finite.

In order to realize all the predicates of a repertoire that are not logical variables, they are enumerated after their order – and place – number. The individuals, as zero-order predicates, are collected in one general class of individuals; next, the first-order predicates are enumerated as their place numbers increase; second-, third-, etc. order predicates are treated accordingly.

Any object of perception and cogitation can be described by the union class of those among the predicates of the complete repertoire of an attributing subject which are the $\mathfrak{X}$-language representations of the object-producing attributes. Let predicates corresponding to object-producing attributes generally be named object-describing predicates. By $0 \cdot \alpha = {}_{Df} \alpha$ is designated the class of object-describing individuals (zero-order predicates), by $1\alpha^1$ the class of object-describing one-place predicates of the first order (properties), by $1\alpha^2$ the class of object-describing two-place predicates of the first order (relations), etc., likewise by $2\alpha^1$ the object-describing one-place predicates of the second order (relations between properties, relations between relations), etc. Then the object under consideration, 0, is described by a predicate class (union class) of the general form

$$P^{(k,n)} = {}_{Df} \alpha \cup \bigcup_{i_1=1}^{n_1} 1\, \alpha^{i_1} \cup \bigcup_{i_2=1}^{n_2} 2\, \alpha^{i_2} \cup \ldots \cup \bigcup_{i_k=1}^{n_k} k\, \alpha^{i_k},$$

where $n = \mathrm{Max}(n_1, n_2, \ldots, n_k)$.

Predicate classes in which occur, besides zero-order predicates, only first-order predicates, are called predicate classes of the first order. Accordingly, a predicate class of the second order is understood to be a predicate class in which occur, besides of zero- and first-order predicates, only predicates of the second order, etc. Predicate classes of second and higher orders may also be called order-heterogeneous.

As each predicate x has a predicative assertion formula, we can say: if $x = \kappa a^i$ belongs to $\mathfrak{T}$, at least the i arguments of x belong to $\mathfrak{T}$ as well.

2. GENERAL NOTION OF MODEL

2.1 *The icostructural mapping*

Definition 1. Let P_1 and P_2 be two predicate classes. Then a one-to-one mapping F is called an icostructural mapping of P_1 onto P_2, if the domain (pre-domain) of F is any subset of P_1 and the range (or post-domain) of F any subset of P_2. F is especially called icomorphic, if the pre-domain of F coincides with P_1, and the post-domain of F with P_2. In the latter case, it can also be said: F is an icomorphism of P_1 and P_2. For 'F is an icostructural mapping of P_1 onto P_2' may be written 'Ico$_F P_1, P_2$'. The *inverse* of Ico$_F$ P_1, P_2, where $U_2 \subseteq P_2$ is mapped onto $U_1 \subseteq P_1$ ($U_1 = F^{-1}(U_2)$), shall be symbolized by $\left[\text{Ico}_F P_1, P_2\right]^{-1}$.

2.2 *Encoded predicate classes*

The $\mathfrak{T}$-language predicates may now be formally interpreted. This requires a semantic metalanguage $\mathfrak{S}$ of $\mathfrak{T}$. Let its only primitive relation be the dyadic relation of designating, symbolized by Des (Designation, designation). By 'Des', the atomic sentential function

$$\bar{a} \text{ Des } \kappa a^i,$$

reads: The $\mathfrak{S}$-term $\bar{a}$ designates the $\mathfrak{T}$-predicate κa^i, is constituted in $\mathfrak{S}$. $\mathfrak{S}$ contains both $\mathfrak{M}$ and (a translation of) $\mathfrak{T}$. In accordance with Martin (1959, p. 30), certain rules of designation are to be observed, e.g. the one that a constant $\bar{a}$ in term of the form $\bar{a}$ Des κa^i designates no more than one object-language predicate κa^i. These rules shall not be quoted here in detail.

Definition 2. A $\mathfrak{T}$-language predicate κa^i is called coded, if there is an $\mathfrak{S}$-language term $\bar{a}$ with $\bar{a}$ Des κa^i. In this case $\bar{a}$ is called the code sign of the predicate. Predicates that are not coded shall be called non-coded.

Definition 3. The complete class of the code signs of a predicate class is called encoding class of the predicate class (of the system aggregate, of the system).

Definition 4. Let P be a predicate class and C an encoding class of P. Then by an encoding of P from C, symbolized by: $\text{Cod}_C\ P$, is meant a coordination function, whose domain is P and whose range is C. It holds: each predicate class P' coded by means of an encoding class C is structurally equivalent to a non-coded predicate class P, which besides P' contains as subclasses a number of one-place predicates equal to the number of elements of the class $\text{Cod}_C\ P'$.

If in many cases code signs are treated as something quasi-material, not merely formal-structural, this is done mainly by reasons of economy of description.

Definition 5. Let P_1 and P_2 be two predicate classes, and F an icostructural mapping of P_1 onto P_2, with the domain U_1 and the range U_2. Moreover, let C_1 be an encoding class of P_1, and C_2 an encoding class of P_2. Then a class of ordered code sign pairs $(\bar{a}_1, \bar{a}_2)$ is called a transcoding class of P_1 and P_2, (symbolized by: $T_{C_1, C_2}\ (P, U_1; P_2, U_2)$, if: 1) $\bar{a}_1 \in C_1$ and $\bar{a}_2 \in C_2$, and 2) it holds: if $\bar{a}_1$ codes the predicate $p_1 \in U_1$, and $\bar{a}_2$ the predicate $p_2 \in U_2$, then p_1 and p_2 are (structurally) identical, hence, being enumerated, they coincide in their number (and, of course, especially in their numbers of order and place).

Definition 6. Let P_1 and P_2 be two predicate classes, and C_1 and C_2 their corresponding encoding classes. Then the transcoding of P_1 into P_2 from the transcoding class T, symbolized by: $\text{Transcod}_T\ P_1, P_2$, means a coordination function, whose domain is (the Cartesian product) $P_1 \times P_2$, and whose range is T.

Definition 7. If in the transcoding $\text{Transcod}_T\ P_1, P_2$ the predicate classes P_1 and P_2 are replaced by the predicate classes P_1^* and P_2^* respectively, then by the recoding of the transcoding $\text{Transcod}_T\ P_1, P_2$ with regard to P_1^* and P_2^*, symbolized by: $\text{Recod}_T\ P_1, P_1^*; P_2, P_2^*$, is meant the transcoding $\text{Transcod}_T\ P_1 \cap P_1^*, P_2 \cap P_2^*$ with a simultaneous inversion of the elements of each pair of the transcoding subclass of T remaining after the substitution of P_1 by $P_1 \cap P_1^*$, and of P_2 by $P_2 \cap P_2^*$.

For $P_1 \cap P_1^* = \emptyset$, or $P_2 \cap P_2^* = \emptyset$ we say empty recoding, for $P_1 = P_1^*$ and $P_2 = P_2^*$ predicate-class-identical recoding.

2.3   *The general concept of model*

(A) Characteristic of mapping. Models are always models of something, namely representations of certain 'originals' (or 'prototypes'), natural or artificial, which themselves can be models again.

(B) Characteristic of shortening (reducing, abbreviation). Models do not generally map all the attributes of the original represented by them, but only those that are relevant for the modeller or model-user.

With the principal characteristic *(B)*, the pragmatic dimension of view in a wider sense is attained. Specifically operational points of view, according to which the selection of the attributes of the original is made, do not yet enter into it. Principally, the attributes of the original can, of course, be selected irregularly and stochastically as well as strictly purposively – with all intermediates possible. In a narrower sense, the selection of attributes becomes pragmatic only when it follows definite operational aims, and, moreover, when it is clear at what times the model does represent the original, and, above all, for whom.

(C) Characteristic of pragmatical model-function. Models are not in themselves coordinated to their originals. They always fulfil their functions of substitution only for subjects with goal-dependent mental or factual operations within certain lapses of time.

On account of the preceding verbal expositions, a formalization of the general concept of model in a pragmatical logic seems to be advisable. To sketch it out, Martin's outline of such a logic may be used once more. The metalanguages $\mathfrak{M}$ and $\mathfrak{S}$, based upon $\mathfrak{T}$, are continued by a pragmatic metalanguage $\mathfrak{P}$.

Before the latter will be characterized, the semiotic structure of languages $\langle \mathfrak{T}, \mathfrak{M}, \mathfrak{S}, \mathfrak{P} \rangle$ shall be complemented to the left, beyond $\mathfrak{T}$, by a semiotic zero-level $\mathfrak{O}$. $\mathfrak{O}$ is the level of the non-linguistic, hence non-semiotic objects, 'attributed' according to 1.1.

In the pragmatical metalanguage $\mathfrak{P}$, two variables are added: k and t. k varies over a given finite class of Kybiak-organisms, i.e. of natural or artificial organisms disposing of function units perceptor, motivator, operator, and effector (Stachowiak, 1965; 1969); t varies over a given finite class of slabs of time.

First shall be briefly sketched out the temporal logic (Martin, 1959, p. 36f.), incorporated in the pragmatical logic. The primitive relation is the relation of the temporal antecedens, symbolized by: An (Antecedens, antecedence), with the atomic sentential function: An t_1, t_2, reading: the slab of time t_1 lies completely before the slab of time t_2. Deduced relations are the relations of temporal overlapping, symbolized by: Co (Contegens), and the relation of being a temporal part, symbolized by: Pa (Participans), for which hold the definitions: Co $t_1, t_2 =$ $_{Df} \sim$ An $t_1, t_2 \wedge \sim$ An t_2, t_1 and Pa $t_1, t_2 =$ $_{Df} \forall t$ An $t, t_1 \curvearrowright$ An t, t_2. The concept of the (temporal) moment, symbolized by Mom, shall be defined as follows: Mom $t =$ $_{Df} \forall t_1$ Pa $t_1, t \curvearrowright$ Pa t, t_1 (a temporal moment then is part of all its temporal parts).

Primitives in $\mathfrak{P}$ shall be: the triadic relation of the semiotical acceptance, symbolized by: Ac (Acception, acceptance₁), the doubly specified five-place relation of extended acceptance, symbolized by: Acpt (Acceptation, acceptance₂), the four-place relation of (semiotic) preference, symbolized by: Praef (Praeferenz, preference), and the sevenfold specified five-place relation of performance, symbolized by: Perf (Performation, performance).

The atomic sentential functions, belonging to the first two primitives, are

$$k \ \text{Ac} \ o, t,$$

to be read as: The Kybiak-organism k accepts the $\mathfrak{T}$-language entity o at time t;

$$k \ \text{Acpt} \ \eta \ o, o', \ t,$$

to be read as: Kybiak k accepts the relation η existing between the (semiotic or non-semiotic) objects o and o' at time t.

η varies here over the repertoire of classes of the acceptance relation

$$\{\text{Descr, Subst.}\}$$

with the meanings:

sentence function	meaning
(*o* and *o'* are attribute- or predicate classes from the corresponding total repertoires)	*k* accepts at time *t*:
k Acpt Descr *o,o'*, *t*	*o* as a description of *o'* (consequently *o* is a predicate class)
k Acpt Subst *o,o'*, *t''*	the substitution *o* by *o'*

Moreover:

$$k \text{ Praef } o,o', t,$$

reading: Kybiak *k* at time *t* prefers the $\mathfrak{T}$-language entity *o* to the $\mathfrak{T}$-language entity *o'*.

k Ac *o,t* and *k* Acpt Descr *o,o'*, *t* can be extended to $\mathfrak{M}$-language entities. For *k* Ac ($\bar{a}$ Des к a^i), *t*, for instance, is then needed a pragmatical meta-metalanguage. Such extensions being admitted, as it shall principally be the case here, it is sufficient for the moment to postulate that in *k* Ac *o,t* '*k*', 'Ac', and '*t*' always belong to an order that is higher than '*o*' by exactly one.

('Ac' and 'Acpt' are obviously classificatory, whereas 'Praef' is comparative. So by the introduction of the ordering relation 'Praef', the classificatory pragmatical logic changes into a comparative one, which may be considered to be a preliminary stage of a quantitative logic (*cf.* also Martin, 1964)).

Among the $\mathfrak{T}$-language entities ($\mathfrak{M}$-language respectively) accepted or preferred by Kybiak-organisms, there may be logical as well as empirical sentences (conjunctions of sentences).

$$k \text{ Ac } L, t$$

indicates that *k* accepts (all the axioms and deduced theorems of) the logic of the language-level $\mathfrak{T}$ (including the type-theoretical structure of orders) and also the logic of the language-level $\mathfrak{M}$. The empirical sentences accepted by *k* will have to fulfill conditions of verification (in the widest sense).

Next, in order to define more exactly the model-theoretically important concept of the rational preference structure of a Kybiak-organism, the deduced relation of indifference (symbolized by Indiff) must be introduced first. Let k Indiff $a,b,t =_{Df} \sim k$ Praef $a,b,t \wedge \sim k$ Praef b,a,t. Then the definition shall hold (Martin, 1964, p. 158): k has a rational preference structure at time t, symbolized by: Rat Praef k,t, if for any two $\mathfrak{T}$-language entities (sentences) a and b ($\mathfrak{M}$-language respectively) holds: 1) k Praef $a,b,t \wedge k$ Praef $b,c,t \curvearrowright k$ Praef a,c,t (transitivity of the preference relation), 2) k Indiff $a,b,t \wedge k$ Indiff $b,c,t \curvearrowright k$ Indiff a,c,t (transitivity of the indifference relation), and 3) k Praef $a,b,t \veebar k$ Praef $b,a,t \veebar k$ Indiff a,b,t (unambiguousness of preference with non-indifference; '$\veebar$' designates exclusive disjunction).

Definition 8. A Kybiak-organism k is called rational at time t, symbolized by: Rat k,t, if at this time k accepts the logic of the language levels $\mathfrak{T}$ and $\mathfrak{M}$ and possesses a rational preference structure.

Finally, the 'atomic' sentential function belonging to the fourth primitive in $\mathfrak{P}$ is

$$k \text{ Perf } \eta' \, o,o', \, t,$$

reading: Kybiak k performs η' at time t concerning the non-semiotic or semiotic objects o and o'.

η' varies over the repertoire

$$\{\text{Descr, Subst, Ico}_F, \text{Rev}_F \text{ Ico}_F \; P_1, P_2, \text{Op}_i,$$
$$\text{Transcod}_T, \text{Recod}_T \; P_1, P_2\},$$

whose 7 elements are classes of performance with the following meanings:

sentence function	meaning
(*o* and *o'* are attribute- or predicate classes from the corresponding total repertoires)	*k* performs at time *t*:
k Perf Descr o,o', t	the description o of o' (consequently o is a predicate class)
k Perf Subst o,o', t	the substitution of o by o'

k Perf Ico$_F$ o,o', t	the icostructural mapping F of P_1 into P_2 (consequently o and o' are predicate classes)
k Perf (Rev$_{F*}$ Ico$_F$ P_1, P_2) o,o', t	the reverse F^* of F (with Ico$_F$ P_1, P_2), i.e. k finds out, or works out, a one to one mapping F^* with $F^{-1} \subseteq F^*$, and composes the predicate class $o' = F^{-1} (P_2 \cap o)$ $\cup F^* (o - (P_2 \cap o))$
k Perf Op$_i$ o,o', t	certain operations i transforming o into o'
k Perf Transcod$_T$ o,o', t	the transcoding Transcod$_T$ o,o' (consequently o and o' are predicate classes)
k Perf (Recod$_T$ P_1, P_2) o,o', t	the recoding Recod$_T$ P_1, o; P_2, o' of Transcod$_T$ P_1,P_2 (consequently o and o' are predicate classes)

It would transgress the limits of this paper to enumerate, however incompletely, the different axiomatic or deduced temporal-logical relationships applying to the above types of performance. A hint concerning 'Perf Op$_i$' may suffice. For this sort of performance, for instance, holds the (trivial) relation: k Perf Op$_i$ o,o', t_1 $\land$ k Perf Op$_i$ o',o'', t_2 $\curvearrowright$ An t_1, t_2. After which the general concept of model can be defined as follows, according to the three principal characteristics:

Definition 9. Let O_1 and O_2 be any (semiotic or non-semiotic) objects. Then, for a Kybiak-organism k, the object O_2, at time t, with regard to certain operations Op$_i$, is a model of the object O_1.

(1)   Rat k,t
(2) $\exists P_1$ $\exists P_2$ k Perf Descr P_1, O_1, t $\land$ k Perf Descr P_2, O_2, t
(3) $\exists F$ k Perf Ico$_F$ P_1, P_2, t
(4) $\exists T$ k Perf Transcod$_T$ P_1, P_2, t

(5) k Perf Subst O_1, O_2, t

(6) $\exists_i$ k Perf Op$_i$ O_2, O^*, t

(7) $\exists P^*$ k Perf Descr P^*, O^*, t

(8) $\exists F^*$ k Perf $(\text{Rev}_{F_*} \text{Ico}_F P_1, P_2) P_2^*, P_1^*, t$

(9) k Acpt Descr P_1^*, O_1^*, $t \wedge k$ Acpt Subst O_1^*, O_2^*, t

(10) k Perf $(\text{Recod}_T P_1, P_2) P_1^*, P_2^*, t$.

In Definition 9, there are to be distinguished: one condition of rationality, 8 conditions of performance (among which one double condition) and one (double) condition of acceptance. Among the conditions of performance, conditions (5), (6), and (8) are the heuristically decisive ones; with an operational conception of Definition 9, they express the main classes of operations of the process of modelling. Among them, condition (6) is creatively to be valued more highly than the others. The creative performances expressed by it include the determination of i-optimizing target-functions.

Though condition (9) expresses but an acceptance, it means nothing less than the 'production' of the 'new' original, 'improved' in some operative sense in comparison with O_1. Condition (9) especially makes possible an increase of information for the modeller k on the modelled original O_1.

Any objects O_1 and O_2 shall, in a more comprehensive sense, be called semantical (symbolical), or else natural, according to whether they belong to the semiotic zero-level $\mathfrak{O}$ (*cf.* p. 150), or are semiotic entities produced out of $\langle \mathfrak{T}, \mathfrak{M}, \mathfrak{S}, \mathfrak{P} \rangle$. After this, it will immediately be clear whether it is a semantic or technical model, and whether a semantic or natural, or technical original is being discussed in a particular case.

The operations transforming O_2 into O_2^* at first furnish changes of O_1 that are only possibly desired, especially new informations about O_1. The modeller k will only accept the transferability to the represented original of the data obtained on the representing model, especially of the new insights into relationships of the model, and will only hold them reliable if he has been able to ascertain that certain 'transferential criteria' have been satisfied. With technical models of natural or technical originals, such criteria are e.g. relations of scales for the comparison of lengths, forces, and energies between original and model, for the comparison of e.g. moduli of elasticity between original and model (Hooke's law of model, Cauchy's rule of scale), of densities and viscosities of liquids (Reynolds' rule of scale), and the like. Particulars may be found in an essay by

P. Füsgen (1959). With semantic models of natural or technical originals, e.g. with theories of the empirical sciences, the transferential criteria become criteria of confirmation or verification, criteria of falsifiability, etc., with semantic models of semantic originals, especially if the latter in some way or other transcend the structure of languages $\langle \mathfrak{T}, \mathfrak{M}, \mathfrak{S}, \mathfrak{P} \rangle$, they become criteria of 'fruitful formation from analogy', of 'legitimate generalization', and so forth. Finally, transferential criteria for technical models of semantic originals are so multifarious that suggestions about them in the present connection would hardly be in place.

The pragmatical character of the concept of model, as determined above, extends beyond the reference of this concept to a pragmatical logic. It also concerns the utility of a model for the modeler. Only a few suggestions may be made to this: A modeler k will accept his model Mod $(O_2, O_1, k, t, \text{Op}_i)$ at time t as usable, if it satisfies certain motives of k within t (if it reduces the strength of the 'motive pressure' of k), and of two models of the same original k will prefer the one that performs a greater satisfaction of motives (a greater reduction of motive pressure) within t, or an equal satisfaction of motives (equal reduction of motive pressure) within only a part of t.

3. MEASURES

3.1 *Structural measures*

Let P_1 and P_2 be two arbitrary predicate classes from $\mathfrak{T}$ and $U_1 \subseteq P_1$ and $U_2 \subseteq P_2$. Between P_1 and P_2 there shall exist the icostructural mapping F with U_1 as its domain, and U_2 as its range. For any finite class Q, $[Q]$ shall, in the following, designate the number of the elements of Q.

Definition 10. By the (ico)structural (or numerical) adequation (or approximation) of P_2 to P_1 (with icostructural mapping F of P_1 onto P_2) (*cf.* 2.1, p. 148) is meant the not-zero quotient

$$(a_{\text{Ico}_F} (P_1, U_1; P_2, U_2) =) a_{\text{Ico}} = \frac{[U_1] \cdot [U_2]}{[P_1] \cdot [P_2]}.$$

Definition 11. The difference $P_1 - U_1$ shall be called the preterition class, the difference $P_2 - U_2$ the abundance class of the icomorphic mapping F of P_1 onto P_2. Then the corresponding quotients

$$a_{\text{Praet}} = \frac{[P_1 - U_1]}{[P_1]}, a_{\text{Abun}} = \frac{[P_2 - U_2]}{[P_2]}$$

are called the preterition measure and the abundance measure of Ico_F P_1, P_2 respectively.

From Definitions 10 and 11 follows that $0 < a_{\text{Ico}} \leqslant 1$, $0 \leqslant a_{\text{Praet}} < 1$, $0 \leqslant a_{\text{Abun}} < 1$. Moreover, it is easy to see that for an icomorphic (p. 148) mapping F $a_{\text{Ico}} = 1$, and consequently $a_{\text{Praet}} = a_{\text{Abun}} = 0$. In which case U_1 shall be called non-pretered, and U_2 non-abundant with regard to the (icomorphic) mapping F of P_1 onto P_2.

According to the characteristic of shortening (B) (p. 150), with modellings where P_1 and P_2 function as describing predicate classes, generally $a_{\text{Ico}} < 1$, and it will, with (physico-, bio-, and psycho-) technical models of natural originals, lie even far below 1. This holds for scientific-semantic models of natural originals; thus, any scientific theory will always cut but certain aspects out of the given fields of pre-scientifically, or at least 'pre-disciplinarily' attributed physical, psychical, social, historical, etc. objects. As to the modeling of natural objects, only some philosophers will try to construct semantic models of 'reality' with the most total original-adequation (-approximation) possible, namely such philosophers as adhere to a realistic epistemology and, perhaps, to a theory of picture-like manner of cognition. If, on the other hand, in the physico-technical sphere there are to be found models with an original-adequation approaching 1 or equal to 1, they originate without exception from technical originals. $a_{\text{Ico}} = 1$ is obtained especially with technical models of geometric (three-dimensional) objects, if these models, no matter on which spatial or temporal scale of mapping, only 'structurally duplicate' their originals.

To get more model-theoretically interesting measures for structural adequations, submappings of the icostructural mapping for order-heterogeneous (p. 148) predicate classes out of $\mathfrak{X}$ will be introduced first below.

In the following four definitions let P_1 and P_2 be order-heterogeneous predicate classes, between which there exists the icomorphic mapping F.

Definition 12. Let α_1 be the individual class of $P_1 = P_1^{(k_1,n_1)}$, and α_2 the one of $P_2 = P_2^{(k_2,n_2)}$. Now, if Ico_F P_1, P_2 is partially individual-preserving, namely, if F maps the individuals (zero-order predicates) of a subclass $U\alpha_1 \subseteq \alpha_1$ onto the individuals of a subclass $U\alpha_2 \subseteq \alpha_2$, then F is called a dichostructural mapping of P_1 onto P_2, and

$$a_{\mathrm{Dicho}} = \frac{[U\alpha_1] \cdot [U\alpha_2]}{[\alpha_1] \cdot [\alpha_2]}$$

the dichostructural adequation of P_2 to P_1.

Definition 13. Let $\kappa\alpha_1^i$ be the class of i-place predicates belonging to $P_1 = P_1^{(k_1,n_1)}$, and $\kappa\alpha_2^i$ the class of i-place predicates belonging to $P_2 = P_2^{(k_2,n_2)}$. Now, if Ico_F P_1, P_2 is partially place-number-preserving, namely, if F, for $\kappa = 0, 1, 2, \ldots, \mathrm{Max}\,(k_1, k_2)$, maps the predicates of a subclass $U\kappa\alpha_1^i \subseteq \kappa\alpha_1^i$ onto the ones of a subclass $U\,\kappa\alpha_2^i \subseteq \kappa\alpha_2^i$, then F is called a hypostructural mapping of P_1 onto P_2. The measure

$$_i a_{\mathrm{Hypo}} = \frac{1}{\mathrm{Max}\,(k_1, k_2) + 1 - r} \cdot \sum_{\kappa=0}^{\mathrm{Max}\,(k_1, k_2)} \frac{[U\kappa\alpha_1^i] \cdot [U\kappa\alpha_2^i]}{[\kappa\alpha_1^i] \cdot [\kappa\alpha_2^i]}$$

where r designates the number of empty predicate subclasses from $P_1 \cup P_2$ with $r \leqslant \mathrm{Max}\,(k_1, k_2)$, where the terms of the sum for (each $i = 0, 1, 2, \ldots, \mathrm{Max}\,(n_1, n_2)$ and) $\kappa = 0$ are replaced by

$$\frac{[U\alpha_1] \cdot [U\alpha_2]}{[\alpha_1] \cdot [\alpha_2]}$$

with $U\alpha_2 = F(U\alpha_1)$, and where each term of the sum with a vanishing denominator is written zero, is called the hypostructural adequation of P_2 to P_1.

Definition 14. Let $\kappa\alpha_1^i$ be the class of κ-order predicates belonging to $P_1 = P_1^{(k_1,n_1)}$, and $\kappa\alpha_2^i$ the class of κ-order predicates belonging to $P_2 = P_2^{(k_2,n_2)}$. Now, if Ico_F P_1, P_2 is partially order-number-preserving, namely, if F, for $i = 0, 1, 2, \ldots, \mathrm{Max}\,(n_1, n_2)$, maps the predicates of a subclass $U_\cup \kappa\alpha_1^i \subseteq \kappa\alpha_1^i$ onto the ones of a subclass $U_\cup \kappa\alpha_2^i \subseteq \kappa\alpha_2^i$ of the same order number, then F is called an orthostructural mapping of P_1 onto P_2. The measure

$$\kappa a_{\text{Ortho}} = \frac{1}{\text{Max}(n_1, n_2) + 1 - s} \cdot \sum_{i=0}^{\text{Max}(n_1,n_2)} \frac{[U_\cup \kappa\alpha_1^i] \cdot [U_\cup \kappa\alpha_2^i]}{[\kappa\alpha_1^i] \cdot [\kappa\alpha_2^i]}$$

where s designates the number of empty predicate subclasses from $P_1 \cup P_2$ with $s \leqslant \text{Max}(n_1, n_2)$, where the terms of the sum for $\kappa = 0$ and $i = 0, 1, 2, .., \text{Max}(n_1, n_2)$ are replaced by

$$\frac{[U\alpha_1] \cdot [U\alpha_2]}{[\alpha_1] \cdot [\alpha_2]}$$

with $U\alpha_2 = F(U\alpha_1)$, and where each term of the sum with a vanishing denominator is written zero, is called the orthostructural adequation of P_2 to P_1.

Definition 15. Let $\kappa\alpha_1^i$ be the class of κ-order and i-place predicates belonging to $P_1 = P_1^{(k_1, n_1)}$, and $\kappa\alpha_2^i$ the class of κ-order and i-place predicates belonging to $P_2 = P_2^{(k_2, n_2)}$. Now, if Ico_F P_1, P_2 is partially both place-number- and order-number-preserving, namely, if F, for $\kappa = 0, 1, 2, .., \text{Max}(k_1, k_2)$, and for $i = 0, 1, 2, .., \text{Max}(n_1, n_2)$, maps the predicates of a subclass $U_\cup \kappa\alpha_1^i \subseteq \kappa\alpha_1^i$ onto the ones of a subclass $U_\cup \kappa\alpha_2^i \subseteq \kappa\alpha_2^i$ of the same order- *and* place-number, then F is called an isostructural mapping of P_1 onto P_2. The measure

$$a_{\text{Iso}} = \frac{1}{\partial + 1 - t} \cdot \sum_{\kappa=0}^{\text{Max}(k_1,k_2)} \sum_{i=0}^{\text{Max}(n_{1,\kappa}, n_{2,\kappa})} \frac{[U_\cup \kappa\alpha_1^i] \cdot [U_\cup \kappa\alpha_2^i]}{[\kappa\alpha_1^i] \cdot [\kappa\alpha_2^i]}$$

$$\text{with } \partial = \left(\sum_{\kappa=1}^{\text{Max}(k_1,k_2)} \text{Max}(n_{1,\kappa}, n_{2,\kappa}) \right),$$

where $n_{1,\kappa}$ designates the maximal number of places of the order κ in P_1, $n_{2,\kappa}$ the maximal number of places of the order κ in P_2, and t the number of empty predicate subclasses with the number of order $\leqslant \text{Max}(k_1, k_2)$ and the number of place $\leqslant \text{Max}(n_{1,\kappa}, n_{2,\kappa})$, where the terms of the sum for $i = 0$ (and each κ) together with the terms for $\kappa = 0$ and $i = 1, 2, .., \text{Max}(n_{1,\kappa}, n_{2,\kappa})$ are replaced by

$$\frac{[U\alpha_1] \cdot [U\alpha_2]}{[\alpha_1] \cdot [\alpha_2]}$$

with $U_\cup \alpha_2 = F(U_\cup \alpha_1)$, and where each term of the sum with a vanishing denominator is written zero, is called the isostructural adequation of P_2 to P_1.

It is obvious that Definition 12 is contained as a special case in Definitions 13 to 15. Moreover, it is easy to see that both Definition 13 and Definition 14 are contained as special cases in Definition 15.

Obviously, according to the icostructural adequation (p. 156) $0 < a_{\text{Dicho}} \leqslant 1, 0 < a_{\text{Hypo}} \leqslant 1, 0 < a_{\text{Ortho}} \leqslant 1$, and $0 < a_{\text{Iso}} \leqslant 1$.

Definition 16. A dichostructural, hypostructural, orthostructural, isostructural mapping F of a predicate class P_1 onto a predicate class P_2, whose adequation measure equals 1, is called dichomorphic, hypomorphic, orthomorphic, isomorphic respectively. In this case, we can also say: F is a dichomorphism, hypomorphism, orthomorphism, isomorphism of P_1 and P_2.

For finite domains and ranges the model-theoretical concept of isomorphism generalizes the usual mathematical one. The total original-adequation, as mentioned on p. 157, would lead to finding an isomorphism of 'reality', and to its theoretical representation, more precisely: to an isomorphic duplication of the predicative description of 'reality'.

Opposite to the case that, in a modelling, the icostructural mapping F, existing between the describing predicate classes, or one of its varieties, reach the value of structural adequation 1, there is the other extreme of a maximal structural shortening of the original. This is the case, if the model consists of one, and only one, attribute, its description then consisting of one, and only one, predicate (encoded or not). Such models shall be called point-models.

Definition 17. Let F be an isomorphic mapping between two predicate classes P_1 and P_2. If the individual classes $\alpha_1 \subseteq P_1$ and $\alpha_2 \subseteq P_2$ are identical and if F maps each individual onto itself, then F is called an auto-icostructural mapping of P_1 onto P_2 (with the limiting case of an auto-icomorphic mapping). Accordingly, upon the equal condition of individual-identical mapping, one will speak of an autodichostructural (in the limiting case autodichomorphic), autohypostructural, etc. mapping of P_1 onto P_2. From the above it will be clear, too, when one is allowed to speak of an auto-icomorphism, autodichomorphism, etc. of P_1 and P_2.

The formulae for measures of structural adequations, as introduced for the icomorphic submappings, can in part be simplified. Thus a_{Dicho} is transformed

$$a_{\text{Auto Dicho}} = \frac{[U\alpha_1]^2}{[\alpha_1]^2}.$$

The structural measures may be specialized to the case that part of the predicates of the predicate classes describing the original and the model are of spatial or time-metrical nature, concerning e.g. linear measures, areas, volumes, curvatures, etc. in the sense of Euclidian geometry. With such predicate classes, which may be called (partially) metrized, the structural adequations obtained after Definitions 10 and 12 to 15 are often transformed into comparisons of scale.

If between the metrized predicate classes P_1 and P_2, describing two space-metric configurations K_1 and K_2 respectively, there exists a (model-theoretical) isomorphic mapping, then either of the two configurations shall be called a structure copy of the other. If in this mapping all space-metrical proportions are preserved, if, therefore, the mapping is equiform and distance-preserving, then the structure copy shall specially be called a space copy. A space copy K_2 of a space-metric original K_1 maps this on a scale $m_r = 1:1 = 1$. If, however, K_1 is equiformly mapped onto K_2, the latter becoming proportionally smaller or larger than K_1, so that $m_r \lessgtr 1$ respectively, K_2 is called a space-metrical contraction model of K_1 or a space-metrical dilatation model of K_1 respectively.

Beyond this, as many specific metrical contraction models, or dilatation models respectively, can of course be dealt with as there are metrizing parameters.

Among the non-space-metrical parameters, the classic-physical time-parameter is of special importance. It will be quite clear what is meant by a time-copy, a time-metrical contraction model, and a time-metrical dilatation model of a time-dependent original with the respective relations of time-scales $m_t \lessgtr 1$.

Of course, space-metrical original-model mappings need not be equiform. In geometry, certain kinds of mapping are investigated, which are of model-theoretical interest as well: affine, projective; conformal (angle-preserving), distance-preserving; conic, cylindrical, azimuthal, polyconical ones, etc.

3.2 *Coding measures*

Definition 18. Let P be a predicate class with the encoding $\mathrm{Cod}_C P$ (p. 149). Then the measure

$$(a_{\mathrm{Codgr}_C}(P) =) \ a_{\mathrm{Codgr}} = \frac{[\mathrm{Cod}_C P]}{[P]}$$

is called the encoding degree of P with regards to C. It holds that $0 \leqslant a_{\mathrm{Codgr}} \leqslant 1$. According to whether for a predicate class $a_{\mathrm{Codgr}} = 0$, or $0 < a_{\mathrm{Codgr}} < 1$, or $a_{\mathrm{Codgr}} = 1$, the predicate class is called non-encoded, partially encoded, or fully encoded respectively.

Definition 19. Let P_1 and P_2 be two predicate classes with the transcoding $\mathrm{Transcod}_T P_1$, P_2. Then the measure

$$(a_{\mathrm{Cod}_T}(P_1, P_2) =) \ a_{\mathrm{Cod}} = \frac{[T]}{[C_1] \cdot [C_2]}$$

is called the code-adequation or material adequation of P_1 to P_2 with regard to T.

Obviously $0 \leqslant a_{\mathrm{Cod}} \leqslant 1$.

The following notations shall yet be introduced:

Definition 20. Let again P_1 and P_2 be two predicate classes with the transcoding $\mathrm{Transcod}_T P_1,P_2$. Then $\mathrm{Transcod}_T P_1,P_2$ is called a realization of P_1, or an abstraction from P_2 respectively, according as, respectively,

$$a_{\mathrm{Codgr}_{C_1}}(U_1) < \mathrm{or} > a_{\mathrm{Codgr}_{C_2}}(U_2),$$

where $T = T_{C_1, C_2}(P_1, U_1; P_2, U_2)$.

$\mathrm{Transcod}_T P_1$, P_2, in particular, shall be called a
partial realization,
full realization,
partial abstraction,
full abstraction,

according as, in the above sequence
U_1 is non-encoded, and U_2 partially encoded,
U_1 is non-encoded, and U_2 fully encoded,

U_1 is fully encoded, and U_2 partially encoded,
U_1 is fully encoded, and U_2 non-encoded.

Definition 21. Let again P_1 and P_2 be two predicate classes with the transcoding $\text{Transcod}_T\ P_1$, P_2. Let P_1 be a description of an object O_1, and P_2 one of an object O_2. Now, if to each predicate of P_1, coded by $\bar{a}_1$, a *new* code-sign $\bar{a}_2$ ($\neq \bar{a}_1$) is co-ordinated in P_2 by T, then O_2 is called an analogy model of O_1. If, on the contrary, in the transcoding Transcod_T P_1, P_2 all code-signs of the predicates of P_1 are preserved, O_2 is called an isohylic model of O_1.

Definition 22. A model of an original that is at once isomorphic and isohylic is called an equate model or a copy of this original.

3.3 *Further measures*

To A. A. Moles and A. Schützenberger (1955) (cf. also Moles, 1958, 1960, 1962) we owe a structural measure of complexity for systems, keeping closely to the entropy measure of Shannon. With certain modifications, this measure can be applied to predicate classes, especially to (predicative) systems, and thereby to the objects (attribute classes) described by them; based on it, comparisons of complexity between original and model can be made and can be related to the structural measures of adequation (3.1).

If, in doing so, predicate classes are conceived as being messages in the sense of the information theory, then, principally, for these predicate classes there can be defined also measures of information (content) on a syntactic, semantic, and pragmatic level, which are a modification, or more strictly, a generalization, of the formula of Shannon.

On the semantic level Y. Bar-Hillel (1953) and R. Carnap have, for very simple object-languages, which contain only a finite number of individuals and one-place predicates, defined a measure of information (content) of predicative statements, which is such a generalization. Any developments of this approach, which uses purely extensional-logical means, could also be of importance for the general theory of models. On the level of pragmatics P. Gäng (1967) has, by means of considerations of the utility theory and the psychology of motives, defined a measure of the pragmatic information-content of messages for Kybiak-organisms, which can still be more closely related to the general theory of models.

Further measures, which, it is true, would meet with great difficulties, if treated in a general way, and could probably be defined only separately for certain kinds of models, ought to be referred to the model-theoretical important concept of contrasting. By 'contrasting' is meant the property of many models specially to expose, to over-stress certain attributes, or classes of attributes respectively, of the original by 'over-quantification'.

4. SIGNIFICANT TYPES OF MODELS

4.1 *Dynamic models*

By a dynamic model is meant a non-semiotic object O_2, which is a time-dependent model of an original O_1, which is likewise time-dependent, and belongs to the semiotic zero-level $\mathfrak{O}$ (*cf.* p. 150). The attribute classes constituting O_1 and O_2 are attributive systems* consisting only of zero-order and first-order attributes. The predicate classes describing O_1 and O_2 are therefore first-order predicative systems, which are symbolized by $O_1^{(1,n_1)}$ and $O_2^{(1,n_2)}$ respectively.

A (first-order) attributive system is, in this connection, called time-dependent (or dynamic), if at least one element out of the complete class of its individuals, properties, and relations is time-dependent, i.e. changes in time. For the describing systems $S_1^{(1,n_1)}$ and $S_2^{(1,n_2)}$ this means that a time parameter occurs in at least one predicate p_1 of $S_1^{(1,n_1)}$ and in at least one predicate $p_2 = F(p_1)$ of $S_2^{(1,n_2)}$, with Ico_F $S_1^{(1,n_1)}$, $S_2^{(1,n)}$. τ

By further definitions within the dynamic type of system, or of model respectively, are specified mainly the open systems and their dynamic models. Here L. von Bertalanffy's investigations can deal with the clarification of concepts such as finality, equi-finality, adaptation, integration and differentiation, centralization and decentralization, growth, decay, etc. of systems.

---

* The limitation of the space available does not allow to explain the notion of system, used here intuitively. An explication was to be given in point 1.3, which had, however, to be cancelled. Of course, attribute systems are a special kind of attribute classes.

4.2 *Cybernetic models*

By a cybernetic model (in a restrictive sense) is meant a dynamic model of a cybernetic attributive system. In this connection an attributive system O_1 is called cybernetic, if 1) at least one (not empty) subset of the set of individuals of O_1 consists of individuals that are time-active elements, so that a change in the state of the input of an element in a certain reaction time brings about a change in the output of this element, and if $2 \cdot O_1$ is a stable – ergodic – system, i.e. a system which, if it is not yet in equilibrium, with each sequence of states (beginning within its domain of stability) tends to an equilibrium.

A necessary condition for the stability of O_1 is the existence of at least one feedback coupling in O_1, i.e. at least one closed chain of time-active elements, so that outputs of one element of this chain are inputs of an element preceding it in the same chain. In stable systems the feedback coupling must, moreover, be compensatory against disturbances.

The reader will find further information in Lange (1962; 1965) to whom we owe a mathematical theory, rather highly evolved already, of the dynamic and especially of the cybernetic systems.

4.3 *Simulation models*

Simulation in a more comprehensive sense is the imitation, considerably shortening, in general, of a (dynamic) original with an alteration of its material qualities. Simulation in a restrictive sense is limited to cybernetic original-systems (*cf.* 4.2). Accordingly, by a simulation model (in a restrictive sense) is meant a cybernetic analogy model (p. 163) – in general reducing its original considerably – of a (cybernetic) original-system. With the original-describing, or model-describing respectively, predicate systems, the analogizing transference of meanings from the original attributes to the model attributes has its formal expression in the transcoding of all encoded predicates of the pre-domain of the corresponding icostructural original-model-mapping.

Normally, the production of simulation models and operations on such models are not immediately performed by the modelling Kybiak-organisms, but by interposed automatic simulators. Analogous simulators generate sequences of simulation models, which map continuously changing original systems. Digital simulators perform the mapping of their originals (which themselves can be, for instance, physico-technical cybernetic function models of bio-cybernetic systems) by means of computer programmes.

Another classification of the simulators follows the different values of the time-scale m_t concerning the simulated and the simulating system. $m_t = 1$ is spoken of as real-time simulators, $m_t \lessgtr 1$ can be spoken of as high-speed-motion simulators or slow-motion simulators respectively.

The present report partly anticipates results which the author will submit in his book *General Model Theory*, soon to be published by Springer-Verlag, Vienna and New York.

REFERENCES

BAR-HILLEL, Y. and CARNAP, R., (1953) 'Semantic information', *Brit. Journ. Philos. of Science*, *4*, 147–157.

FÜSGEN, P., (1959) 'Modelle und Modellregeln', *Wehrtechn. Monatshefte*, *56*, 241–251 (first publication in 1939).

GÄNG, P. (1967) 'Pragmatische Information', *Grundlagenstud. Kyb. Geisteswiss.*, *8*, 77–90.

LANGE, O., (1962) *Caloéś i rozwój w świetle cybernetyki*, Warsaw, Państwowe Wydawnictwo Naúkowe; *Wholes and Parts. A General Theory of System Behaviour*, Oxford-London-Frankfurt, Pergamon, 1965 (in English).

MARTIN, R. M., (1959) *Toward a Systematic Pragmatics*, Amsterdam, North Holland. Publ. Co.

MARTIN, R. M., (1964) 'Toward a logic of intentions'. In: J. R. Gregg and F. T. C. Harris (eds.), *Form and Strategy in Science*, p. 146–167, Dordrecht, D. Reidel.

MOLES, A. A. and SCHÜTZENBERGER, A., (1955) 'Sociométrie et créativité', *Rev. Psych. Appl.*, *V, 3*.

MOLES, A. A., (1958) *Théorie de l'information et perception esthétique*, Paris, Flammarion.

MOLES, A. A., (1960) 'Über konstruktionelle und instrumentelle Komplexität', *Grundlagenstud. Kyb. Geisteswiss.*, *1*, 33–36.

MOLES, A. A., (1962) 'Produkte: ihre funktionelle und strukturelle Komplexität', *Ulm* (J. Hochschule für Gestaltung), *6*, 4–12.

STACHOWIAK, H., (1965) 'Gedanken zu einer allgemeinen Theorie der Modelle', *Studium Generale*, *18*, 432–463.

STACHOWIAK, H. (1969) *Denken und Erkennen in kybernetischen Modellen*, Vienna-New York, Springer (second edition).

9   Management in cybernetic terms

STAFFORD BEER

1. THE HISTORY AND NATURE OF CYBERNETICS

The science of cybernetics has been developed under that name for a quarter of a century. It was defined with unique clarity and authority by the late Norbert Wiener to mean the science of control and communication in the animal and the machine.

This statement is pregnant with meaning: a meaning latent rather than hidden. People have been slow to understand it, although it has been there all the time. The point is this. There are general laws which govern control processes, whatever the system under governance. These laws apply to computers and servomechanisms, to the human nervous system, to populations of animals, to the economy, and to every other large, complex probabilistic system – such as the business firm. We include the adjective 'probabilistic' in this list of words qualifying 'system', since even well-specified systems that are truly complex can in practice be described only in this way.

A full historical review of the subject would systematically reveal how, quite gradually, scientists expert in many branches of knowledge came to understand the invariant nature, at an abstract level, of the processes which control large systems. With hindsight, we can be more brief. It turns out that we recognize systems to be such for four main reasons:
- because they cohere within some frame of experience;
- because they survive through time within some appropriate definition of continued identity;
- because, to achieve these ends, they prescribe unto themselves certain rules of equilibrial activity which are tolerable to their continued existence;
- and because they assimilate their unfolding experience into self-regulating processes of learning, adaptation and evolution.

If these are the common characteristics of large viable systems, then cybernetics sets itself to determine how the relevant mechanisms work. Having understood something about mechanism, science may then be relied upon to generalize its understanding – across the various types of system that it studies. This process leads to concepts of law, whereby science makes a further generalization: we expect that any *new* complex viable system that is going to survive will be found to utilize the generalized mechanisms of survival already elicited. But to make the concepts of mechanism and of law effective in designing or re-designing systems, we shall need concepts of behaviour, by which to understand the practical application of the models which embody our laws and our mechanisms.

All of this means that the scientific apparatus required to understand, design and regulate large viable systems is becoming available. It is this very apparatus, based on a corpus of knowledge, of which the management community stands most in need. For if cybernetics is the science of control, management is the profession of control. Every manager, whether he runs the firm itself or a major department of government, whether he runs the country or an aspect of international affairs, faces an identical problem. He faces, that is, the need to maintain a viable system far more complicated than he personally can understand. And the beginning of wisdom for management at any level is the realization that viable systems are, in large measure, *self*-regulating and even *self*-organizing.

Cybernetics reveals the nature of these natural phenomena. It must do so, if it is to help at all. For although management must accept responsibility for everything that happens, it cannot assume direct autocratic control of everything that happens. The systems concerned are just too big. This is why cybernetics turned to the study of self-regulating systems (such as those found in the relationship between organisms and their environment) and to self-organizing systems (such as the brain) for its insights. There simply is no *manager* identifiable in an ecological or a neurological system. Yet both of them work. Management theory, say cyberneticians, has been led astray in studying the nature of the existent and accepted managerial process itself. To make studies of the manager was the obvious thing to do; and yet 'the manager' turns out to be the embodiment of something we might call 'management principle' – that set of characteristics discovered in any viable system which conduces to viability. In this sense, then, the people who call themselves 'managers' are really catalysts of a systemic metabolism which is already at work.

But of course this considers managements as something which happens to be there in an on-going system, and something which is acknowledged by the system's components as having authority. The major problems arise when matters are *not* going well – or at least when it is obvious that 'something needs to be done'. Managers, the men themselves, are then expected to take some kind of action.

I think it is a major cybernetic conclusion to draw from these remarks that managers generally approach this problem in the wrong way. They usually try to intervene in the equilibrial processes of the self-regulating system – thereby, perhaps, making it fundamentally unstable. The sensible course for the manager is not to try to change the system's internal behaviour which typically results in mammoth oscillation, but to change its structure – so that its natural systemic behaviour becomes different. All of this says that management is not so much part of the system managed as it is the system's own designer.

What are the aspects of the system with which management can sensibly interfere, which it can design – or re-design? They are the *mechanisms* of that system: the structures, and the rules governing the behaviour of structures, which are usually taken as given. They are the arrangements already accepted as institutional conventions. It is these that need investigation.

2. CONCEPTS OF MECHANISM

One of the major mechanisms, perhaps the most important of all, which operates in the self-regulation of systems is the mechanism of *feedback*. This term has become very popular, and is often wrongly – because too loosely – used. Explicitly: feedback does *not* refer to a response provoked by a stimulus. (Managers commonly say: 'I have had some feedback about my suggestion on so and so.') This usage perverts a critically important idea.

The idea is this. When a system is in full operation it produces an output. Depending on the view we take of this output, we shall feed back a signal to those elements of the system which govern the nature of the output – a signal which actually alters them. When the system at large – as it already exists – next operates on its inputs, it will procure a different output – one hopefully nearer to our desire. The main reason why this mechanism is so important is that it does not require us either to understand or to intervene in the major operations of the system. These are left alone, and treated as self-controlling. What we are doing is to take a logically (and not necessarily managerially) superior view. If we have a perfectly good system the outputs of which are always exactly half what we require, then we alter the inputs to that system (in the simplest case) by a factor of two. Then the perfectly good system, quite unaffected by this, produces the anwers we want. It has not been denatured, or thrown into confusion, in the process.

The simplest form of feedback to understand is called error-actuated negative feedback, which is the one just mentioned. In this situation, we have an explicit statement of what the output is intended to be. 'A profit of ten million dollars', 'a fifteen percent return on capital', are examples of such a criterion in the firm. If the output of the system is different from this, a device is needed which measures the difference between the actual and the intended result. This 'error' is fed back to the start of the system, where it is enabled to change certain parameters of the system, so that the result – next time round – is nearer to the target than before. So far, so good. But there are other aspects of feedback, of which the notion of amplification is the most important. Instead of a fixed output criterion, we may have simply a statement of preferred trend. 'Let us increase the profits' is an example. Then, if the system is tending to increase the profit, the *positive* feedback signal encourages the system's critical variables to enhance yet further the final effect. This is called a reward system (its negative is a punishment system), the objective of which is to cause the system to *learn* from its past experience. These are unworked examples, but they illustrate the vital notion.

The whole point about any feedback mechanism is that, having set it up, the manager may go away. After all, he cannot attend to everything simultaneously. When he has set up a useful feedback mechanism, he should be able to forget about the subject; because what happens will henceforth regulate itself.

Now although we may think of a large organization, such as a firm, as having a single output (labelled profitability for example), and although we may imagine a large feedback loop which would adjust the inputs to the system so as to keep the output at a desired level, this is no more than a conceptualization of how management works. It is inconceivable that the complexities of a company's operations could actually be stuffed into a single mechanism of this kind. But we may start by this method to account for the way the business works. Then we ask questions about the way the system breaks up – into divisions of the company and divisions of the market, for instance, and model those. Thus we shall gradually be able to devise a more complicated model, redolent with feedback loops, which is of practical value. In doing all this we pass from the notion of a straightforward feedback mechanism to the notion of multiple loop systems. Outstanding in this area of study is the work of J. W. Forrester (1961; 1969).

There are three basic characteristics of viable systems which can profitably be studied by cybernetics in terms of multiple feedback loops. First, the significant outputs must be under control: we must know how to manipulate the system so as to produce a desired effect. Second, and this is vital, the system as a whole must be stable. Instability is the major symptom of a badly-managed organization, and we detect this symptom in terms (for example) of wild stock fluctuations; of surges of work-in-progress; of recurring panic in the conduct of day-to-day business; and of stop-go policies in the area of development. But cybernetics has indeed intensively studied the mechanisms which govern equilibrial behaviour – and can incorporate them in its management models.

The major concept which emerges from such studies is that of homeostasis. This means the capacity of a system to hold its critical variables within physiological limits. Note that we do not say: within prescribed limits. The point is that there is no satisfactory way of specifying acceptable limits of variation, except through a study of the system's dynamic behaviour. This should lead to the discovery of that degree of variation for critical parameters which the organism as a whole can tolerate before it is denatured.

It turns out that we can design a simple system, and prescribe limits for it, because we understand it completely. We know how it works, and we know both the kind and the magnitude of the perturbations it must withstand. This design-process yields a stable system: think of regulating a central heating installation for example. When systems become unthinkably complex, however, we can be sure of none of these things; we do not really understand the process itself, nor the perturbations which affect it, nor the interaction of these two. Therefore we adopt the principle that we need not only self-regulation (the feedback mechanism), but a capacity to generate internal elements of control which can adjust to everything else that is going on.

The best known example of homeostasis, which illustrates this, is the control of body temperature. This is achieved by myriad interactions within the body, taking account of the total set of circumstances from moment to moment, and not by some kind of thermostat working to fixed temperature limits. That is why we say that homeostatic controllers use self-organizing principles to hold critical variables within physiological limits. And so we have identified a self-organizing characteristic (the mechanism of which is homeostasis). The work of W. Ross Ashby (1954) provides the management cybernetician with fundamental knowledge on this score: he knows now how to go to work.

We said earlier that a relatively simple multiple loop feedback system could be designed – in full knowledge – which could be stable. In designing very complicated systems (without full knowledge) to be self-organizing by homeostasis, we emerge with a new criterion: ultrastability. This criterion relates to the capacity of a system to withstand perturbations which have not been foreseen by the designer.

This capability at first sounds impossible to realize. That is because we take the wrong model: a model drawn by our training from energy-systems (with which we are familiar) rather than from information systems (with which we are not). All we are really doing is to construct control devices which recognize unknown threats to the system – through their preliminary effects on the smoothness of operations. Gyroscopes and engine governors, for instance, are examples of homeostatic controllers. They are intended to keep ships and aircraft, or engines, running in a regulated way – regardless of the reasons why the ship is off course, or the engine racing. They achieve this, not by analysing the causality of the situation and coming to terms with the root problem, but by detecting within themselves pathological symptoms which are directly used to take regulatory action. I have called this principle 'intrinsic control'.

Similarly in the firm, we require managerial control devices to damp down oscillations (such as those recorded above as symptoms of instability), regardless of their cause. This idea is very important in management, because it may often take too long to identify the cause of trouble and to correct it at source. The common belief that this is the only scientific way of proceeding is mistaken, and derives from a very old-fashioned view of science itself. Keep the engine governor in mind.

So far we have concentrated on cybernetic mechanisms intended to hold things steady, to keep outputs and critical variables under control, to make systems at large both stable and ultrastable. All these things are necessary to managers if they are not to live in a state of continuous crisis. But there is another side to the picture. The ultimately stable state is death. If we are not careful, we shall have devised a paradigm of the firm which is a recipe for peaceful demise. All viable systems, cybernetics points out, are geared not only to tolerate a degree of tension, but to make constructive use of it.

Muscle 'tone' makes a good example of this tension-by-antithesis in the human body. Without it we should just fall down. Therefore we look for mechanisms in management systems which provide antithetic internal stresses, maintaining tonality short of the crisis level. From these mechanisms spring others which alone can lead the firm forward. It is a cybernetic result that systems cannot learn unless they make errors; they cannot grow without mutation; they will not adapt unless they experiment; they never evolve unless learning, growing and adapting.

All this, and the cybernetic understanding of it, means that it is now possible to design into a management system a proper machinery for generating innovation. That is the raw material of evolutionary development, and of the company's growth.

3. CONCEPTS OF LAW

When science has acquired an understanding of mechanisms which appear to be general to its area of study, it seeks out the common principles which must underlie their operation. For example, a tour of industry would reveal that (whereas many objects are moved about by a power source) in almost every factory there are examples where objects are deliberately and successfully moved in the absence of a power source. From the observation of these instances we should (if we were scientists from Mars, wholly unfamiliar with terrestrial mechanics) be able to infer the general principle of gravity feed. And from this we should in turn suspect the existence of the law of gravity itself. So it is with cybernetic mechanisms.

The 'stuff' of control is not any kind of object; it is something called *variety*. Variety is defined as the number of possible states of a system.

In what sense can this mathematical construct be called the very fabric of system? Consider the electric light on your desk. Its variety is two, because it is either on or off. The control of this situation is a simple matter, because we have a switch marked 'on' and 'off'. Consider a labour force of ten men, operating under a rule that anyone who did not immediately do what he was told would be shot. This system has a variety of ten and is readily controlled by anyone with a gun and ten bullets. Now relax the constraint that disobedience means death. At once the variety of this ten-man team rises to something approaching infinity. These men may now do anything at all: obey orders, disobey orders, vary orders, ignore orders. Or they may go away and play cards.

In short, the cybernetician calls any ordinary situation, in which an enormous number of possible states might be realized, a variety generator. The management problem is precisely a problem in handling variety: if we examine any managerial action, we shall find that it is a variety reducer. In the limit, when any particular goal has been achieved (for example, the order has been accepted by the customer) there is no variety left. The system has only one state: it is success, and that is a terminal state.

Now the kinds of action open to managers appear to be many and varied. There are high-level policy decisions; there are low-level short-term instructions; there are decisions about organizing the firm; there are verdicts which choose between alternative courses of action. It is interesting that so many different managerial activities, categorized as they normally are by function and by rank, discussed as they normally are in terms of different criteria applied by widely differing techniques, should share a common measure of success. This is precisely the measure of variety reduction. It will also quickly be noted that the higher-level decisions eliminate more potential variety than the lower-level decisions.

These observations indicate that it might be possible to design an organization, and with it a system of management control, based on the measure of variety. And so it proves to be. Now let us look for the natural law, exceedingly simple but exceedingly potent, which actually governs variety regulation. We have clues to its form already in the two-state electric light with its two-state switch, and in the ten-man team made obedient by ten bullets. The principle is this: only variety can absorb variety.

Once this is said it appears very obvious. But there is no difficulty in thinking of innumerable everyday situations in which people behave as if it were not the case. As to management, the application is clear: the managerial system, taken as a whole, must be capable of generating as much control variety as the situation is capable of proliferating uncontrolled variety. When these conditions are not met, and often they are not met, untoward events occur which the management cannot bring back into line.

Examples of well-known attempts to control proliferating situations with variety-starved controllers are legion. For example, we find governments attempting to control a variety-rich economy by changes in bank rate; we find managing directors (who should know better) setting out simple administrative rules about the way the company should run – rules which are immediately and readily circumvented by people lower down, because they operate in a variety-rich environment. We find policement attempting to regulate traffic at individual cross-roads, when their information does not extend around corners – never mind to the next policeman at another cross-roads. And so on. None of these managers can possibly be in control; they are attempting to disobey a natural law. I repeat: only variety can absorb variety. This is known as Ashby's Law of Requisite Variety (1954).

If a manager must needs deploy as much variety as the situation he seeks to bring under control, how is he to do it? The simplest method is by producing a precise match between the variety of control and of the controlled – as we saw in our preliminary examples. Most games are organized on this basis – we have the same number of players on each side, having the same resources. If we move to a more serious form of the 'game', such as a war, we can see how the same rule is applied. As civilian life becomes increasingly complex, which means that every individual has high variety (compare feudal times), it becomes increasingly necessary to match the total variety of half the citizens with a control variety consisting of the other half. Today we have just about reached the point where the policing of the state – in terms of taxation, welfare, education and so forth, as well as criminality – consumes half the total effort of society.

All this may seem to be necessary, if Ashby's Law is to be obeyed. But that is not the case. There is another way to deploy requisite variety, and that is to generate matching variety through a variety amplifier. If we say that all traffic will keep to one side of the road, we have set forth a low-variety rule. This is matched, in any individual case, by a low-variety acquiescence: 'I will do it'. But if everyone is truly acquiescent, then the control variety has been amplified by the number of individuals in the system. Should the population of drivers at which this rule is aimed not acquiesce, then (naturally enough) the low-variety rule will not work. We should need a high-variety rule such as a law enforcement officer driving in every car.

Thus all managements are faced with a triple choice: they may absorb proliferating variety by the amplification of control variety, or by one-to-one matching, or by reduction of uncontrolled variety. The first method has the demerit that a high-variety situation overthrows the control system completely – in the simple act of disobedience. The second method appears to have the demerit that it *ipso facto* uses up half one's total resources. The third method works very well; but it reduces opportunity and is inimical to major innovation.

But once again there is an alternative solution. Remember the game situation in which one team absorbs the variety of the other team. This control device does not consume managerial variety at all. It uses the rule of judo: one's opponent is defeated by his own strength, not yours. Most management situations can be defined in terms of two antithetic sets of activity. For example, the company and its market, each generating very high variety, can be modelled by a homeostat in which each set is deliberately organized as a variety sponge *vis-à-vis* the other set.

Then we are presented with a further problem. We may certainly conceive of two aspects of the situation for which, as managers, we are responsible, as absorbing each other's variety. And we may take organizational steps to ensure the accomplishment of this plan – whether we use variety generators, variety absorbers, or variety reducers. But recall what was said in the last section about the homeostat as a machine for running to a standstil . The homeostat is itself a controller of variety. But unless there is a controller of the homeostat, we shall not be able to intervene in the situation as managers at all.

Not that managers do not attempt this feat. A senior manager often has the notion that he may intervene in the homeostatic systems which operate under his aegis. He has the authority to do so, of course. But the minute he directly engages in a highly complex situation, on level terms as it were with those whose interactions are performing the balancing activity of the homeostat itself, the senior manager abandons his olympian role. His own personal variety is that of a human being, however elevated his status. No: the role of the senior manager is to remain above the homeostatic fray, and to consider what is happening in terms of his higher level understanding. Because he is outside the system, in fact, and because he partakes in another system which is no concern of his subordinates, his method of control is explicitly to alter the criteria according to which the lower level system is operating.

Let us go back to the illustration from games. Suppose that as a higher manager you have the responsibility to ensure that team A wins in a game which is already being played between team A and team B, where the scoring is already even. You could dress yourself in the appropriate regalia and charge onto the field of play. The players would recognize you. Your own side might defer to your tactics (but perhaps you are not a very good tactition?), while the other side would do their level best to put you out of action. This is not the way to behave at all. If you really had authority over this situation, the clever action would be to change the rules of the game so that your side must win it. You belong to a higher order system than the game system; your information is better; you command the facilities for variety generation. Then do not act as if none of this were true.

This illustration seeks to define the notion of metasystem. A metasystem is a system over-and-above the system itself. Its major characteristic is that it talks a metalanguage; and this is a richer, better informed, way of talking than is available to the system lower down. It should be noted that the *raison d'être* of the metasystem is given in logic; it is not necessarily anything to do with the hierarchy of status.

4. CONCEPTS OF MODELLING

Having talked about mechanisms and the laws which underlie them, we may be able to see how cybernetics provides a basis for modelling a management system. Now a model is neither a literary device, as is a simile, nor a logical device, as is an analogy. A model is a formal account of a system which identifies how it actually works (see Beer, 1966).

Interestingly enough, the rules of modelling turn out to duplicate the general laws of cybernetics which we have already been discussing. Consider: a model seeks to match the variety of the situation modelled – and in so far as it fails it is a less effective model. Thus the ideal model of anything is itself; while a model almost as good as this identity model is one which matches every element of the real system with an element in the model. Obviously such an arrangement provides requisite variety in the modelling process. Technically, such a model is called *isomorphic* with reality, because every element is matched. A paste copy of a piece of jewelry is an isomorphism.

If we cannot have an isomorphic model, and this is indeed unusual, we may have instead a model whereby many elements in the real system are represented by one element in the model. For example, if we make a model of Shakespeare's birthplace which is about six inches long, we may fairly readily produce an item which is identifiable as the building in Stratford-upon-Avon. But every brick in our model stands for many bricks in Stratford. It follows, then, that we are totally unable to produce every feature of the real building. This representation of the many by the one, technically called a many-one mapping, is not an isomorphism but a homomorphism of the original. We have lost variety. But the important point is that – if we are sufficiently clever – we will not have lost variety that matters.

Everything here depends on the purpose for which the model is constructed. Suppose we wish to make people think about Stratford. We build our six-inch model, and we produce a photograph of it. This photograph, at a casual glance, immediately says: 'Stratford-upon-Avon' to anyone who has seen Shakespeare's birthplace. So there may be no loss of information at all. A homomorph helps to regenerate the variety of the isomorph, when it is correctly used. But if we wished to know how long it will be before the Stratford building falls down, nothing at all will be gained by studying degeneration in the model.

In a management system, we know (or ought to know) the features of the situation that matter. Suppose we offer to provide the manager with a system which correctly predicts whether the man who will be operating the lathe in the third shop on the left next Tuesday morning will be wearing brown boots. This would be a high-variety model indeed; but one would certainly expect the manager to say that he was not interested in the least. So it is clear that we may eliminate variety in the process of modelling provided that we do not eliminate information which the manager most wants included.

In order to achieve these ends, we should begin with the macrostructure of the system we are studying. This system has major outlines. There are manifestly several identifiable processes, markets, trade unions, etc. Then our modelling process begins by specifying the major items and the connections between them. Already we have a model, which may be considered complete, although it has no detailed infrastructure. The model is homomorphic, and thus of very low variety compared with the original. Nevertheless, the manager may well – even at this point – be able to recognize the situation which he must control.

It is easy to imagine that the form of this model, written on a piece of paper, consists of boxes connected by lines. Each box refers to a major activity, and is a very high variety box. Nonetheless: there it is, with a label on it. We know what it is, but nothing at all about what is inside it. Such boxes are called 'black boxes', for the very simple reason that they are not transparent. We cannot see what is going on inside. Never mind, for the moment. These boxes are connected by lines, which may be used to indicate all manner of things. Above all, however, they indicate the way in which the boxes are connected in terms of communication between them. Communication, here, may mean anything from a production flow line (by which one box certainly communicates with another) to a message (about the size of the stocks for example); or it may be a more subtle form of communication, having more potency, which carries feedback information.

What can we say about these black boxes at this moment in time? Very little. But it may well be that we have a measure of their variety. Therefore, if one box is supposed to handle the output of another, we already know that it will fail in this attempt unless its variety is as high as the second. That is an immediate inference, by the Law of Requisite Variety. So although the boxes are black, they have a distinct *persona* within the cybernetic system.

Let us then turn to the lines by which boxes are connected, which we have already said represent communication. Now we may treat the problem of communication as a variety problem also. The least effective means by which two boxes can be related in terms of communication is by noise which passes between them. 'Noise' is defined as a signal having no meaning. But we must note in passing that even noise identifies a channel – the path through which the noise has passed. When we manage to identify a pattern in the noise, we declare that something meaningful is being communicated. Whatever is passing through the channel might now be called data. Data is pattern become meaningful. But data of themselves have no influence upon anything – after all, they may well be ignored; they may be stored for further reference (which never happens); they may engulf the recipient, as anyone who has bought a news-paper or a book which he has never read well knows. Noise become data becomes information at a precisely identifiable point. Information is what changes us. We never change without an information input (why should we?) If we really have received information, we are *bound* to change – because our variety is thereby increased.

Just as we can infer a great deal about our situation, using a model in which all the boxes are black, so we can infer a great deal about our capacity to react by looking at the communication channels whereby the boxes are connected. Do they contain merely noise? Are there receptors at the other end which are capable of transforming noise to data? Do 'thinking' elements lie behind these input transducers which are capable of transforming data to information? All these are highly relevant questions. But there is more to say. Consider two black boxes, A and B, which are mutually in a state of homeostatic equilibrium. What can we say about the communication channels which connect them? Well, we know that each box must have roughly the same variety as the other. And this equation would be useless if the communication channels were not adequate to transmit that variety – in both directions.

By these means we are able to identify the structure of communication channels which will complete the necessary stabilizing loops, and be able to specify their measurable capacity. There is a complete mathematical theory of communication, due especially to Claude Shannon (1949), which provides us with many formal theorems for the elucidation of communication problems. It sounds trivial to say that the channel capacity must be able to handle the variety of the black boxes. But this rule is often disobeyed in practise – with dire consequences. If we consider the managing director of a firm and one of its most humble employees, what could we possibly say about the communication between these two men? The answer is likely to be that they cannot (not do not, but cannot) communicate at all – because the channel capacity is simply not there. Shannon's theorems elucidate much of what the cybernetician needs to know in his modelling process. From his point of view, at least, one of the most important results of the mathematical theory of communication is Shannon's tenth theorem. This says, in effect, that it is *not enough* to provide channels with a capacity to transmit the variety of the black boxes. We need extra-channel capacity to elucidate ambiguities in the message.

From all of this it follows that if one is modelling a management system even in the most crude and macrocosmic fashion, a great deal can already cybernetically be said about its structure, and even about the way it works and fails to work. Black boxes juxtaposed in homeostatic equilibrium must have requisite variety; channels connecting them must obey the laws of communication; and we shall already be looking for emergent metasystems. All of this can be said before we have even approached the modelling of detailed operations within the firm. Perhaps this will never be necessary: we may settle for a low-variety homomorphism, depending on the object of the exercise.

More important than the details is the structure. We shall soon find that we are building a hierarchy of systems, based on the principles already uncovered. For every system demands a metasystem; and therefore a second metasystem will be identified beyond that. There is no logical end to the chain, because at each level of language there are propositions which logicians call 'undecidable' except in terms of a metalanguage.

Then when shall the process cease? How do we know when to stop modelling? The answer to this lies in the concept of the black box once again. For, when we have reached the limits of the system we are studying, we are compelled to say that it subsists within the framework of a higher order system – which we have no brief to penetrate. This does not mean to say that it can be ignored. What we must do is treat this extrasystemic system as an encompassing black box – and look for its effects upon the totality which lies under our jurisdiction that cannot be decided. Then we have to accept the resolving input of the superior black box as given, as insusceptible to analysis.

Now this statement is true for every system governed by a metasystem. In so far as we are designing a total management structure, we ourselves understand everything. But we must realize that each metasystem exists precisely because there is no logical sense in which the system to which it is 'meta' can cope without this unanalysable help. Although, in logic, this is a matter of some theoretical sophistication, it seems likely that real managers usually understand the point very well. When one explains things to a child, one perforce speaks the language of the child; and one may have to do violence to ones own insight in so simplifying the explanation given that it is almost incrorrect. Similarly, the head of a firm may find it totally impossible to explain his actions to the work force, in terms which they understand, without virtually falsifying the true basis of his policy. This is not in the least because either the child or the labourer is stupid; the point holds even if they can each be proved more intelligent than the father and the boss. They are just not part of the metasystem, and they do not speak the metalanguage. And when one comes to government, it is a necessary duty – on occasion – to declare that the reasons why a minister took certain action is not in the public interest to divulge. But the real point behind many ministerial failures of communication is not a matter of security at all, but a matter of metalinguistics.

These are a few examples of the operation of another fundamental principle of applied cybernetics. It is named the Principle of External Complementarity (Beer, 1967). That is because, at some point, all hierarchic systems, however sophisticated, rely for their logical completion on a black box lying outside.

5. CONCEPTS OF BEHAVIOUR

The identification of mechanisms led to concepts of law; and we have just seen how the laws of cybernetics govern our view of modelling. But models are useless unless they are applied; we go into action in a managerial situation armed with a model which – hopefully – embodies the laws and applies the mechanisms.

In doing this, we find ourselves confronted with a behavioural situation. This is a real world: a world in which models have no status, cybernetic laws are unrecognized, and the very mechanisms themselves are not understood. For this is the region of managerial action; it is the world the manager himself understands, it is the arena where he demonstrates his own competence as a leader and maker of decisions. And today, in a way unexampled by any previous epoch of history, this world is a scene of change. Change has always happened; and it is a *cliché* to observe that change is more fundamental and happens much more quickly than ever before – thanks to an exponential advance in technology. We are observing, indeed, a change in the rate of change.

It is for this very reason that management, which has hitherto developed its own competence to handle increasingly elaborate situations fairly successfully, now appears to be failing. Throughout the world, and at every level of operations, there is a management crisis of one kind or another. Now, although we said that tension was necessary to uphold the tonality of a system, we explicitly noted that the degree of tension within a viable system must remain short of persistent crisis. Today, on the contrary, crisis is persistent – and almost universal. We face environmental crisis in terms of pollution; by pesticides, by carbon monoxide, by noise, by chemical effluent, and so on. We face a technological crisis also, one which began with the threat of thermo-nuclear war – a threat to which almost unaccountably we have become inured. The fact is that the risk of thermo-nuclear devastation is more serious today than it ever has been before, thanks to the extension of nuclear capability, and the ever-increasing elaboration of the control systems required to restrain proliferating variety.

But beyond these existing problems there is the threat of the computer, which is hardly imagined yet in the minds of most authorities, nor even of those who will sooner or later abuse its immense power. There is the development of the laser, which will produce a revolution quite as impressive as that already attained by computers themselves. And thirdly, there is the threat of a new social crisis of disorder and violence, begotten largely by the other two, aided and abetted by the collapse of social metasystems which proved so stabilizing to the social homeostasis of the past. This is a reference to the contemporary loss of respect for organized religion, for law, and for inherited *mores* of every kind.

The problem may be summed up as a need for the management of change, which outclasses any previous experience which mankind has had of this requirement. It was said much earlier that most of our management technique was devoted to the smooth running of affairs, and that special measures had to be taken to ensure that the capability to innovate was not lost. Without this, we said, there could be no growth, no learning, no adaption, no evolution. All this is sufficiently difficult to underwrite when the world is standing virtually still – and indeed the capacities of mankind to undertake any kind of effort (whether in the speed of travel, the capability to compute, the capacity to lift and project, or anything else) remained, with hindsight, virtually static for five thousand years. It is in the last hundred years that we have seen the change in the rate of change which has left our management capacity gasping for breath.

Then we must organize; we must design control structures competent to cope with an unprecedented task of adaption. In general, the method which people adopt appears to be this. They look at existing trends and extrapolate them, hoping thereby to create for themselves a scenario which expresses what the future will be like. They then ask themselves whether they can create policies and undertake decisions which will enable the system for which they are responsible to survive in these circumstances. But this approach will not do.

Thanks to the exponential characteristics of contemporary change, these extrapolations reach points of singularity well within the compass of the period under review. That is to say: the forecast expansion becomes infinite at some finite point in time. That makes nonsense of the accepted approach to adaptation. The issue is nowhere more poignant than in consideration of the world population, which – at the present rate of expansion – is predicted (by these jejune methods) to become infinite within the lifetime of people already alive. Since this is impossible, we must look to the mechanisms which will inevitably flatten the exploding curves.

We find those that are natural to ecology all too readily: they are the threats to the extinction of mankind which have already been listed. Not only does it take variety to absorb variety; variety *will* absorb variety. Thus we face the ultimate task in control. Casting must be done; but it is not a question any longer of contemplating how to adapt to the predicted change. Quite clearly, the predicted change itself must be deliberately modified. As Gabor has put it, we must invent the future. If we do not, the future will happen to us. We shall not like it. Above all, in the terms of this paper, we have to lay hold on the exploding outputs of our situation, and drag down these outputs to a level which society can contain. Then regulatory mechanisms which can hold those outputs steady at the desired level must needs be instituted.

The science of cybernetics has, just in time, come to understand something about the fundamental processes which are causing loss of control, and also about those processes which are needed to contain explosive disorder. If management is to make use of these discoveries in time it will need to work at the metasystemic level. We can no longer afford the time to tinker with the internal mechanisms of established institutions.

These issues, which are in my opinion critical to the very survival of mankind, were extensively discussed at an OECD conference held at Bellagio, Italy, in 1968 (see Jantsch, 1969).

REFERENCES

ASHBY, W. R., (1954) *Design for a Brain*, New York, John Wiley (revised edition in 1960).

BEER, S., (1959) *Cybernetics and Management*, English Univ. Press (revised edition in 1967).

BEER, S., (1966) *Decision and Control*, New York, John Wiley.

CHURCHMAN, C. W., (1968) *The Systems Approach*, Delacorte Press.

FEIGENBAUM, E. and FELDMAN, J., (eds.) (1963) *Computers and Thought*, New York, McGraw-Hill.

FORRESTER, J. W., (1961) *Industrial Dynamics*, MIT Press and John Wiley.

FORRESTER, J. W., (1969) *Urban Dynamics*, MIT Press.

JANTSCH, E. (ed.) (1969) *Perspectives of Planning*, OECD.

KLIR, G. and VALACH, M., (1967) *Cybernetic Modelling*, Iliffe.

SHANNON, C. and WEAVER, W., (1949) *The Mathematical Theory of Communication*, Urbana (Ill.), Univ. of Illinois Press.

WIENER, N., (1948) *Cybernetics*, New York, John Wiley.

10 Concerning the notions of operation and optimation

ARNOLD KAUFMANN

As long as man had relatively little control over his environment, he regarded his ways of changing it either in general terms or in relation to certain micro-phenomena that were considered as having little connection between them. Now however, he is transforming nature by his industrial activities: his environment is a technosphere in which he exercises increasingly effective control. These industrial activities increasingly require energy and information – the most expensive components, limited in time and in space, components which must be used to best advantage and clearly demarcated. This is why operations analysis and optimation have acquired such importance in management thinking at all levels in modern society. The manager needs his operations map and processes for choosing between the solutions it indicates. Hence the growing use of what Kotarbiński calls 'praxeology' (decision theory) and the operations maps that might consequently be called 'praxeograms' or 'praxeographs', with the associated processes for preparing and selecting decisions that constitute the essence of operational research.

The demarcation of operations is the first concern; in the succeeding stage, the relations between them are investigated. The most suitable mathematical language for these purposes at present is the König and Berge graphs theory, as the operations are considered as members of countable sets and the most frequently encountered relations (numerical or otherwise) permit configurations with which mathematicians are now more at ease.

The analysis of operations should be non-prescriptive, its object being to describe, as correctly as possible, that which exists or is postulated. The difficulty of so describing the structures of production or distribution can be seen from a glance at the combinations involved. They can run to thousands of separate or continuous variables; to be usable, graphs to represent these problems have to be fragmented and the parts taken separately. This complexity influences not only the computing techniques, but forecasting, management and economic activities generally. The large but limited possibilities of the computers have made it possible to overcome of the major difficulties, but for new kinds which have arisen it is still impotent.

Before particularizing, it may be useful to give a few examples. Building a hospital necessitates thousands of diverse and not very repetitive operations. So does the running of a commercial port. Urban traffic sets engineers problems of disturbing complexity. Administration in industry and the public services alike is beginning to drive specialists to despair, despite all their data processing resources. Research may involve endless parameters. Education in and out of school is an immensely complicated combination of problems.

How can operations be analysed, particularized, have the relations between them determined? Here enters the model, representing something real or hypothetical. As all the parameters cannot be incorporated, a model is necessarily simplified and arbitrary, but it does give the mind something it can grasp.

These models can be very different:

1. *Deterministic:* For each set of causes there is one set and one set only of results (these models also called 'programmes', but this word is used for many, widely-differing concepts).

2. *Stochastic* (Probabilistic): For each set of causes there is more than one set of results, but the coefficient of probability of all the possible states of the system can be evaluated. Most often selected for describing phenomena which alter with time.

3. *Uncertain but structured:* By hypothesis, all the possible states are known but at least one is not and its coefficient of probability cannot be evaluated. Applies to cases where nature or other determinants intervene.

4. *Uncertain but imperfectly structured:* Not only are the probabilities of the states inadequately known, but also the actual states themselves. In this last case, constructing the model of a system means working back by modifications and simplifications to case (3). Here, however, the ignorance of probabilities for each of the possible states in the model is so great a difficulty that the only thing to do is attempt to measure the chances as accurately as possible. So, further changes and simplifications are introduced. However, decisions can rarely be taken on the basis of

statistical information or probability laws; resort is had to more precise measures (averages, variances, medians, quartiles and other coefficients) to bring the hypotheses down to earth.

Deterministic models are much used in preparing decisions, e.g.:

– Short-term forecasting (Graphs): Each operation or activity is situated in time in relation to others. Examples: PERT (Programme Evaluation and Review Technique) graphs, Roy's 'potential' graphs.

– Sequencing and combining. Preparation and timing of tasks. Often hard to translate into mathematical language and usually highly complicated, hence difficult to manipulate.

– Location and allocation. Example: various activities have to be assigned in relation to a given set of positions, tasks, executants, means of production, localities.

– Economic transfers (*cf.* Leontiev matrices).

– Economic programmes involving linear or non-linear constraints, integer or discrete variables.

– Modular representations for analysing flows of all kinds (model constituted by the resulting graphs and the inter-flow relations).

– Transport, circuit and distribution models.

Stochastic (probabilistic) models are also much used. The best known and simplest is the Markov chain, a sequence of random events in which the probability of each event depends on the outcome of immediately previous trials. For operational analysis, their use requires a delicate manipulation of probability theory; if the models are quantifiable, graph theory can help to simplify and clarify. Some major uses: inventory, queuing, reliability, and equipment replacement problems.

In practice, stochastic models are seldom wholly or even adequately exploitable. The statistics are generally ill-known and the probabilities derived from them dubious. The typical model is more likely to be uncertain but structured (3) than stochastic (2). It might be thought that knowing the events possible but having little idea of their respective probabilities would rule out usable conclusions. However, these models are of universally acknowledged value for risk assessment. As the probabilities are poorly known, an attempt is made to evaluate the consequences of certain situations. But there are so many possible combinations that only a limited number can be studied, despite the ever-growing possibilities of simulation methods.

Description, i.e. the non-normative analysis of the operations, is of course necessary, but is not concerned with the human mind's demand for efficiency or, more precisely, for the best. What do we mean by the best?

To a mathematician, the notion is clear. Because of certain constraints, there is a subset of possible solutions; of these, one (or more) which will give a maximum or minimum result in relation to a chosen numerical criterion, e.g. a production programme whose execution takes least time, a works organization which yields maximum profit. Mathematical programming rests on the assumption that there is a single criterion for action; in real life, this is rarely the case (*cf.* Pareto).

The real aims of a business executive, politician or other decision-maker may be extremely complex, and depend on a multitude of criteria, as often as not contradictory. Making a decision or decisions is a very delicate matter, with no unique, exclusive rules. Consciously, and even unconsciously, free choice enters in, but is rarely decisive in making the first order of activities. A comparative review of the possibilities will sometimes yield this first order, but this is still not enough to indicate a maximum (or minimum) in the set theory sense. Other eliminations or additions must follow and even then, the result will be inadequate in certain cases. Ideally, the items to be compared will fall into a total, strict order, but this is very rare.

Hence the major importance of criteria selection in all optimization problems. Operational research originally tended to be somewhat academic, it being taken for granted that it had a single, unique objective. The trend is now away from this view (*cf.* Roy, 1969).

There is a growing tendency nowadays to break down the ultimate aim into its major components, convert these in turn into objectives, and then seek the best means of achieving them. Work done for the United States Department of Defense from 1961 onwards under Secretary of State Mc-Namara clearly affected research in business corporations and public services. PPBS (Planning, Programming, Budgeting System) analysis involves considerable changes in the way of paying regard at highest level to intentions and possibilities. The terminology is intended to help in determining the ultimate aim as a function of intermediate tasks, missions and objectives, and vice-versa. Discussions still continue regarding terminology and programming methods. It will be interesting to see the cybernetic follow-up, the indications provided by electronic simulations, and effective results.

In this new approach in the choice of the solutions there are reflections of the contributions of von Neumann and Wald to value theory viz., seeking to determine the preference of one solution to others by weighting, and making a sequential readjustment accordingly. However, numerical adjustment methods have serious drawbacks (non-additive, non-homogeneous) and research tends, instead, to look to the pattern of possible preferences (where, in any case, numerical evaluations can be used). It is difficult to convert a combination of intentions into criteria to be used in making a selection which must itself be consistent with the original combination of intentions. As the objectives are not homogeneous, the theory of probabilities affords little help in deciding subjective weightings, while measurement theory is not (as was originally hoped) suitable. However, distributive lattices seem to offer interesting possibilities.

When one criterion stands out but the others nevertheless cannot be neglected, optimization by changing parameters or by k-optimality, can be attempted. Altering one or more of the parameters may give optimal solution(s) much better adjusted if the combination of preferences is complex. k-optimality can be taken in several ways. If the sets are finite, class 1-optimal is the subset of optimal solutions, class 2-optimal the subset of optimal solutions of the whole less the class 1-optimal solutions, and so on. A certain arbitrary order of solutions that might be of interest for other criteria can be found by taking in classes made up of solutions which vary from the optimal solution or solutions by a difference equal to k (k-optimality).

What do we mean by optimality in a system? In nature – in biology for instance – it is not easy to see what the notion of optimality can correspond to. On the other hand, the idea of equilibrium very frequently recurs. All the same, it still remains necessary to give a better definition of exactly what is understood by equilibrium. In economics and sociology the notion of optimality is probably artificial and might not be able to stand up to certain contradictions, but the habit is now ingrained and the term 'optimal' is increasingly used. It will not disappear until we find a better. Let us then recall what optimization consists in or, to use the terminology accepted by a number of authors in France, let us study the optimization of systems.

Take a system comprising men or/and machines or/and products. The constraints in the model of this system involve two sorts of variables:

1) those the decision-maker can control, and 2) those he cannot. The model is assigned a single-valued function. The aim is then to find out which values of the controllable variables will give an optimal value for the function assigned to the model (maximal or minimal as appropriate). The values assigned to the non-controlled variables follow a series of hypotheses.

A few examples will clarify. A factory has m machines with which it proposes to make n products. An operation O_{ij} consists in getting product i off machine j. There are various constraints: order in which certain operations must take place, operating times having to be fitted in at specified intervals, and so on. The value function to be optimized (minimized) is total machine idle time.

Such problems are frequent in industry. They are usually highly complex, and when the quantities m and n are greater than ten, the time needed to process them, even with high-capacity computers, may be much too long. The decision-maker accordingly settles for a reasonable compromise. Methods which provide a passable (even though non-optimal) solution are often termed heuristic (from the Greek verb 'to find out'); they take much less time.

Depots in central points supply distribution centres with variable quantities of a product. Lorries of known capacity are available. The distances between the depots and the centres and between the centres are known. The problem is to reduce to a minimum the total distance the lorries must cover in a given period, e.g. a week. This kind of problem occurs in the distribution of oil and petrol, milk collecting, operation of school buses, and so on. Here again, heuristic methods can often give adequate solutions.

Locating a centre or centres of production. One or more products will have to be delivered to other localities. Transport and labour costs in the possible site areas are known. Other factors include accessibility, availability of housing, local charges, climate. Seldom in such cases is there one criterion only, and several value functions could be proposed for optimization. Usually, one is selected and heuristic methods are used to find optimum values for the others.

The algorithmic, and some of the heuristic methods used for the above three types of problem are based on a very general procedure. The set of solutions is broken down by an n-partition (very often $n = 2$) and each of the subsets thus created is given an upper (lower) bound. The process is repeated for a subset having the greatest lower bound, and each new subset is again bounded. It is then continued with a subset having the least upper bound, selected from the subsets which have not yet been subjected to breakdown, and so on until a subset containing only one solution, a minimal solution, is obtained. This elegant evaluation process is known as the 'branch and bound' method in the United States and as the *méthode de séparation et évaluation progressive* in France. It is of very general application, provided that the bounding and branching can be properly done, which is not always easy. However, the 'rooted-tree' curve followed acquires more and more peaks as the evaluation continues, and it may take much too much time, even with high capacity computers. In such cases, heuristic methods can be used at a certain point. Branch and bound optimization can be used to find either a maximum or a minimum after adjustment of the algorithm, and it works in problems involving continuous or mixed variables.

It can also be used in conjunction with Polya's 'screening' methods. The human mind commonly tries to find the optimal solution by stages – by successive screenings or siftings.

Linear programmes are among the complex-system models in widest use today. All the constraints of the model are linear equations or inequalities and the solutions are situated in a convex domain. These equations or inequalities will take the form of a set of relations such as:

$$\sum_{j=1}^{j=N} a_{ij}\, x_j\, b_i \odot i = 1, 2, ..., M$$

The symbol $\odot$ indicates that the equality or inequality may be in either direction. The variables x_j are non-negative, whilst the coefficient a_{ij} and b_i may be any real numbers. A value function is taken which is also a linear function:

$$f(x_1, x_2, ..., x_m) = \sum_{j=1}^{j=N} c_j\, x_j \text{ where the } c_j \text{ are real numbers}$$

The object then is to find a solution or solutions giving an optimal (maximal or minimal) value of f.

Much used with this type of model is the Simplex algorithm, developed some twenty years ago by G. Dantzig in the United States and Kantorovitch in the USSR (although the actual idea was mooted much earlier).

The following is an example of a linear programme model of a production system. A firm has to turn out 14 different types of products. There are three assembly lines on which each of the products can be processed. The order in which the products come off the line is unimportant. The capacity of each line, the production cost per ton of each product on each line and the hourly output of each line for each product are known. The demand for each product is also known. The model accordingly takes the following form:

$$\sum_{j=1}^{j=14} \frac{x_{ij}}{d_{ij}} \leqslant c_i \qquad i = 1, 2, 3.$$

$$x_{1j} + x_{2j} + x_{3j} = d_j \qquad j = 1, 2, ..., 14.$$

where x_{ij} is the quantity of the product j to be produced on the line i;
d_{ij} is the output of product j on line i;
c_i is the capacity of line i;
d_j is the demand for product j.

The value function whose minimum is sought (the total cost of production) can be written:

$$f = \sum_{i=1}^{3} \sum_{j=1}^{14} \gamma_{ij} \cdot x_{ij}$$

Computers can now process programmes containing thousands of variables and thousands of constraints, as major economic programmes require. Variants of the Simplex method, devised to make the processing more rapid, are often used in conjunction with approach processes which are more rapid in certain cases (gradient method, Lagrange's method of multipliers). A considerable literature exists on this subject.

Constraints are again presented in the form of equations or inequalities in models known as 'integer-valued linear programmes' or 'mixed-variable linear programmes'. In these models, the controllable variables can take only non-negative integer values or else Boolean values (0 or 1) or, again, some variables can take only integer values while the others can have continuous values. These problems are much more difficult to solve, and a great deal of work has been done on them in recent years. Many forms of algorithms have been suggested, nearly all based on branch and bound processes. Economic and other problems of this type, with hundreds of variables, can now be processed, but require much more computer time than in cases where all the variables have continuous values.

In some models, the value function or/and the constraints are not linear, but may, e.g. be quadratic or mixed. Methods have been suggested by Wolfe, Beale and Rosen, to mention only recent work.

Before considering models whose subject matter is randomizable, we must look at dynamic programming, i.e. models in which the changes in the states of the system occur sequentially. At moments distributed discontinuously or continuously in time, the system changes. At these moments the vector of states may change. For our present purpose, we shall assume that this change takes place in a predetermined manner (the case of the stochastic processes will be considered later). In these deterministic processes, an optimal trajectory will be sought by sequential processes. The principle for the resolution of sequential programmes of this nature has been stated by R. Bellman in the United States, and may be resumed as: 'An optimal trajectory can only be formed by optimal subtrajectories.' To apply this principle, it is necessary to prove certain theorems deriving from it which, as a rule, are very easy to prove and in certain cases are simply truisms. If an optimal trajectory could be formed of non-optimal subtrajectories, then the optimal trajectory would have to pass through other subtrajectories and could no longer be optimal, which contradicts the hypothesis. But the deterministic sequential processes treated in dynamic programming must be carefully examined before being subjected to optimation processing; in particular, they must be associative.

Certain combination problems can be processed by dynamic programming, needing only to have a suitable structure that is either sequential or can be rendered such. But it no longer works – even with computers – when the variables of state are numerous. Its possibilities are thus limited, but valuable in undertaking the construction of sequential models. One interesting point is the boundary within which dynamic programming operates. For each problem, the model must have a suitable boundary, upon which the results usually very largely depend. According as the value function used is short-term or long, the optimal trajectories will be widely different.

If discrete variables are involved, dynamic programming may often need k-optimality processes (see above), especially if there can be more than one single selection criterion.

Sequential models are used in inventory, sequencing, investment and equipment control problems; hence the practical value of dynamic programming. A 'theory of optimal processes' will be discussed below.

Deterministic sequential processes immediately evoke stochastic processes. If randomization is feasible in constructing a model, the model itself will more often than not be stochastic. Markov chains, which play so important a part in heredity phenomena in biology, are similarly important in the human sciences.

Assigning a value function to states in Markov chains can provide good and representative models of various inventory and equipment replacement problems. R. Howard first drew attention to the advantage of considering the normative aspect of Markov processes, and highly interesting ergodic properties have been brought to light in subsequent studies; for these discrete processes, the use of demonstrations employing graphs represents another appreciable advance. Although stationary processes are rare in real phenomena, the hypothesis of their existence in the selected model makes it possible to bring out clearly the essential conditions for equilibrium. In the case of processes where the variables take their values in the continuum, the time element being 'discretized' or not, rather tricky problems of integration and differentiation are posed and their exhibition is difficult or still remains to be worked out.

Decision-hazard processes represent an interesting extension of Markov chains. A sequential 'decision-hazard' process is a process in which nature and the decision-maker intervene alternately. It is assumed that sufficient statistical observations of nature have been made to assign probabilities to all the relevant changes of state; that each change of state has an associated value; and that the changes of state consequent upon decisions can be evaluated. Thus, to any strategy, a total value can be assigned which is the sum of the values of all the changes of state and those that derive from the decisions. In this kind of model, the process need no longer be stationary, and it can approximate fairly closely to a diversity of real-life situations. In these processes, the interval of anticipation or economic horizon involved plays a very important part. However, in cases which are not stationary, or stationary for a small number of decision-hazard phases only, ergodic equilibrium is ruled out.

These notions have a theoretical importance for learning and adaptive processes which goes well beyond that of their practical applications.

The linear relations which enter into Markov processes permit the use of common functional transformations: the Laplace transform for continuous processes, or the z transformation for processes discontinuous in time. These transformations help to demonstrate convergences which are particularly useful in studying and comparing various long-term policies.

Stochastic processes also have a very wide application in problems of economics, sociology and even psychology (in queuing, inventory, investment, and other phenomena previously mentioned). Queuing occurs in many aspects of social and economic life. Service points provide services for 'users' (machines and products as well as people). Service points and users together form a 'queuing system'. It is assumed that probability distributions can be assigned to the states of this system, and that integral or differential equations will yield working estimates. Policies can then be worked out to avoid bottlenecks. Different forms of impatience can be studied. Priorities are established to facilitate the traffic and satisfy legitimate demands. The problem is often to minimize the total cost of queuing for service points and users alike; or to reduce risks. The sociologist can study and quantify individual and group behaviour. Queuing theory can be applied to road, air and sea traffic, to production – if execution times are variable and can be measured statistically – and to many physical phenomena. Phenomena which are too complicated for complete analysis by such models can be studied by simulation. Since Erlang's initial work, thousands of publications have discussed cases of the most diversified kinds.

Inventory problems are crucial in many systems. Stationary random processes can be used in certain rather rare cases, for which equilibrium conditions and permanent policies can then be worked out. Various kinds of costs are involved: management and holding costs, costs deriving from shortages or extent of shortage, cost of re-stocking. If equilibrium is possible, it is worth while determining the optimal policy or policies. This may be relatively easy, but if the inventory involves several stages of distribution and management and transport difficulties, no acceptable analytical study may be feasible and simulation will have to be used. Generally speaking, inventory problems change too rapidly to have any stationary aspects. Study has to depend on short-term changes and forecasts which often work out quite well, in factories, big stores, warehouses, and so on. These forecasts rely on simulation processes that are also learning and adaptive processes.

The increasing extent and complexity of modern technology demand an increasingly close check on its constituent parts (*cf.* in the production of energy, transport, transfer of processing of information) and, for maintenance purposes, increasingly refined studies of reliability. Economic optimization has to pay attention to maintenance and repair costs, masses (e.g. for space rockets), volumes, and so on. Several criteria may have to be satisfied, and parametric transformation (see above) is often necessary.

Markov chains are often used in reliability and equipment replacement studies. The equations are the same for the life and death of equipment as for the life of cells in biology, except that, in nature, man can only very rarely impose his control systems, whereas he can incorporate them in his technologies. But the analogies between technological and biological life should not be stretched too far. However, biologists can get ideas from models constructed for economic and social studies, and economists and sociologists have much to learn from examining the methods of biologists. A machine is a generalized automaton that resembles any living being, except that its use can be controlled in endless ways.

Normally, this article should consider the models commonly used to study systems that are uncertain but structured (see 3, page 188), i.e. where all possible states are known but the coefficient of probability of at least one cannot be evaluated. The cases are in fact covered under games strategy and dealt with by another contributor to this book. However, to tie in what has just been said about optimization more closely with what is to follow, games strategy can be considered from a special angle, i.e. games against one or more opponents or/and against nature. Here we take games against nature only, in which the possible states must be defined and a value assigned to each. Depending on the purpose of the author (e.g. von Neumann, Laplace, Hurwitz, Savage), the optimization may be either minimax or maximin, a simple weighting, minimal regret, and so on. There could be endless argument about the relative merits of various criteria – this is obviously a subjective matter. But a critical examination of these criteria gives an excellent insight into the contemporary psychology of decision-makers; in particular, the procedures suggested by certain dominating ideas make it possible (*cf.* page 191 above) to bring a combination of preferences or intentions into line with criteria for action. Another advantage of these rather academic studies is that they give a better idea of what is meant by a strategy against nature and, more especially, what is meant by a mixed or weighted strategy. For the sake of accuracy, a distinction must be made between 'policy' and 'strategy'. A 'policy' applies in a case which is deterministic (see 1. on page 188) and involves scalar or vectorial decisions; a 'strategy' applies in cases which are not deterministic but either probabilistic, or uncertain but structured (see 2. and 3. on page 188).

In games against nature, sequential games are extremely important. The sequential form of the decision-hazard process (see 3. and 4. on page 188) recurs, but this time, nature intervenes, and the coefficient of probability cannot be evaluated. As the combination element enters fairly extensively into these games, it is difficult to apply them in practical cases. The computer doesn't seem to be able to do much to help (machines are needed with circuits in parallel to high degree; sequential machines are too slow, even if they can work at the rate of a nano-second for each bit). The interest of these games is that they allow a scientific approach to decision preparation.

More elaborate control processes are described as 'learning and adaptative'. In the real, technological world in which men take decisions, such decisions are seldom final, or even regular and systematic. When too large a change occurs in the object, the system or the environment, the decision-maker intervenes and adapts the system to bring it into line with his criteria. Starting from a relatively modest knowledge of the system and the environment, he acquires – over a period of time which varies in length – a better knowledge of both and of all the conditions involved. He can thus work out a control process that takes account of the widest range of observed human habits and behaviour.

This 'piloting' makes optimization much more realistic. The decision-maker goes about it as follows. He locates a model of the system he wishes to control in a future which may or may not be finite, but in principle always will be. To deal with the combination of hypotheses he has adopted, he seeks the strategy that gives the best results in relation to his criterion, or the best compromise if his criteria are plural. He feeds in the decisions for the present and the future that the strategy dictates. The strategy proves correct up to a point only because nature also intervenes. He studies the new situation. He can continue with the same model or choose another more realistic. He again works out an optimal or compromise strategy, for e.g. a shorter or longer future, or for different values of the variables over which he has control. Another new situation arises ... and so on.

This is the approach most frequently used in cybernetics. It is used in its most advanced and realistic form in economics, for example, to work out fundamental patterns, but can equally well be used in guiding a spacecraft, steering a ship or other machinery, in government, in management, or in studying the way in which an individual behaves in his environment under the impulse of his reason and his feelings.

'Piloting' is of particular practical importance in macro-economics. Until quite recently, planners drew up development plans for a specific period (e.g. five years). The authorities then tried by every possible means to achieve the objectives, even if, meanwhile, conditions and opinions changed. In practice, no medium or long term plan was carried through to achieve the objectives as set. Planners now prefer a sliding scale of objectives or even a sliding and variable scale. Yearly, or sooner if necessary, the plan is examined to see how it is working out, and it is suitably modified. It is surprising that economists in advanced countries are only now discovering this idea which common sense would seem to suggest, probably because of ingrained habits and all kinds of brakes on the necessary but not always foreseeable changes in society.

In facilitating this more flexible approach in planned or semi-liberal economies, computers will have an important part; for, after each 'learning and adaptative' phase (see page 199), it will be necessary to simulate the new situations that correspond to new hypotheses. As these simulations become more complex and delicate, the mathematical resources of computers become indispensable to the analyst. The approach of economic planner and decision-maker here is almost exactly that of McNamara and Kantorovitch (see page 190 above); the main difference is in the manner and order in which the PPBS evaluations and classifications are made.

Civilians now fairly often follow the military practice of applying the cost-effectiveness criterion to decision problems. In many economic problems, cost and effectiveness are the main criteria, and it is difficult to say which is the more important. A graph plotting variations in effectiveness against cost (or vice-versa) indicates the best solutions in terms of individual preferences or those of supposedly coherent groups.

The cybernetic flow chart on page 201, showing the phases in their correct positions, summarizes the ideas about economic 'piloting' set

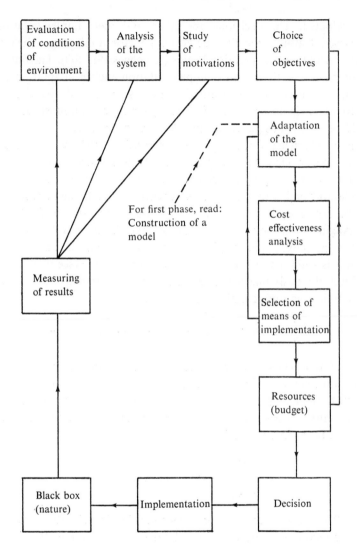

out above. The analysis of the system is preceded by an evaluation of the environment and followed by a study of motivations, after which the objectives are defined. A model is constructed or adapted. Once total cost has been worked out and effectiveness specified (both can have vectorial forms), the possible means of implementation and the possible resources are evaluated. The decisions are taken and their implementation is supervised. Nature is the ultimate deciding factor at this stage. The results are tested and a new operation begins (see pages 199–200). The links will be noted between the means of implementation and the adaptation of the model, and between the evaluation of resources and the choice of objectives. (This flow chart is of course given only as an illustration, and would be adapted as particular problems may require.)

These cybernetic forms can be expressed in strictly mathematical terms – particularly necessary in technological procedures, where the decision has to be programmed in advance and intervenes at a speed considerably higher than that of the reactions of the human brain.

A theory of optimal control in sequential processes put forward by Pontryagin and his Soviet research group takes up and develops variation calculus principles and involves programmed control. The cases for which it is valid may be deterministic or probabilistic (see page 188). In brief and obviously inadequate outline, it can be summarized as follows.

The following differential equations apply:

$$\frac{dx^i}{dt} = f^i(x^1, ..., x^n, u^1, ..., u^r), \; i = 1, 2, ..., n.$$

where x^i represents the state variables, and u^j the control variables. What values can be assigned to the u^j variables in an interval between two instants t_0 and t_1, assuming that the u^j variables are functions of time, and that the initial values at $t = t_0$ of the x^i variables are known, viz. x_0^i?

Take a functional integral

$$J = \int_{t\,=\,t_0}^{t_1} f^0\,(x^1, ..., x^n, u^1, ..., u^r)\,dt$$

where f^0 is a given function. For every control defined by the u^j variables in the interval t_0 to t_1, the integral takes a finite value. If a control exists which converts the system from state vector x_0^i to state vector x_1^i, the integral J becomes minimal.

Pontryagin's method to some extent combines Bellman's optimality principle with the usual variation calculus version, allowing a strict control of the processes in many important cases. This was because reliance could no longer be placed on more or less intuitive mathematical methods. Pontryagin's method has proved almost ideal for optimality analysis and control and, with the many variants since worked out, has been of vital importance in space navigation, in the real time control of continuous manufacturing processes, and in the study of many still unsolved theoretical optimation problems.

REFERENCES

AUMALE, G. D', (1968) *Programmation des décisions*, Paris, Presses Universitaires de France.

BECKENBACH, E. I., (1964) *Applied Combinatorial Mathematics*, New York, John Wiley.

BELLMAN, R., (1960) *Dynamic Programming*, Princeton Univ. Press.

BERGE, C., (1962) *La Théorie des graphes et ses applications*, Paris, Dunod.

BOOT, J. C. G., (1964) *Quadratic Programming. Algorithms. Anomalies. Applications*, Amsterdam, North Holland Publ. Co.

CAUDE, R. and MOLES, A., (1964) *Méthodologie. Vers une science de l'action*, Entreprises modernes d'édition.

DANTZIG, G. (1963) *Linear Programming and Extensions*, Princeton Univ. Press.

HAMMER, H. P. and RUDEANU, S. (1968) *Boolean Methods in Operations Research*, Springer-Verlag.

HOWARD, R. (1960) *Dynamic Programming and Markov Processes*, New York, John Wiley.

KAUFMANN, A., (Vol. I, 1970; Vol. II, 1968) *Méthodes et modèles de la recherche opérationnelle*, 2nd edition, 2 vols. Paris, Dunod.

KAUFMANN, A. (1966) *L'Homme d'action et la science*, Paris, Hachette.

KAUFMANN, A. (1968) *Introduction à la combinatorique*, Paris, Dunod.

KÖNIG, D. (1936) *Theorie der endlichen und unendlichen Graphen*, Leipzig, Akad. Verlag.

KÜNZI, H. P. and KRELLE, W., (1962) *Nichtlineare Programmierung*, Springer-Verlag.

LUCE, R. D. and RAIFFA, H. (1957) *Games and Decisions*, New York, John Wiley.

NEUMANN, J. VON and MORGENSTERN, O., (1944) *Theory of Games and Economic Behavior*, Princeton Univ. Press.

PONTRYAGIN, L. S. *et al.* (1962) *The Mathematical Theory of Optimal Processes*, New York, John Wiley.

ROY, B., (1969) *Algèbre moderne et théorie des graphes*, Paris, Dunod.

THRALL, R. M. *et al.* (1957) *Decision Processes*, New York, John Wiley.

WALD, A. (1950) *Statistical Decision Functions*, New York, John Wiley.

11 Game theory

NICOLAI N. VOROBYEV

1. FUNDAMENTAL CONCEPTS OF THE THEORY OF GAMES

1.1 Game theory is the theory of mathematical models for decision-making in conflict situations (e.g. in contests).

The implications of this very wide definition need detailed analysis.

The theory deals with models, i.e. not with actual optimal decisions but with idealized schemata of them. All the general statements that may be made about arbitrary models apply in game theory. These models are not just any kind of model, but formal, symbolic, mathematical models. This means that all the game-theoretical statements must be sufficiently precise to lend themselves to complete formalization.

In particular, the very object of the game theory, the optimal decision-making under conflict must be formalized, and this in turn requires the formalization of the concepts of 'decision-making', 'optimality' and of the 'conflict' in question.

The formalizations for each of the three concepts are problems of entirely different complexity.

1.2 Decision-making is understood in the simplest sense as the choice by the decision-maker of an arbitrary decision from within a set of possible decisions given in advance. Game theory is not necessarily concerned with the physical or social nature of the decision, the decision-maker's reasons for or the means of selecting his decision, much less his manner of implementing it – these are partly matters for cybernetics and operations research. Nevertheless, in dealing with specific cases, game theory may also have to bear these aspects in mind. An elementary but very instructive exposition of game theory contains in the book of M. D. Davis (1970).

1.3 The formalization of the idea of a conflict is appreciably more complex.

A conflict is a phenomenon in which we know who is involved and how; what are the possible outcomes; and who is concerned by these outcomes and how. This description can be enlarged upon.

First, we must list all the acting factors. These can be collective and possess some internal structure. Therefore they may be called acting coalitions. The total of all such coalitions constitutes a set, which we can designate $\Re_a$.

Secondly, all permissible decisions for each operational coalition must be indicated. Usually, in the theory of games no distinction is made between the decision and its implementation (a kind of identification frequently used in mathematics). The actions, behaviours and decisions of each acting coalition are called its strategies. The set of all strategies of acting coalition K can be designed S_K.

Thirdly, we have to indicate all the possible outcomes, which are basically the results of the choices of strategies by all the coalitions. These outcomes are called the situations. The set of all situations we designate S.

The coalitions having chosen and carried out their strategies (1.2 above), the outcome is assumed to be completely predetermined, i.e. the situation is univocal. This assumption is less restrictive than it might seem. Suppose the choice of strategy by the coalitions does not lead univocally to a particular physical outcome but leaves open the possibility of any of the outcomes of a subset of the set of all outcomes. The uncertainty here could be of two kinds. 1) The outcome is random and the probabilities of its realizations depend on the strategies chosen by the acting coalitions. We can consider it as a single, complex outcome, i.e. a single situation; for example, the conflict is a chess match in which the winner gets a lottery ticket as a prize. 2) The strategies chosen by the acting coalitions can have different outcomes to which no probabilities can be assigned. Here, at least one other factor not included in constructing the model is playing a role. Hence, the model does not describe the conflict adequately, and must be revised.

Fourthly, we must include all the parties interested in any way in particular outcomes of the conflict. Like the acting factors, they too may be collective and structured and can be called interest coalitions. The set of all interest coalitions is $\Re_i$.

In real conflicts, the operational and interest coalitions usually coincide, but this is not a rigid rule. A football fan watching a match on television has an interest in the outcome but cannot influence the result. On the other hand, the referee has no interest in the result, (or should have none...), but exercises considerable influence on the course of the match and its result.

Fifthly, we must indicate in what the interests of the interest coalitions consist. This is done by showing, for each, pairs of comparable situations and indicating, for each comparable pair, which of the two is preferable. It is not essential, however, that any two situations for each interest coalition be comparable. Indeed, it may happen that a particular situation will be absolutely non-comparable (exactly as in ethics no comparison is allowable between the value of money and the value of human life). The fact that situation s for interest coalition K is preferable to situation t will be designated by $s \leftarrow_k t$.

Very often, the preferential relationship for interest coalitions is described as follows. For each coalition of interests K for all situations S is defined a numeric function H_k and $s \leftarrow_k t$ is accepted where $H_k(s) \rangle H_k(t)$. The function H_k is called the payoff function of the coalition.

It follows that any conflict may be formally described as a quintuple

$$\langle \, \Re_a, \left\{ S_k \right\}_{k \in \Re_a}, \; S, \; \Re_i, \left\{ \leftarrow_k \right\}_{k \in \Re_i} \, \rangle \qquad (*)$$

in which the meaning of each letter is as explained above; the subscript near each of the braces indicates that the content of the braces is variable and depends on the index that accompanies it and that the index itself varies within the bounds of the set, as follows from the symbols adjacent to the braces.

The formal model of the conflict, represented by the system (*), is called *the game*. Basically, the mathematical theory of games deals with the study of conflicts treated as games, in the sense of this definition.

This definition of games may appear too complicated and abstract. However, it reproduces in a formal language all the features which are inevitably inherent in any conflict, without at the same time containing any of the indices proper only to special isolated classes of conflicts.

1.4 The formalization of the concept of conflict led us to the game concept. The formalization of the notion of optimality, on the contrary, is not a preliminary step for working out game theory, but a fundamental problem of the theory itself. Moreover, it is in game theory that optimality, its nature and its variants, becomes a major scientific problem and, above all, a mathematical one (see Section 4).

2. EXAMPLES OF GAMES

The following examples will help to explain.

2.1 'Morra': Three players, I, II and III, each simultaneously show 1 or 2 fingers. If all three show the same number of fingers, the payoff for each is nil. If one of the players shows a number of fingers different from the number shown by the other two, he wins as many units as the number of fingers he has shown. The win is paid from the bank, which is independent of the game. What are the principal components of this game?

Clearly the players are involved in both acting and interest coalitions. Therefore we can write:

$$\mathfrak{R}_a = \mathfrak{R}_i = \{\text{ I, II, III}\}$$

Each player has two strategies, 1 and 2. Formally, this is represented:

$$S_I = S_{II} = S_{III} = \{1, 2\}$$

Each triplet consisting of a strategy I, a strategy II and a strategy III forms a situation. The game clearly involves $2 \times 2 \times 2 = 8$ situations. The preferences are determined by the payoff functions. The payoff values may be represented as follows:

SITUATIONS

	111	112	121	122	211	212	221	222
Payoff of Player I	0	0	0	1	2	0	0	0
Payoff of Player II	0	0	2	0	0	1	0	0
Payoff of Player III	0	2	0	0	0	0	1	0

2.2 Two bandits ('Prisoner's dilemma'): Two bandits (Players I and II) guilty of a serious crime are in prison on remand. Each can confess or deny. If both confess they will both be imprisoned, with allowance for the mitigating circumstances of the confession (mandatory sentence 8 years). If both persist in denying the crime, then, given the lack of direct evidence, they will be convicted only for the illegal use of arms (mandatory sentence 1 year). If one confesses and the other does not, the one who has confessed goes free (such are the laws of the State in which the action takes place) and his accomplice receives all the punishment (a 10-year sentence). In this game each player has two strategies ('Confession' or 'Denial'), so that the total number of situations in the game is $2 \times 2 = 4$. The payoffs can be summarized in two matrices:

		I's payoff II's strategy	
		C	D
I's strategy	C	−8	0
	D	−10	−1

		II's payoff II's strategy	
		C	D
I's strategy	C	−8	−10
	D	0	−1

The payoffs shown in the matrices are negative, because they represent losses to the players.

2.3 'Stone, paper, scissors'. Two players (I and II) simultaneously make the sign for one of the three (stone, paper, scissors) (a clenched fist means stone, the cupped hand paper and the 'V-sign' scissors).

If the two players signal the same objects, the payoff for each is nil. In other cases, 'stone' wins 1 against scissors (stone breaks scissors) and loses 1 against paper (paper covers stone), and in turn paper loses 1 against scissors (scissors cut paper).

As in the previous example, the players here are involved in both acting and interest coalitions.

Thus,

$$\Re_a = \Re_i = \{I, II\}$$

Each player has three strategies: stone, paper, scissors. Formalized, this looks like:

$$S_I = S_{II} = \{S, P, SC\}$$

Each pair consisting of a strategy I and a strategy II forms a situation. Clearly the game presents $3 \times 3 = 9$ situations. The preferences are determined by the payoff functions. The values of the payoff function for I can be described as follows:

II's strategy

		S	P	SC
I's strategy	S	0	−1	1
	P	1	0	−1
	SC	−1	1	0

The payoff of Player II is equal to I's payoff but with the opposite sign, that is, to his loss.

2.4 The duel: The adversaries move towards each other from starting point a to a final point b; each may fire one shot at his opponent. The duel ends when at least one of the duellists is hit. The duellist who has hit his adversary and remains untouched himself scores 1 (his opponent at the same time loses 1). If by shooting simultaneously, both score a hit or both miss, each scores 0. The precise moment in which he will fire is planned by each player in advance. The probability of hitting the opponent from distance x is $p(x)$.

Here the players' strategies are the distances at which they plan to fire. By a suitable selection of the origin and of the scale of the distances, it can be posed that $a = 0$ and $b = 1$. Thus the strategies will be represented by numbers between 0 and 1, and the situations by the pairs of those numbers. Elementary calculations of probabilities show that the value of the payoff function for Player I in situation (x,y) is defined by the equations:

$$H_1(x, y) = \begin{cases} p(x) - p(y) + p(x)\,p(y), & \text{if } x < y \\ 0 & , \text{if } x = y \\ p(x) - p(y) - p(x)\,p(y), & \text{if } x > y \end{cases}$$

The payoff function of Player II differs from the above only in its sign.

2.5 *Chess:* A game of chess is supposed to be played according to ordinary rules. There are two players, Black and White. The strategy of each is a system of choices of admissible moves in every position in which he plays. More formally, the strategy of each player is every function defined for all the positions he plays, and the value of the function for the position is an admissible move in that position.

The situation as a pair of two strategies completely determines the course and outcome of the play. The payoff for each player is 1 in each situation in which he wins, −1 in each situation in which he loses, and 0 in a draw.

2.6 Dividing the cake: A mother (sole 'acting coalition') has made a cake (which we can take as a unit) for her three children. She is able to divide it arbitrarily into three parts: x_1 for the oldest (to be called 1), x_2 for the second (called 2) and x_3 for the youngest (called 3). This means that the set of strategies for the mother is the set of all possible triplets of the form (x_1, x_2, x_3) where $x_1, x_2, x_3 \geqslant 0$ and $x_1 + x_2 + x_3 = 1$.

Geometrically, for each of these triplets it is possible to find a corresponding point of a triangle for which the numbers x_1, x_2 and x_3 will be the barycentric co-ordinates (readers unfamiliar with this geometry need not bother about its exact meaning and may be satisfied merely with the possibility of such correspondence).

It is plain that here the mother's strategies are the situations of the game. The children persuade one another of the fairness (and hence necessity) of one division or another of the cake, by using any arguments available (and probably also their fists). It soon becomes clear that none of them (not even the eldest) acting alone can get himself even the smallest crumb of the cake. Together the two older ones (1 and 2) can ensure a division that allows the two of them 0.7 of the cake. If they receive more, they can consider it a windfall, to which they have no reasonable claim. Similarly, 1 and 3 might together obtain 0.6 of the cake, and 2 and 3 together 0.5.

Figure 1

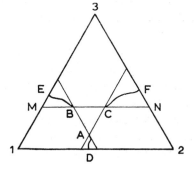

Thus the interest coalition is represented here not by the three individual children but by their possible pairings, three in number.

To describe the preferential relations for each of the three coalitions of interests, we can consider two situations (two partitions that are frequently called imputations) $x = (x_1, x_2, x_3)$ and $y = (y_1, y_2, y_3)$. The (1,2) coalition prefers partition x to partition y (the formal expression is $x \leftarrow_{1,2} y$) if, first, $x_1 + x_2 \leqslant 0.7$, and second, if the share of x of each member of the coalition is larger than his share of y, that is, if $x_1 > y_1$ and $x_2 > y_2$. Further, it is not any two partitions which lend themselves to comparison, but only those where the sum of the first two components does not exceed 0.7 (in Fig. I this is the triangle M3N).

The preferential relations for the other two coalitions of interests are described similarly. Thus the game takes the form indicated at (*) above.

3. CLASSIFICATION OF GAMES

3.1 The definition of games as systems (*) formulated in Section 1 provides a convenient basis for the classification of games. An elaborated, though in no way exhaustive, classification is given in Vorobyev (1970).

It may be noted that, from the point of view of formal development, items of the form (*), in which the interest coalitions set is empty or comprises only one coalition of interests, are also games, but the first belongs in the study of the purely descriptive theories which describe processes occurring in nature or society, without having any objective. The study of second type items is concerned with problems whose mathematical content consists in the definition of extremes of given functions under given constraints. Proper games begin from the point where genuine conflicts arise, i.e. where at least two parties are involved. Accordingly, we shall deal from now on with games involving two or more coalitions of interests.

The first indicator by which to classify games proper is the unicity or multiplicity of the acting coalitions. With several coalitions the theory of course becomes more complicated, but immediately brings to light questions of much interest and practical importance; in the case of games with a single coalition, extremely deep problems have to be tackled right away. We shall begin by examining an important class with many acting coalitions, non-co-operative games.

3.2 In a non-co-operative game each acting coalition is at the same time an interest coalition, and vice-versa. The set of all the players is designated by I, the players themselves by the numbers 1, 2 ... n. So that in non-co-operative games we have $\Re_a = \Re_i = I = \{1,2 \ ... \ n\}$. The strategy of player i constitutes a set S_i and each n-tuple $s = (s_1, s_2, ..., s_n)$ where $s_i \in s_i$ is a situation. Since the set of situations is well defined by the set of strategies, it will not necessarily be specifically mentioned in the identification of the game.

Let the payoff of player i in situation s equal $H_i(s)$. The fixing of the payoff functions of H_i completes the identification of the non-co-operative game, which takes the form:

$$<J, \{s_i\}_{i \in J}, \{H_i\}_{i \in J}>$$

'Morra' and 'Two bandits' are examples of this general type of non-co-operative game.

3.3 Among the varieties of non-co-operative games a special place is reserved for those in which the number of players is two: $n = 2$ (traditionally called Player I and Player II) and the payoffs of Player II in any situation are of equal value but opposite sign to those of Player I:

$$H_I(s) = - H_{II}(s). \qquad (**)$$

Such games are called zero-sum two-person games (because the equation (**) may be rewritten $H_I(s) + H_{II}(s) = 0$) or synonymous, antagonistic games.

The set of players in the two-person game being always the same, it is not necessary to indicate it every time; also, it follows from (**) that the value of the payoff function for Player I it is always possible to find the value of the payoff function for Player II. Thus, in identifying the two-person game one states only the payoff function for the first player, and the number of the player as the subscript of the function is omitted. In this case, we sometimes speak only of the payoff function of the game, meaning thereby the gains of Player I in the various situations or, what amounts to the same thing, the losses of Player II.

3.4 The second indicator that provides a natural basis for classification of two-person games lies in the nature of the players' set of strategies. In particular if the sets are finite, the game is also called finite. In the opposite case, the game is called infinite. The game of 'Stone, paper, scissors' is a two-person finite game. Taking this game as an example, we can see that the values of the payoff function in a two-person finite game can be arranged as a matrix. Accordingly, two-person finite games are often said to be matrix games.

As an example of a two-person infinite game we can take the 'duel'. In this game the situation, being a pair of numbers between 0 and 1, may be shown as a point of a unitary square on the plane of the co-ordinates. All two-person games for which such presentation is possible are often called games on a square.

3.5 We have so far assigned no specific properties to the players' strategies, considering them simply as elements of abstract sets. However, in reality, the choices made by the players often prove to be, not momentary decisions but sequence of partial decisions or even processes constantly unfolding in time. Such games are called games in extensive form (or positional or dynamic games). Chess is an example. Other examples are most outdoor games and card games, and conflicts with pursuit or capture elements of any kind.

3.6 We now come to the games with only one acting coalition. The behaviour of this single coalition obviously completely determines the outcome of the conflict. Accordingly, the coalition's strategies can be identified with the situations and need be mentioned no further in what follows. That is why we sometimes call such games non-strategic games.

As a rule, in non-strategic games, a set of interest coalitions is regarded as a particular family of subsets of the set of players I. Usually, the payoffs (in this case it would be appropriate to say the payoff vectors) of all the players in each situation are given and the preferred choice from the comparable situations for each interest coalition is that giving the best payoff for each of the players in the coalition.

A very important class of non-strategic games consists of those in which the situations are various partitions ('imputations') of some unlimited divisible object; for each coalition the maximum share of the object that that coalition can ensure for itself is indicated. Such games are called co-operative games. 'Dividing the cake' is an example.

4. FUNDAMENTAL PROBLEMS IN GAME THEORY

4.1 The content of game theory is optimal behaviour in conflicts rather than the study of the conflicts themselves. That is why both the descriptive examination and exposition of the game as a formal conception, and the constructive questions concerning the process of identifying the game, take a subordinate place in game theory, at least at present. The main aspect of game theory is normative; it specifies the goals of interested parties and reveals the expedient activities of acting parties.

Optimal situations and strategies in a game are usually said to be its solutions. Game theory is occupied with mathematical representation of the relationships between the conditions of the game and its solutions. Therefore for every game, as well as every class of games the three fundamental questions are: What do we mean by solution? (what is the very notion of optimality in this game?); Do optimal solutions exist for this particular game?; What are they and how can they be found? These are the three main questions of game theory.

It was J. von Neumann who posed and resolved in part these questions in his article of 1928. They are also the essential theme of the monograph by von Neumann and Morgenstern, published in 1944, which laid the foundations of game theory as a mathematical science.

4.2 Let us begin with the first question. So far, no one has found optimality principles sufficiently precise to apply to all games, but they have been formulated for certain classes of games.

Many behaviour principles intuitively felt to be optimality principles are in fact nothing of the kind – formal analysis shows them to be unachievable, e.g. the naive idea of each interest coalition achieving its optimal situation and the maximum value of its payoff function is practicable in only a very few cases of very little interest.

As a basis for many principles of optimality we can take certain features of traditional non-conflict optimality, e.g. 'the situation is optimal if no deviation can improve it'. Let us extend this to non-co-operative games. The optimal situation will now be a situation in which no player who deviates from it (and all other players keep to the strategies already chosen) can increase his win by so doing. Such situations are called equilibrium situations.

4.3 In a two-person game, the equilibrium of a situation means that any deviation from it by Player I can only reduce his winnings, and deviation by Player II would reduce what he in turn stands to win, i.e. reduce the losses of Player I, which amounts to increasing payoff I. This lends itself to an interesting geometrical interpretation. Let a two-person game consist in the choice of a point on a terrain, Player I choosing its latitude, Player II its longitude, and the altitude of the point representing the payoff function. Suppose there is a chain of mountains rising above the terrain, running north-south; a low saddle in the chain corresponds to the equilibrium situation in the game. Because of the possibility of such an interpretation, situations of equilibrium in two-person games are often called saddle-points.

Again, it so happens that for two-person games (as can be demonstrated mathematically without much trouble) the principle of optimality requiring the aiming at (striving for) saddle-points is equivalent to the principle requiring aiming at (striving for) maximization of the least possible, i.e. the absolutely guaranteed, gain; this is known as the maximin principle. The strategies whereby Player I maximizes his minimum gain (and Player II minimizes his maximum loss) are called optimal strategies.

4.4 Equilibrium situations, and they only, can secure an agreement between the players which it will be in no party's interest to violate unilaterally. If any attempt is made to incorporate non-equilibrium, it will be in the interest of at least one player from the very start to violate the agreement.

Another principle of optimality in non-co-operative games is Pareto's optimum: a situation is Pareto-optimal if there is no other situation which would be at least as favourable as for all players and even more favourable for at least one of them.

Pareto's optimality is in a way at the opposite pole to Nash's equilibrium. In a Nash equilibrium situation, individual improvements cannot be secured by individual deviations, while Pareto optimality signifies that general improvement is not possible under general deviations. Pareto's optimality may be in formal contradiction with Nash's equilibrium. For example, in 'Two bandits' the confession of both bandits results in an equilibrium situation, while the situation when the bandits refuse is optimal in Pareto's sense.

In two-persons games, Pareto's optimality has no relevance since, there, any situation is optimal in his sense.

4.5 As non-strategic games have been more deeply studied than non-co-operative games, a larger number of relatively refined optimality principles have been worked out for them.

One classical definition of the optimum is the value of a function such that no other value is preferable to it. Applying this to non-strategic games, the optimal situation is one to which no other is preferable for any coalition of interests. The set of all situations with this property is called the core of the game (which may comprise many situations). In 'Dividing the cake' the core consists of all the situations belonging to the triangle ABC.

If such optimization has several solutions, i.e. if the objective function has several optima, we may define optimality in the following manner. The set R of values of the function consists of optima, if

1) none of these values is preferable to another;

2) for any value taken outside the set R, a preferable value can be found within it.

Now let us apply this notion of optimality to non-strategic games. The outcome is that the set of situations R is composed of optima if

1) for neither of two situations r_1, $r_2 \in R$ and $K \in \mathfrak{R}_i$ is it possible that $r_1 \leftarrow_K r_2$;

2) whatever the situation $s \notin R$ there will be a situation $r \in R$ and a coalition of interests $K \in \mathfrak{R}_i$ such that $r \leftarrow_K s$.

Any set of situations possessing these two properties is called the solution of the game in the von Neumann-Morgenstern sense or the stable set (1944); the properties themselves are referred to as internal and external stability.

Such a solution can be applied to a particular system of legal and ethical norms in a society, that is, applying to a majority of players I. Internal stability then means that in the society in I there are no 'forces' (interest coalitions K) interested in passage from one norm to another; external stability means that in the event of any deviation from the norm (i.e. any going outside of the limits of the solution) some forces in the society will want to re-establish it.

By simple logical analysis it is easy to confirm that, if a game has a core and a solution (*cf.* von Neumann-Morgenstern, 1944), the core must lie in the solution. For example, in 'Dividing the cake' the solution is represented by the triangle ABC plus the curvilinear segments AD, BE and CF. These segments are not univocally determined and may be traced under some restrictions very arbitrarily; in particular they may be rectilinear segments perpendicular to the corresponding sides of the great triangle.

4.6 As principles of optimality one can consider satisfying, situations should contain certain conditions of fairness. If a player increases the gain of any collective by exactly the amount he secures for himself acting individually, in a fair situation he must receive as much as he would have received without joining any collective. Again, if two players increase the gains of any collective by equal amounts, in a fair situation their shares must be equal. Developing this approach, Shapley constructed the definition of a fair situation. For example, in a fair division in 'Dividing the cake', the eldest child would receive $\frac{1}{3} + \frac{1}{20}$ of the cake, the middle child $\frac{1}{3}$, and the youngest $\frac{1}{3} - \frac{1}{20}$.

4.7 The second of the main problems of the game theory is that of the realizability of particular principles of optimality. Otherwise, the whole exercise is pointless. As indicated earlier, an intuitive attractive principle allowing the most favourable situations for all interested parties is very rarely workable in practice and is thus virtually useless.

Other principles of optimality mentioned above appear more promising, but the actual demonstration remains difficult.

Zermelo has proved the existence of optimal strategies in a broad class of dynamic games, including chess. Yet, simple games like 'Morra', 'Stone, paper, scissors' and 'Duel' have no equilibrium situations. This can be confirmed very easily.

To escape from this impasse one can apply an approach that is typical in pure mathematics.

Alongside the players' original strategies, new generalized strategies are introduced; from these, situations are constructed to which the definition of the payoff function is extended. Equilibrium situations are sought among these new situations. The new strategies, situations and expanded payoff functions must of course have a natural and plausible interpretation in terms of the original strategies, situations and payoff functions.

The following extension of non-co-operative games is very fruitful. Suppose each player can not only choose any particular strategy, but select strategies at random, with arbitrary, but well-defined probabilities.

These courses of action are called mixed strategies. The independent choice of mixed strategies by the players gives a mixed strategy situation, in which the gain of each player is a random variable whose mathematical expectation is considered to be its payoff function value.

On the basis of each non-co-operative game a new game is now constructed which is called the mixed extension of the first game. Nash has shown that each finite non-co-operative game has an equilibrium situation in mixed strategies, i.e. in its mixed extension. This was demonstrated earlier by von Neumann for finite two-person zero-sum (matrix) games.

The equilibrium situation in 'Morra' appears to be when each player shows one finger with the probability of $1/(1 + \sqrt{2})$ (and therefore two fingers with the probability of $\sqrt{2}/(1 + \sqrt{2})$).

In 'Stone, paper, scissors', each player's mixed optimal strategies consist in choosing between the three strategies S, P, and SC with a $\frac{1}{3}$ probability each.

4.8 For the non-strategic games – even for the special class of co-operative games – the situation seems to be not as satisfactory as for the non-co-operative games.

Games with no core (or more accurately, where the core is empty) are easy to find. In 'Dividing the cake' for example, if the shares that the pairs of children can secure increase to 0.8, 0.7, and 0.6 respectively, the resulting game has an empty core.

Have individual co-operative games stable sets (i.e. solutions in the von Neumann-Morgenstern sense)? The question is very complicated. For many (but very narrow) classes of games, the existence of a solution is proved; for arbitrary 5-person games, the question is still open. Quite recently (1967), an example of a 10-person game with no solution has been constructed by Lucas.

Further, if the game has a stable set, firstly, it may be non-unique and, secondly, may consist of several situations. Consequently, a complementary problem has to be dealt with for solvable games: selecting, from all of the solutions, and then from all the situations composing the solution selected, the solution and situation with, so to speak, the highest optimality.

It is at least some relief to remember that a Shapley vector exists for every co-operative game, that it is unique, and consists of a single situation.

4.9 The third fundamental question (see p. 215) is, what are the optimal solutions (if such exist) and how can they be found? This is an autonomous and very important problem which is still open, despite the amount of game theory literature devoted to it. Hitherto, 'solutions' have been found for fairly narrow classes of games only. Even then, the final answer usually appears not in the form of analytic formulae, but as an algorithm. Hence, further development is closely tied in with the mathematical development and the use of computer techniques.

5. GAMES PLAYED AGAINST NATURE

As a rule, in conditions of conflict, no party intends to give his adversary information about his plan and impending actions. Consequently, optimal decision-making in conflict conditions means decision-making under uncertainty.

In conditions of uncertainty, in turn, there is a set of variants of the conditions in which the decision is to be taken; and the party taking the decision has no precise knowledge either of these conditions or even of the *a priori* probability distribution of the variants. The different variants can be treated as the strategies of a player labelled 'nature', so that decision-making under uncertainty is equivalent to decision-making under conflict (i.e. conflict with nature).

Uncertainty and conflict being thus closely related, we can define game theory as a theory of mathematical models for the making of optimal decisions under conflict or uncertainty. Let us now translate this into the language of game theory.

To take the simplest case: a party who is making the decision and nature, his opponent, are the two players in the non-co-operative game we are constructing. His strategies are obviously the decisions available to him and nature's strategies are, as already noted, the possible combinations of circumstances which cannot either be predicted or forecasted exactly.

The value of the player's payoff function is the extent to which he attains his purpose, this depends on his decision and on nature's actual strategy. What is nature's payoff function? By the way in which the definition is made, the anthropomorphization of nature can be avoided by attributing to the player some psychological attitude towards his uncertain gain (or, what amounts to the same, towards his uncertain losses).

Assume he is concerned to maximize his guaranteed (minimum) gain. This means he must act as if nature is his conscious enemy, animated by the desire to inflict maximum damage on him. This makes the game played against nature, i.e. decision-making under uncertainty, a two-person game; regarding it as such is a logical consequence of the assumption that the decision-maker assumes the max-min principle as his principle of optimality (see 4.3). Thus, to establish the case for the two-person game against nature, all that is required is to establish the soundness of the max-min principle.

In decision-making problems it is extremely difficult to verify the principles of optimality from a consideration of their consequences. The alternative is to deduce the principle we want from a few axioms that seem to be reasonable or that can immediately be experimentally verified.

A set of axioms that necessarily brings in the max-min principle has been proposed by Milnor (1964); Vilkas has constructed another based upon the idea of a fair gain under uncertainty.

Naturally, max-min does not satisfy all the usual requirements for optimality. Milnor himself has shown that if, in his set of axioms, some axioms are replaced by others, sometimes no less likely, another principle of optimality is obtained instead of the max-min principle. Nothing that has been said should be taken as discrediting the max-min principle, but merely as evidence that decision-making under uncertainty bristles with psychological nuances with still elude formalization. We may hope in time to learn how to circumscribe exactly and formally the classes of problems of optimal decision-making under uncertainty in which the max-min principle could be used without reservations, as well as the classes of problems where it could not be so used.

6. GAME THEORY AND STATISTICAL DECISIONS

6.1 Certain authors (e.g. Chernoff and Moses, 1959) define mathematical statistics as a theory of decision-making under uncertainty. In the light of what has been said above, that means that statistics is closely related to game theory. In point of fact, statistics is quite clearly going to be considered a constituent part of game theory, distinguished by its specific problem range and its terminology. This of course in no way diminishes the range and significance of mathematical statistics.

6.2 Wald (1950) has systematically studied the approach to statistical problems from the viewpoint of games theory. His book cites several points of correspondence between fundamental concepts in statistics and two-person game theory.

Two-person game	*Problem of statistical decision-making*
Player I	Nature
Player II	Statistician
Set of strategies of Player I	Class of distribution functions ('states of nature' set)
Set of strategies of Player II	The statistician's 'Decision function'
Payoff of Player I	The statistician's risk
Mixed strategy of Player I	*A priori* distribution over 'states of nature' set
Optimal strategy of I	Least favourable *a priori* distribution over 'states of nature' set
Optimal strategy of II	Decision on the mini-max principle.

These correspondences can be taken further. The further development of the correspondences between concepts and results in statistics and in game theory (especially in the theory of games in extensive form) is at present under discussion.

7. APPLICATIONS OF GAME THEORY

7.1 When we speak of applying the theory of games, a distinction must be made between: 1) the description, in game theory terms, of phenomena found in nature or in society, and 2) real decisions arrived at by games theory methods in dealing with specific, practical questions.

The second are still sporadic and isolated. It is not proposed to go into detail, but simply to indicate the difficulties.

First, to solve a practical problem by game theory methods, it is first necessary to formulate it with precision, i.e. give an exact description of the relevant game. All the players and their strategies must be determined, and the preferential relationships over the set of situations shown. This in turn requires accurate information about the phenomenon involved. If the preferential relations are determined by the payoff functions, the information must be quantitative. But this implies exact measurements, and the methods for obtaining them have not yet been satisfactorily worked out.

Secondly, the game theory solution does not always satisfy the executor who carries out the decision. For example, a mixed strategy recommendation raises the question of responsibility in the event of unfavourable consequences. Moreover, the multiplicity of the game's solutions (already discussed) makes it impossible to obtain a specific recommendation on which to rely.

We therefore discuss only the possible rather than actual applications of game theory, in cases in which the phenomenon involved lends itself to description in game-theoretical language.

As its definition indicates, game theory is in principle usable in conflicts of any kind, and these can be found in nearly all disciplines. Accordingly, many phenomena in nature and society lend themselves to treatment in game theory terms.

7.2 Its originators saw game theory mainly as a mathematical tool to help in making optimal economic decisions. The title of the first basic monograph by J. von Neumann and O. Morgenstern, *Theory of Games and Economic Behavior* (1944), is fairly explicit. In a competitive economy, game theory could be used in studying competition for markets, advertising, price questions, stock market operations, and so on.

The theory has proved to have much broader possibilities. It can equally serve in the conditions of a planned economy, in studying for example the respective merits of centralizing or decentralizing industrial management, optimal planning in terms of several indices, planning under uncertainty arising, for instance, from technological progress, and so on.

7.3 War is of course the most obvious of all cases of conflict. Military applications of game theory are dealt with in Drescher's monograph (1961) and a multitude of articles. In 1964, NATO held a conference devoted mainly to game theory; its proceedings constitute a bulky volume (1966). However, it must be emphasized that games theory also produces mathematical models for disarmament studies. Saaty's book (1968), despite some debatable propositions, indicates some very promising developments.

7.4 The law is another scene of evident conflicts – first between those who make up a society. But the making of the law is itself based on a conflict; for the legislator is at grips with the factors, not always very clear or specific but nevertheless very real, which give rise to crime or breaches of civil law. Legislation to anticipate mass developments that have juridical consequences and accordingly may need to be incorporated in law also falls within the purview of game theory. Court trials are competitive, involving optimal behaviour and norms of procedure. Verdicts are ordinarily made in conditions of uncertainty; and law-makers and courts alike can be considered as players making decisions.

7.5 Ethical and legal norms having much in common, applications of game theory to moral questions are very similar to those in jurisprudence. The fact that, in contrast to law, ethics is not codified only increases the uncertainty in the choice of optimal ethical behaviour.

7.6 Sociology has a variety of openings for game theory – social and class conflicts, the utilization of resources (particularly those which cannot be described in purely economic terms), relations of the individual with the collectivity and with other individuals, and so on.

7.7 Applications in biology are rather special. The animal and, even more, the vegetable kingdoms can hardly be said to take deliberate decisions with a precise end in view, or to be conscious of interests that conflict or do not conflict. Nevertheless, the interpretation in game theory terms of such phenomena is both possible and useful. For example, the struggle for existence between two species can be treated as a two-person game in which the admissible forms of behaviour of either species figure as their strategies and the number of individuals in each as their objective functions. It is particularly worth while to treat questions of symbiosis and parasitism in game theory terms.

Another natural subject for game theory treatment is the study of evolutionary processes, which may be considered as conflicts between the species complicated by random external conditions, with the line of evolution of a species as its strategy and the principal evolutionary trends in species as their objective functions. Since optimal strategies are ordinarily mixed, it is natural to assume that it is the mutations that represent the mixed strategies in this case. The description of these phenomena in terms of game theory may lead to new discoveries in heredity and in the shaping of the genetic inheritance.

REFERENCES

BERGE, C., (1957) *Théorie générale des jeux à n personnes*, Paris, Gauthier-Villars.

CHERNOFF, H. and MOSES, L. E. (1959) *Elementary Decision Theory*, New York, John Wiley.

DAVIS, M. D., (1970) *Game Theory*, New York, London, Basic Books.

DRESCHER, M., (1961) *Games of Strategy. Theory and Applications*, Englewood Cliffs (N.J.), Prentice-Hall.

KLAUS, G., (1968) *Spieltheorie in philosophischer Sicht*, Berlin, Deutscher Verlag der Wissenschaften.

LUCE, R. D. and RAIFFA, H., (1957) *Games and Decisions. Introduction and Critical Survey*, New York, John Wiley.

MENSCH, A. (ed.) (1966) *Theory of Games. Techniques and Applications. A Nato Conference*, New York, American Elsevier Publishing Company.

MILNOR, (1964) in *Game Theory and Related Approaches to Social Behavior*, M. Shubik (ed.), New York, John Wiley.

NEUMANN, J. VON, (1928) 'Zur Theorie der Gesellschaftsspiele', *Math. Annalen, 100,* 295–320.

NEUMANN, J. VON and MORGENSTERN, O., (1944) *Theory of Games and Economic Behavior*, Princeton (N.J.), Princeton Univ. Press.

SAATY, T. L., (1968) *Mathematical Models of Arms Control and Disarmament*, New York, John Wiley.

VOROBYEV, N. N., (1970) 'Modern State of Game Theory' (in Russian), *Uspehi Mat. Nauk*, Vol. XXV, 2.

WALD, A. (1950) *Statistical Decision Functions*, New York, John Wiley.

12   Metatheory

MARIO BUNGE

INTRODUCTION

Strictly speaking, a *metatheory* is a theory about some theory or class of theories. And a *theory* or deductive system is, in turn, a set of statements (e.g. equations) ordered by the relation of deducibility. In this way no statement in the theory remains isolated: every statement is either an assumption or a conclusion. More precisely, a theory is a hypothetico-deductive system, as it can be formulated in such a way that every formula in it is either an initial premise (hypothesis, axiom or datum) or a logical consequence of a set of initial assumptions. Strictly speaking, for a body of theory to qualify as a metatheory it has got to be a theory itself: a more or less loose set of remarks on a theory does not constitute a metatheory proper.

Metatheoretical research started in mathematics at the turn of the century with the central aim of strengthening the rigour of proofs and ensuring consistency. Metamathematics was accordingly often called 'proof theory'. It soon became apparent, though, that metamathematical investigation is interesting in itself and, moreover, that it can be useful in other ways. Indeed, it can also lead to the discovery of structural similarities among otherwise different mathematical theories and it can establish relations (or, more precisely, mappings) among whole sets of theories, thus throwing new lights on the architecture of mathematics. The same can be said of logic, particularly when viewed as a branch of mathematics and handled with the help of mathematical tools. Metalogic and metamathematics are in any event flourishing. They can safely be ignored by the applied logician and mathematician, but they are no longer neglected by the inventors of new basic theories and by those who are interested in the foundations and in the structure of logical and mathematical theories.

Outside logic and mathematics, metatheoretical progress has been slow – probably for two reasons. The first is the belief that a factual (empirical) theory is, after all, an inductive synthesis of empirical data, hence something 'based' on (rather than tested by) experience, itself a non-theoretical item; on this view, the foundations of theoretical science should be sought in empirical procedures, not in hypotheses, let alone in fundamental hypotheses, i.e. postulates. Secondly, there is the pragmatic attitude of most contemporary scientists, who are in a hurry to do some 'hard' and publishable work even at the price of conceptual obscurity. It is hardly necessary to point out that this policy of neglect of, or even contempt for, the conceptual foundations of factual science is bound to lead to superficiality and even to inconsistency – as it did lead in mathematics not too long ago.

Be that as it may, there are hardly any metatheories proper concerning factual theories: field, though enormous, is still largely unexplored. If we were to stick to the strict meaning of the term 'metatheory' we might ignore it altogether in the present survey. Instead, we found it more interesting and useful to use a lax definition, one that will enable us to explore in a preliminary fashion the various aspects – formal, semantic, epistemological, pragmatic, and philosophical – of the metatheory of scientific theories. In general, less attention will be paid to the more classical and therefore more talked about metamathematical achievement (like Hilbert's, Gödel's and Tarski's) than to some promising new lines of research in the metatheory of mathematical and scientific theories. The succinct bibliography at the end should aid the reader anxious for further information.

1. LANGUAGE AND THEORY

Every theory is expressed or formulated in some artificial or symbolic language, which is often a combination (or, more precisely, the union) of several languages. A language is here taken to be a set of signs that can be grouped into expressions which can in turn be transformed into other expressions. Admissible expressions in a given language are called its well-formed formulae, while admissible transformations of expressions are called the valid transformations. In a formalized language both the rules of formation of admissible expressions and the rules of valid transformations must be stated explicitly. Whether the expressions say anything about reality, and whether the transformed expressions say anything new, are questions that go beyond the limits of a formal characterization of languages. For our purposes, what matters is that an artificial language of some sort or other is indispensable in order to formulate a theory proper: the natural languages are too poor and inexact for this purpose – so much so that even one of the simplest mathematical theories, the theory of semi-groups, cannot be formulated without the assistance of elementary logic and of a handful of extralogical technical notions (set, binary operation on a set, and associativity).

Theories are often referred to as languages, but this is mistaken on several counts. First, while some theories are true, languages cannot be called false even though they may be exact or inexact, rich or poor, abstract or concrete, and so on. Second, a single language may be used by a number of theories and, conversely, some theories can be expressed or formulated in alternative languages. Third, every language contains well-formed expressions that are inadmissible as formulae of some theory – e.g. $1 \neq 1$ can certainly be said in the language of arithmetic but it is not a valid formula of this theory. Consequently we must distinguish between a theory and its language. While a mathematical (biological) theory concerns mathematical (biological) objects such as sets (organisms), its language concerns nothing at all: it is non-referential, it is just a framework for building statements concerning something.

There are universal languages and regional ones. The former are the languages of the logical theories: all others are non-universal, as they contain specific terms such as 'set' or 'atom'. Indeed, every formula, whether in theoretical chemistry or in mathematical sociology, fits some pre-existing formula of logic: more precisely, it has the form of some formula of the predicate calculus with identity, and this quite apart from its meaning and of its truth value. That is, the language of logic is a ready-made, exact and universal language. Set theory, too, has a ready-made, exact and almost universal language – but not quite so universal. Every other theory has a language of its own that can often be used by several other theories as well. Thus, the language of physics is the union of the languages of predicate logic, set theory, and many others. This does not mean that physicists explicitly employ many theorems of logic or of set theory: it does mean that they use, in some way or other, the concepts (though not always the corresponding terms) of statement and of deduction, of class membership and of set intersection, and so on.

A non-logical theory is not one that is illogical but one that goes beyond logic in that it contains at least one extra-logical assumption, i.e. a statement concerning some extra-logical concept, such as the concept of function or the concept of society. Accordingly, the basic assumptions (axioms) of a theory are the assumptions of its underlying logic – i.e. of the logical theory it presupposes – plus specific initial assumptions (that depend on the subject matter). Every other statement in a well-organized theory will follow from those basic assumptions in accordance with the rules of inference admitted in the underlying logic.

2. METALANGUAGE AND METATHEORY

It came as a shock when Gödel proved that any domain of some complexity, e.g. ordinary arithmetic, contains true statements that cannot be proved within its own formalized theory, i.e. by resorting exclusively to the axioms of the theory and the rules of inference of the underlying logic. Either such statements must be justified by other means, or else the theory must be enriched with further assumptions that make the derivation possible – but even with the extension, other true statements will still be excluded. Gödel's incompleteness theorem is a standard example of a metatheorem in metamathematics, i.e. of a provable statement that concerns (is about, refers to) mathematical statements rather than mathematical objects such as sets, maps or spaces. In general: a *metatheorem* is a provable metastatement and, in turn, *a metastatement* is a statement about another statement or statements.

[The following, based on the notion of predicate, is a more precise elucidation of the notions of statement and metastatement. A predicate P may be regarded as a function that maps n-tuples of objects of any kind into statements, i.e. $P : O^n \rightarrow S$, where O^n designates the nth cartesian power of a set O of objects and S designates a set of statements. Likewise a metapredicate MP, like 'provable' or 'complete', may be analyzed as a mapping of statements into metastatements, i.e. $MP : S \rightarrow MS$, where MS is included in S. These partial elucidations bring out the reference class and they are independent of the concept of truth – which is an advantage in the case of factual science, where total truth is so hard to attain.]

Every theory contains metatheorems. The earliest examples of metatheorems were the duality principles in projective geometry, ensuring the interchangeability of 'point' and 'line', or of 'line' and 'plane', in the statement of the theorems. Similar duality principles were later discovered in logic. Moreover, the inference rules may be regarded as metatheorems rather than as pragmatic items or rules of procedure. In general, every provable statement of the form '*A* entails *B*', where *A* and *B* are statements, is a metatheorem. Likewise every provable statement of the form '*T* has the property *P*', where *T* is a set of statements (e.g. a theory), is a metatheorem.

Even factual science contains metatheorems, and not only those in the formal (logical and mathematical) theories it presupposes. Any statement to the effect that a given formula is (or fails to be) co-variant under a certain group of transformations is a metatheorem. The famous *CPT* theorem (charge-parity-time) in physics is a metatheorem of this kind, as it asserts that a certain set of formulae (viz., those of all relativistic field theories) retain their form under combined charge, parity and time reversals. Far from representing a law of nature, this is a typical illustration of the concept of *metanomological statement*. The point is important not only from a logical but also from a practical point of view: for, if the *CPT* theorem is indeed a metatheorem, then it cannot be expected that it will be confirmed or refuted in the laboratory. Only the theory it concerns can be so tested. If confirmed, the *CPT* metatheorem stands; if refuted, it becomes pointless.

The collection of metatheorems of a given theory need not itself constitute a theory, i.e. a system of formulae closed under deduction. Thus the *CPT* theorem is not part of a comprehensive metatheory of physics, but a stray metatheoretical statement. Whether it might be possible to build a metatheory for a whole class of physical theories is another matter – one, incidentally, that has not been explored. As pointed out in the introduction, it is only with reference to logical and mathematical theories that we find fully developed metatheories.

Whether stray, or systematic (belonging to a deductive system), a metatheorem is always expressed in a *metalanguage*, i.e. a language used to talk about another language (a language enabling us to talk about the objects referred to by a theory is called an *object language* of the theory). A metalanguage may or may not be formally as well developed as the primary or object language; its level of development will depend primarily on our needs. To state a stray metatheorem it is accordingly often sufficient to employ ordinary language, supplemented with some semantical terms such as 'designates' and some metalogical terms such as 'proved'. Richer metalanguages are needed only for fully developed metatheories. In present-day metamathematics, a number of such sophisticated languages are in fact employed. Thus the algebraic characterization of a deductive system as a filter requires a metalanguage containing, at the very least, the expressions 'precedes', 'partially ordered set' and 'filter'. Metamathematics at present uses as its language the union of the languages of all the basic theories of mathematics – algebra, category theory, set theory, topology – in addition to a number of expressions of its own ('theorem', 'proof', 'model', 'decidable', 'categorical'). Although there should be no conceptual obstacle, nothing of the sort exists in connection with factual theories.

A metatheory, whether fully developed (strict sense) or not (lax sense), i.e. whether it is in turn a theory or merely a set of more or less rigorous and logically connected remarks, can bear on any of the following aspects of the object theory (or class of theories) it concerns: the syntax or structure, the semantics or content, the pragmatics or use, or, finally, the philosophy of the theory (or set of theories) in question. Thus a metatheory of physical theory could deal, severally or jointly, with the following aspects of physical theory: the logical structure, the mathematical structure or formalism, the interpretation, the empirical validation and the technological application, and the underlying metaphysical and epistemological assumptions. Before briefly considering these various aspects of metatheory, we must first examine the concept of theory formulation.

3. THEORY FORMULATION

All theories in logic, mathematics and science are more or less formalized. It is not only that ordinary language may lack the technical terms – after all, these can be added to any vocabulary. But these terms usually are interrelated in such a way as to constitute technical expressions that go beyond the resources of ordinary language. Formalization provides a means of attaining conceptual richness and precision, and of rendering deductive inference as rigorous and mechanical as possible.

However, there are degrees of formalization. We may distinguish the following stages of development of a theory in this regard: 1) *natural* or semi-formalized, 2) *axiomatic*, and 3) *fully formalized*. A natural or naive formulation of a theory is one in which the basic ingredients are not clearly singled out, and one in which the scientist is allowed to introduce foreign elements at any stage if they are necessary to prove something. At this stage relevance (to the subject matter) and consistency (non-contradiction) are the only mandatory requirements. Most of mathematics and theoretical science follow this semi-formal pattern, which is often modestly called 'informal' or 'non-formalized'.

The next stage, *axiomatics*, is attained when: 1) the basic (primitive or defining) concepts of the theory are found and listed; 2) the remaining concepts are defined in terms of the basic concepts; 3) all the basic concepts are unambiguously and exhaustively characterized by means of initial assumptions (postulates or axioms); 4) these initial laws lead on to the remaining statements of the theory.

Axiomatics is nowadays taken for granted in logic, set theory, algebra and topology, where it has become standard practice to formulate the bases or foundations of theories as axiomatic definitions, i.e. as definitions by means of axioms.

Example. T is a topological space if and only if T is an ordered couple $\langle X, I \rangle$ where X is a set and I is a unary operator such that:

1) if $A \subset X$, then $I(A) \subset X$,
2) $I(X) = X$
3) for every $A \subset X$, $I(A) \subset A$,
4) for every $A \subset X$, $I(I(A)) = I(A)$
5) for every $A, B \subset X$, $I(A \cap B) = I(A) \cap I(B)$.

These five axioms give jointly an implicit definition of the interior operator I, and are necessary and sufficient to develop the general theory of topological spaces. But surely this is not how the theory was born. Moreover, the formulation is so abstract that it is useless to anyone who has not got the 'feel' of it – an intuitive understanding that can only come by working on examples and applications. Nevertheless, the axioms manage to convey some of the intuitions behind the formalism. Thus, one can read I as an operator that 'peels off' a set, and $I(A)$ is helpfully called an open set. The aim of axiomatization is not to kill intuition but to exploit it to the full, by rendering explicit all the tacit components of intuitive reasoning, while at the same time avoiding being misled by intuition. In short, axiomatics equals explicitness plus exactness plus order.

The possibility of axiomatizing a theory is independent of its content, if any. In principle, indeed, every clear and well-knit body of ideas can be axiomatized. Even theories in political science can be axiomatized provided they are first mathematized. However, 'axiomatization' can be understood either restrictively or broadly. In the former 'axiomatization' means not only the orderly arrangement of all the components (basic concepts and initial assumptions) but also the extraction of all non-mathematical content, i.e. the conversion of the given theory into a purely formal structure. Thus if mechanics is axiomatized, forces will be described as vectors, neglecting the physical meanings. If however the factual content is taken into account, then axiomatics can be attempted in the broad sense, taking care of meanings, at least partially, by adding rules of designation and assumptions for the referents of the symbols in question. One may thus speak of physical, biological, or sociological axiomatics. A few factual theories, mainly in physics, engineering, chemistry, biology, and psychology, have been formulated axiomatically.

The formalization process can be carried beyond axiomatization by 1) supplementing the symbolic language so as to minimize the function of ordinary language, and 2) stating or at least mentioning all the assumptions and presuppositions, including the logical ones. This complete formalization is simply called 'formalization', although it might more significantly be called *full formalization*. A few elementary mathematical theories have been fully formalized. A full formalization of any of the richer theories is practically impossible. Rationalism must be content to know that there are no obstacles in principle to a full formalization of any theory – but that it is more rewarding to invent new theories, even if they are only half-formalized.

4. STRUCTURE OF THEORIES

The general characterization of a theory hinges on the metalogical notion of deducibility or entailment. But this is insufficient, for it does not tell us anything about a theory as a structured whole. A deeper view calls for certain mathematical notions. Three possible mathematical treatments of the structure of theories in general are set out below.

The most elementary way of handling the concept of a theory is to regard it as a set S of statements partially ordered by the relation $\vdash$ of entailment $[T = \langle S, \vdash \rangle]$. This *set-theoretic* approach allows a number of metatheoretical notions of the syntactic kind to be formalized. In particular, the idea of the union of two (axiomatizable) theories can be clarified. If T_1 and T_2 are theories expressed in certain languages $L(T_1)$ and $L(T)_2$ respectively, then their *union* $T = T_1 \cup T_2$ is a third theory T such that its language is the union of the given languages and the axioms of T are those of T_1 jointly with those of T_2. Likewise for the *intersection* $T = T_1 \cap T_2$ of two theories. Finally, T_1 may be said to be a *subtheory* of T_2 if the set S_1 of formulae of T_1 is included in the set S_2 of formulae of T_2 and, in addition, T_1 is closed under deduction. If T_1 is a subtheory of T_2, then T_2 is called an *extension* of T_1.

The set S of formulae of a theory is the collection of all the logical consequences of its initial assumptions (axioms) A, i.e. $S = Cn(A)$. The closure of S under deduction is expressed in the metatheorem: $S = Cn(S)$. Not every set of formulae has this property. Thus the union $S_1 \cup S_2$ of the formulae of two totally unrelated theories may not constitute a third theory. The consequences of $S_1 \cup S_2$ constitute what is called the logical sum $S_1 \dotplus S_2$ of the two systems. A typical metatheorem involving this new notion is the following: If A_1 and A_2 are two formulae (e.g. axioms) of a given theory, then the set of consequences of their conjunction is the logical sum of their separate consequences. On the other hand, the set of consequences of the disjunction of A_1 and A_2 equals the common part of their separate consequences. In other words, conjunction enriches while disjunction impoverishes. So much for the calculus of systems.

A different characterization of a theory is given in terms of the algebraic concept of filter. A *filter* F in a partially ordered set P is a structure such that: 1) if x is a member of F and x precedes y, then y too is in F; 2) the infimum (greatest lower bound) of any two members of F is in F; and 3) the empty set is not included in F. On interpreting 'precedes' as 'entails' and 'infimum' as 'conjunction', it is possible to prove the central metatheorem: *every deductive system is a filter*. From here on the study of the structure of theories becomes the study of a particular interpretation (model) of filter theory, a branch of abstract algebra. Which is one more example of the algebraization of metalogic and metamathematics and, at the same time, of the mathematization of philosophy. So much for the algebraic approach to the analysis of theories. Let us now mention an even deeper approach to the same problem.

Mathematical theories are usually formulated and analyzed in set theoretic terms, i.e. they are specified as sets together with certain relations and/or operations and/or functions on those sets. Thus, a lattice is said to be a partially ordered set together with two binary operations on that set, meeting certain conditions (axioms). When constructed in this style, a theory can usually be formulated in more than one way. There is no point in asking which formulation is the best, except for aesthetic, didactic, or computational purposes. The mere multiplicity of equivalent formulations makes inter-theory comparison difficult and even misleading, as the differences may be minimized in some cases and exaggerated in others. A deep characterization of a theory, or family of theories, should be free from such ambiguities: it should seize on what is essential to the theory beneath the accidents of its particular presentations, which are often a matter of taste. If this is so, one may suspect that any set theoretic characterization of a theory is married to a particular presentation of a deeper structure that remains beyond the reach of that mode of theory building but might be disclosed by a deeper look. This is indeed the case: there now exists an alternative way of formulating, hence of analyzing algebraic theories, and surely more complex theories as well, which is more abstract and therefore less ambiguous. This alternative is offered by category theory, a new basic branch of mathematics.

The *categorial* (usually spelt 'categorical') approach consists in emphasizing the morphisms (e.g. functions) at the expense of the elements of the classes. In the categorial view an algebraic theory, and perhaps every theory, is a particular type of category, and an algebra is a realization of that category. In turn, a *category* C consists essentially of: 1) a class *ob C* of objects (e.g. sets, groups, topological spaces), 2) a class *mor C* of morphisms (structure preserving mappings) from one object to another and 3) the composition of morphisms (a generalization of function composition), the whole satisfying two axioms:

– the associativity law for morphisms: if f, g, h are any composable morphisms, then $(f.g) \cdot h = f \cdot (g.h)$;

– the identity axiom: if f is any morphism from the object A to the object B, then $I_A \cdot f = f = f \cdot I_B$, where $I_A : A \to A$ is the identity morphism on A and I_B the one on B.

Examples of categories: 1) the category of sets: its objects are all sets and its morphisms are all functions; 2) the category of lattices: the one whose objects are all lattices and whose morphisms are all lattice homomorphisms.

One can investigate relations among categories that are not related in obvious ways. Indeed, under certain restrictions, one can map whole categories on other categories. Every such mapping is effected by a functor, or morphism of categories, i.e. by a function that takes objects into objects and morphisms into morphisms. More precisely, given two categories C and D, a functor F from C to D is determined by two laws: one from *ob C* to *ob D*, the other from *mor C* to *mor D*, such that 1) morphism composition is preserved, i.e. if f and g are morphisms of C, then the composition $F(f) \cdot F(g)$ of their images in D equals the image $F(f \cdot g)$ of their composite, and 2) identities are prserved, i.e. if B is an object in C and I_B the corresponding identity morphism, then its image $F(I_B)$ in D equals the identity morphism $I_{F(B)}$ of the image object. In turn, functors can be composed and, correspondingly, whole bunches of categories can be handled at one stroke. Thus the *category of categories* is built: its objects are all categories and its morphisms all functors. This is the supreme mathematical object.

Since in the categorial approach the accent is on form and on the whole, it is reasonable to expect that it will elicit a deep and fruitful insight into the structure of theories and their mutual relations. It may end up by reorganizing the whole of mathematics and by re-shaping metatheory.

5. DEGREES OF ABSTRACTION

Theories vary in their degree of abstraction. Thus the theory of partially ordered sets is abstract as long as the nature of the sets and of the ordering relation are not specified. If the relation is interpreted as the inclusion relation for sets but the set is still regarded as unspecified or abstract, then a somewhat more concrete theory results. Finally, if both the nature of the members of the set and the ordering relation are fixed, a concrete theory, or model of the abstract theory, will result.

All the basic theories in modern algebra are abstract: they concern uninterpreted operations and relations on abstract sets. These theories often originated in an effort to disclose the common essential structure beneath a collection of specific or concrete theories: in a way, then, those theories emerged as a result of metatheoretical investigations. Thus an abstract semi-group is a structure shared by all objects containing an associative operation. Clearly, such objects are found not only in mathematics but also around us: for example, the set of all physical systems – in particular linguistic signs – constitutes a semi-group in so far as its individuals can be combined or concatenated associatively. An abstract theory T is like a dummy, while a model M of T is like a set of clothes fitting T.

Consider an abstract theory T formalized to the extent that all its specific or non-logical constants have been identified and arranged in a sequence C_0, C_1, C_2, ..., C_n, ... Now consider a 'parallel' sequence $M = \langle U, S_0, S_1, ..., S_n, ... \rangle$ of definite mathematical objects, each with a definite status: U is a set and every one of the S_i's, for $i = 1, 2, ...,$ is defined on U in a way that corresponds to the structure of the constants in the abstract theory. More precisely, if C_n is an individual constant (a variable of the lowest logical type), then the corresponding S_n is an element of U. If C_n is a unary predicate, then S_n is a subset of U. If C_n is a binary predicate, then S_n is a set of ordered pairs of elements of U – and so on. Such a sequence M of specific mathematical objects defined in set-theoretic terms is called a possible extensional mode (realization) of T. Whether M is an actual model of T will depend on the formulae formed in T with the help of its specific constants C_i and the logical or universal concepts (negation, conjunction, existential quantifier, etc.). A formula in T may or may not become true when every constant C_i occurring in it is replaced by the corresponding specific concept S_i occurring in M. If every valid statement of T is satisfied (or holds, or is true) under such a specification or interpretation of the non-logical constants of T, then M is said to be an (actual) extensional model of T.

Every abstract theory has a number of models. These models may be structurally identical (isomorphic) to one another or not. If they all are, the theory is said to be *categorical*; otherwise it is non-categorical. Most theories are non-categorical. Indeed, isomorphism is harder to come by than it would seem. To ruin isomorphism it is enough to take non-isomorphic basic sets (domains of individuals). For example, the theory of partial order may be realized by infinitely many pairs $\langle A, \leqslant \rangle$, $\langle B, \leqslant \rangle$, ... where A, B, ... are sets with different cardinalities, i.e. unequally numerous. The best one can usually do is to prove that the set of all models of a given theory T includes a subset of models that are isomorphic to one another: a statement to this effect is called a *representation (meta) theorem* for *T*. But full categoricity is both exceptional and far from desirable, as it amounts to rigidity. Only non-categorical theories can have wide fields of application.

The semantic concept of model has proved to be important, not only for mathematics but also for logic. Thus, if a given statement couched in the language of *T* is satisfied in every possible model *M*, that statement is said to be *valid*, or *logically true*, or *analytic* in the model-theoretic sense. In this sense, logical truth is model-free, i.e. it does not depend on the particular interpretation assigned the functional symbols concerned. The mere fact that there are such interpretation-free formulae and that they are universally valid throws doubt on the thesis that every idea is concerned with facts. And the fact that the set of such model-free formulae, i.e. logic, is rationally prior to any special enquiry, in particular any investigation concerning matters of fact, suffices to ruin altogether the doctrine that whatever can be thought concerns the world.

The semantic concept of model is also of importance in exact philosophy, and in particular in methaphysics. For example, it enables us to elucidate the notion of structural identity, or formal analogy, between two fields of fact, such as molecular diffusion and human migration, or two concrete systems, such as organisms and societies. Indeed, it can be said that two such concrete objects are *formally analogous* (structurally identical) if and only if they are adequately accounted for by two structures that are isomorphic models of an underlying abstract theory. Analogy in a weaker sense will obtain if the morphism concerned is a homomorphism of one of the models into the other.

The semantic concept of model differs from the various other senses of the same word, except in the trivial sense that every theoretical model, or specific theory, of some sector of reality is in turn a model, in the semantic sense, of some abstract theory. The theory of semantical models was adumbrated at the turn of the century in connection with certain metamathematical questions, mainly consistency and independence, but it was not worked out systematically until the 1950's. It is now the most advanced branch of semantics and a flourishing area of research, but it remains practically limited to logic and mathematics. The semantics of factual theories is hardly under way (see Section 7).

6. METAMATHEMATICAL PROPERTIES

A theory can have, or fail to possess, a number of global properties of a formal kind. The study of these properties and their mutual relations, as well as the finding of practical criteria for establishing whether a given theory does have any such properties, constitutes the very heart of *metamathematics*.

Chief among all metamathematical properties is *consistency* or non-contradiction. It is mandatory for every theory worth its name that it be consistent or that it can be repaired so as to become consistent. This, not only because a blatant falsity is a blemish, but also because a single contradiction (logically false statement) will generate an arbitrary number of arbitrary statements, i.e. it will induce irrelevant digression. The usual consistency test is based on the following metatheorem: *A theory is consistent if and only if it possesses a model*. The actual test is as follows. First, axiomatize the theory. Next, strip the axioms of their usual meaning, leaving an uninterpreted (abstract) formalism. Finally, try to find a model of this abstract theory in a well-known theory the consistency of which is either established or assumed: that is, try to find an interpretation of the basic symbols under which the formulae of the theory become formulae of a familiar theory whose consistency is not questioned (at the moment). If such a model is found, then the theory can be pronounced consistent: for, if it did hide a contradiction, the latter would show up unmistakably in the new interpretation.

Notice that this procedure does not yield absolute but rather *relative consistency*, in the sense that the given theory is pronounced consistent relative to some other theory, i.e. provided the latter is consistent. There would be nothing wrong with this if the base-line itself were demonstrably consistent, but this is usually not the case. Indeed, more often than not in a consistency proof, the symbols in the given theory are given number-theoretic meanings – but it so happens that number theory has not been proved consistent. Note also that the consistency test we have mentioned is a semantical one: it employs a semantic means for achieving a formal (syntactical) end. The same holds for most other metamathematical properties: either purely syntactic (model-free) methods are not available, or they are laborious.

A second metamathematical property of importance is *postulate independence*. It is desirable, though not necessary, that the axioms of a theory be mutually independent, i.e. that none of them be entailed by the others. This is not just a matter of elegance and economy but also one of practical importance. Indeed, if one wishes to subject a theory to repairs, one has to proceed step by step, and this is possible only if the replacement of any given axiom by another formula does not force changes in all the others: au independent axiom system is one that does not reject transplants.

Axiom independence can be tested in the following way. Take all the postulates and single out one of them. Negate the latter and adjoin it to the remaining postulates. Then find out whether the new axiom system is consistent. If it is, then the postulate under scrutiny is independent – so much so that its negation has produced no contradiction. The same procedure is then applied to all the remaining postulates, one at a time. If a non-independent is spotted, it is removed from the postulate set: a theorem has been won. In the last resort this technique, too, is of a semantic nature, as it boils down to a number of consistency tests. There is an alternative independence test which is semantic all the way through, as it consists in reinterpreting the basic (primitive) symbols so that all the postulates except the suspect one are satisfied. If such a model is found then the candidate must be independent: if it were dependent on (entailed by) some of the remaining axioms it, too, would be satisfied under the given interpretation.

A third valuable metamathematical property is *primitive independence*. It is desirable but not mandatory that the basic (primitive) concepts of the theory be mutually independent, i.e. that they be not interdefinable. This is mainly of philosophical importance: it allows one to spot definitions and avoid confusing them with non-conventional formulae, e.g. law statements. The test is again of a semantic nature and is as follows. First collect all the primitives and then re-interpret the one under examination. Then check whether the postulates still hold after this partial re-interpretation: if they do, the candidate has passed the test.

A fourth metamathematical property is *completeness*. A theory *T* is complete if and only if every formula couched in the language of *T* is either provable or refutable in *T*. Clearly, completeness amounts to incapacity to grow while remaining consistent. Test: take the postulate set and consider a new premise couched in the language of the theory. There are two possibilities: either the 'new' premise is entailed by ('contained in') the axioms, in which case the latter are pronounced complete; or the axiom set enriched by the new premise is inconsistent, in which case, too, the original theory is complete. A different test, of a semantic nature, is based on the metatheorem: *If a theory is categorical then it is complete.*

One of Gödel's shattering discoveries was that, if a recursively axiomatizable theory is moderately rich (e.g. if it contains elementary arithmetic) and moreover consistent (demonstrably so or by assumption), then it is incomplete. And, not being complete, it can be extended without necessarily becoming inconsistent. This has sometimes been viewed as a limitation on rationality. It may be construed in the opposite sense, by just replacing 'incomplete' by its synonym 'extensible'. Indeed, if practically all theories are incomplete, then there is no end to the task of building stronger and stronger theories, and applying them. This is particularly obvious in the case of factual theories: indeed, in factual science, theories must be able to grow by the addition of subsidiary hypotheses and data: i.e. they must be incomplete. Otherwise they cannot be general, or they cannot be applied to special cases nor, consequently, subjected to empirical tests. Irrationalism should not rejoice in the essential incompleteness of almost every theory: what is incomplete makes further rational investigation possible and desirable.

The fifth and last metamathematical characteristic we shall touch on is *decidability*. A theory T is called decidable if a decision procedure for it exists. And a *decision procedure* for T is a general and effective (mechanical) method allowing one (or a computer) to decide whether any given formula couched in the language of T is indeed a *bona fide* member of T or just a stranger dressed up in the same linguistic garb. Decidability, i.e. the existence of such an effective procedure, can often be proved without actually exhibiting the technique. As it happens, the vast majority of mathematical (hence scientific) theories are undecidable. Not even the elementary theory of groups is decidable – let alone arithmetic and the theories presupposing any such undecidable theories. Moreover, it can be proved that, if a (first order) theory is deductively complete, then it is undecidable if and only if it is not recursively axiomatizable. This metatheorem is far less catastrophic than it looks. Indeed, the completeness clause is seldom satisfied, so the metatheorem does not always apply. Hence it constitutes no real limitation on the possibility of axiomatizing any branch of knowledge.

Moreover, the non-existence of a decision procedure does not preclude admitting or rejecting any particular formula as a member of a given theory *T*, by using means obtained outside *T*, e.g. lemmas not proved in *T*. This is, after all, the way proofs and counter-examples are usually constructed in non-formalized mathematics, namely, with the help of auxiliary constructions and notions borrowed from other chapters of mathematics. Surely by proceeding in this way the crust of a formalized theory is pierced, but everything proceeds within the self-imposed bounds of reason. Reason cannot be confined within one theory or even within one arbitrarily demarcated field. Every formalism is artificially separated from all the other theories. Inventive reason puts together what formalizing reason puts asunder.

7. THE SEMANTICS OF SCIENTIFIC THEORIES

Model theory, touched on in Section 5 and applied in Section 6, has become the bulk of the semantics of logic and mathematics, as well as an important tool for proving theorems, or rather metatheorems, concerning certain aspects of any theory as a whole.

But model theory cannot, without further ado, be applied to a semantic analysis of factual theories, i.e. theories with a factual reference; and this for two main reasons: because both the concept of meaning and the concept of truth suffer radical changes when entering the territory of factual (usually called 'empirical') science. This, in turn, should be obvious: unlike pure mathematics, factual science concerns concrete things and is tested by checking its performance in relation to the observable behaviour of concrete things.

Consider first the problem of interpretation, which is intimately related to the one of meaning. An interpreted mathematical theory (i.e. a model of some abstract theory) is a structure interpreted in some other mathematical theory. For example, ring theory can be interpreted in arithmetic terms. Here interpretation remains within mathematics and it consists in assigning a specific arithmetical object (number or operation) to every primitive symbol of the uninterpreted theory. By contrast, a theory with a factual content (reference) is interpreted by reference to extra-conceptual objects such as physical things, their states, and changes in these states. In short, whereas a mathematical model is yet another formalism, a scientific theory is a formalism endowed with an interpretation pointing beyond the conceptual domain. Two different concepts of interpretation are then involved.

The difference can be elucidated roughly in the following way. An interpretation ensuing in a mathematical model may be construed as a mapping I_m on the set S of symbols of a theory into a set C of specific mathematical concepts. In short, $I_m: S \to C$. If we wish to produce a factual theory we must assume that, in turn, every one of the basic concepts in C refers to some concrete object (thing, property thereof, event, etc.). That is, we must introduce a further map R, one assigning every member of C a set in the family P of classes of concrete objects. In brief, $R: C \to P$. Finally we compound the two maps, R and I_m, obtaining the map called *factual interpretation*, namely $I_f = RI_m$. The three arrows constitute a commutative diagram. This allows us to go directly from the set S of basic symbols to the family P of referents of the theory, i.e. $I_f \updownarrow: S \to P$. (The elucidation of the notion of empirical interpretation is even more complex, for it involves further theories as well as a reference to facts as experienced by some subject.)

Once the notion of factual interpretation has been elucidated, one can explicate the one of *factual* (e.g. physical) *meaning*. For example, one may regard the meaning of a symbol occurring in a factual theory as the sense (connotation) of the corresponding concept together with the reference class (set of indended referents) of the latter. This poses, of course, the problem of building a calculus of senses to elucidate the elusive notion of connotation: this is difficult though possible. But the problem will not even be tackled if one believes that current model theory fulfils the needs of factual science, or if one confuses factual meaning with empirical meaning or, worse, with empirical test operations.

Finally, once the concept of factual meaning has been elucidated, one can approach the task of building a theory of factual truth or material adequacy. Such a theory goes beyond the simple concept of truth employed in logic and mathematics; 1) because factual truth involves factual reference, and 2) because factual truth is rarely total or complete: in the best of cases, if interesting and deep it is approximate: only trivialities can be squarely true or false. Now, since a concept is best elucidated by a theory that contains it, we need an exact theory of *inexact factual truth*. Only thus will the semantics of science be realistic and hence in a position to help scientists, who every day employ the concept of partial truth.

So much for the outline of a research project in the semantics of science.

8. THE EPISTEMOLOGY OF SCIENTIFIC THEORIES

Unlike mathematical theories, scientific theories are supposed to enrich our knowledge of reality. Hence they must have certain epistemological properties in addition to their syntactical and semantical characteristics.

A first epistemological condition every scientific theory is required to meet is *external consistency* or compatibility with the bulk of corroborated data, hypotheses, and theories. No matter how original a theory, it must respect logic and mathematics – not just by leaving them alone but by using them – and it must not question every item of factual knowledge. For, if it does clash with the whole of tradition, then it will be impossible to put it to the test, as every test of a given theory calls for the collaboration of further theories, hypotheses, and data. (For example, the test of a psychological theory requires items of physics, sometimes also of chemistry and biology, always some logic and mathematical statistics.) The surest sign of pseudo-science is that it makes a clean break with the whole of our formal and scientific background, thus rejecting the normal mode of testing for truth.

For a theory to be testable, all of its predicates must be *scrutable*: they must be open to critical analysis and they must somehow, however deviously, show up in observable facts. For example, the phase of a wave is scrutable (though not by direct observation) whereas a repressed wish, one that does not manifest itself, is inscrutable. The requirement that we keep only measurable predicates (which is sometimes made in the name of an obsolete variety of empiricism), would kill every hypothesis, hence every theory as well, for the mark of a hypothesis is that it goes beyond experience. It is not direct observability that we must have but scrutability: this is necessary and sufficient for empirical testability.

A specific scientific theory should be testable by observation, measurement, or experiment: it should stick its neck out by betting that such and such will be the case. It should do so with precision and boldness. In short, specific scientific theories should have an appreciable *predictive power* composed of accuracy and originality. The predictive performance of a theory is, together with its external consistency, the main though not the only factor allowing us to estimate its degree of truth, hence its credence and its acceptability. This does not arise in connection with very general theories: these are so many comprehensive frameworks, each consistent with any number of specific theories, or theoretical models of a given piece of reality. The relativistic theory of gravitation, automata theory, and the theory of evolution are such comprehensive frameworks: they are untestable unless enriched with detailed models but, on the other hand, they have an appreciable explanatory power.

Predictive power is not essential and, even when possessed by a theory, predictive power is not enough: we want every theory to explain the facts in some domain and we want some theories to explain certain lower level theories. Every theory should be able to explain, at least in principle, the bulk of what it purports to cover: in short, it should have an appreciable *explanatory power*. The explanation should be as accurate as possible but it should preferably also give some insight into the referents of the theory. A theory accounting for the behaviour of its referents, without disclosing what makes them tick, can be a good scientific theory but it is not the best possible theory. A richer theory will be a deeper one, a theory hypothesizing unseen mechanisms responsible for the overt behaviour of the system. For example, of the various theories of bilogical evolution proposed so far, the synthetic theory is the deepest because it tells us what the main evolutionary mechanism is, namely, the natural selection of spontaneous variations. (This does not mean that the theory is final, i.e. completely true.) In any case, we want our theories to have a substantial explanatory power without, however, explaining everything under the sun, as pseudo-science attempts to do. Further, we distrust explanations contrived wholly after the event: we do not value a high explanatory power unless it is accompanied by a reasonable predictive power.

The above features are some of the signs or indices of the *degree of truth* of a scientific theory, i.e. of the extent to which the theory constitutes a faithful or adequate conceptual reconstruction, or symbolic picture, of a sector of reality. In evaluating the degree of truth of a theory it is not enough to count its hits and misses and to compress this information into a degree of confirmation. A theory may often succeed, or fail through no merit or fault of its own: the experimental techniques may have been faulty, the observations may have been careless, or the in-inferences from them may have been invalid. Observation, measurement and experiment are seldom fool-proof: they utilize assumptions that may be false; they involve a host of variables that are not adequately controlled; and their outcomes may be misinterpreted. A careful analysis of the actual test of any scientific theory must take all these empirical and conceptual factors into account. While such critical analyses of individual cases are sometimes found in the scientific literature, no general theory of the testing of theories is available. Nor, for that matter, do we have more than the beginnings of theories concerning the external consistency, testability, predictive power, and explanatory power of theories. This whole matter is practically virgin, and what metatheories there are in it seldom concern real science, and, in particular, theoretical science. And in any case they have hardly been subjected to tests: they are usually believed on authority. In short, the epistemology of scientific theory – the supreme item of scientific knowledge – is still underdeveloped.

9. THE PRAGMATICS OF SCIENTIFIC THEORIES

Pragmatics is concerned with the workings of symbolic forms in real life. In particular, the business of the pragmatics of scientific theories is to investigate their origin, growth, use, and disuse, rather than to look at them as if they were ready-made and self-existent.

The study of the ways in which theories are invented and expanded, accepted and criticized, should be an interdisciplinary enterprise, for it has psychological, sociological, historical and methodological aspects – not to mention the aesthetic and ethical ones. Unfortunately no such collective effort seems to have been attempted. There are only a number of half-baked and untested opinions on the life of theories, and on the process of theory construction and decay.

A popular view on theory construction is that it can be subjected to rules, hence reduced to routine operations. This view rests on the opinion that every scientific theory is just an inductive synthesis of empirical data that could in principle be made by a cleverly programmed computer. The trouble with this opinion is that it mistakes scientific theories for empirical curves (or data interpolations) and it overlooks the fact that scientific data are collected in the light of theories and in response to problems posed within theories. At the other end of the spectrum we find the view that theories are totally free inventions subject to no canon whatever. This opinion is surely right in emphasizing that theoretical creation is akin to artistic creation, in so far as, in either case, the imagination produces something radically new and often far beyond the frontiers of perception. Nevertheless, one can discern styles and standards in both cases. Thus we find the phenomenological (black box or kinetic) style on the one hand and the dynamical on the other. And it is obvious that, no matter how imaginative a theory may be, it is constrained by certain norms, such as logical consistency, cohesion, external consistency, scrutability, predictive power, and so on. Were this not so, metatheory would be impossible. In short, although there are no rules for securing theoretical originality and depth, there certainly are standards which every theory must respect if it is to be regarded as scientific rather than as a piece of pop science.

As to the use of scientific theories for practical purposes, this is a central theme of the philosophy of the various technologies – physical, chemical, biological, psychological, and sociological. A first problem in this regard is to determine the way theories must be prepared or worked out in order to be applied to the deliberate production or prevention of some practical outcome, such as the manufacture of a commodity or the cure of a disease. This problem is related to, but different from, the problem of the preparation of a theory for its empirical test: in either case one has got to deduce low-level theorems and summon the help of subsidiary assumptions and auxiliary theories but, in the case of the practical application, one will look for maximum efficiency rather than for maximum truth. This will influence the actual choice of theory: for practical purposes, one will usually prefer the theory which is the easier to handle, perhaps also the one involving the lower cost, even at the price of superficiality and inaccuracy.

Open problems of this kind are plentiful, indicating that the pragmatics of theories, once they are taken seriously and without pragmatist prejudices against theory, will grow considerably and enable us the better to understand the interactions between theorizing and doing.

10. THE PHILOSOPHY OF SCIENTIFIC THEORIES

It is clear that scientific research is guided by a number of heuristic clues of a philosophical type about the nature of the world and our knowledge of it. Thus, one assumes that things are grouped into natural kinds, that facts fall into objective patterns that can be known, even if only gradually, that space and time constitute the basic structure of the world, that there are no minds separate from bodies, and so on. In short, scientific investigation presupposes a number of ontological and epistemological hypotheses – not to mention a good slice of logic – which are in turn suggested by science and philosophy. This is hardly deniable: the question is whether any such philosophical hypotheses are retained in scientific theories once they have been built, or whether they disappear with the scaffolding.

This problem cannot be solved without regard to special cases: here, as in every other budding domain of research, one should proceed empirically. Moreover, an adequate answer cannot be offered before axiomatizing the theory in question. This is necessary, but may not yet suffice: to disclose the philosophical ingredients of a theory, if any, we must subject its key concepts to philosophical analysis. It is thus that we have come to learn that every scientific theory dealing with complex systems more or less overtly employs the innocent-looking concept of part – a concept that is usually taken for granted but calls for a special theory (mereology), one that belongs to metaphysics and must be formulated in mathematical terms.

On the other hand, an axiomatic and philosophical analysis may show that certain philosophical tenets commonly assigned to some scientific theories are really alien to them. A famous case in point is the doctrine of absolute space and time, which we have become accustomed to associate with Newtonian mechanics. We have only recently come to learn that classical mechanics does not depend on this metaphysical hypothesis: indeed, whether space and time are construed as absolute (self-existent) or as relational (anchored to things and their changes), one gets the same testable formulae. Hence that metaphysical hypothesis (or its negate) is redundant to classical mechanics and it must be judged by criteria other than empirical success or failure. Another celebrated case is the thesis that quantum mechanics is always concerned with systems under observation and, more precisely, with unanalysable units mysteriously constituted by physical objects and observers. This metaphysical thesis, too, has recently been dissociated from the theory thanks to a semantical analysis of its basic (primitive) concepts and to the axiomatic reconstitution of the theory: it turns out that the concept of observer does not even occur in the theory.

In short, a critical analysis of the axiomatic foundations of any scientific theory is bound to reveal a number of genuine philosophical items – chiefly metaphysical categories like those of system, change, and cause – and to discard certain philosophical ideas that had been wrongly assumed to be countenanced by the theory. Moreover, a philosophical look at current science reveals a number of scientific theories that belong by right to metaphysics, as being both extremely general, and untestable without further ado: this is the case of general systems theory, the general theory of machines, automata theory, and information theory. Paradoxically enough, high-powered engineering has become genuine exact metaphysics. This new metaphysics, created in the engineering schools, may eventually replace the dying metaphysics of the philosophy departments.

SUMMARY

In our time all of mathematics and much of science consist of theories. Hence metatheory, or the theory of theories, is at the heart of the analysis of mathematics and science.

A theory, whether mathematical or factual, has certain formal (logical and algebraic) characteristics that distinguish it from a body of opinions. These characteristics are studied by metamathematics. This discipline is also concerned with the relations among theories as far as their structure and their extension are concerned. A powerful new tool for the meta-mathematical analysis of whole classes of theories and their relations is category theory. Model theory, another newcomer, tackles the problem of the interpretation of abstract theories and of the relations among the models of one and the same abstract theory; in addition, it supplies methods for the metamathematical analysis of theories. In the light of these studies, most theories prove to be incomplete and undecidable – which, far from constituting a defeat of reason, points to boundless possibilities of expansion of the realm of reason.

A theory with a factual content poses not only metamathematical and model theoretic problems but also a number of metascientific problems: semantical, epistemological, methodological, pragmatic, and even ontological. Central among them are those of factual and empirical interpretation, factual and partial truth, empirical scrutability, predictive power, and metaphysical commitment. All branches of philosophy are relevant to the study of theoretical science and both are bound to benefit from such contacts. After all, metatheory is the conscience of theoretical science and a test of philosophy. Only a philosophy which accounts for the nature and central role of theory in contemporary science deserves to be taken into consideration.

REFERENCES

ADDISON, J. W., HENKIN, L. and TARSKI, A. (eds.) (1965) *The Theory of Models*, Amsterdam, North-Holland Publ. Co.

BELL, J. L. and SLOMSON, A. B., (1969) *Models and Ultraproducts: An Introduction*, Amsterdam, North-Holland Publ. Co.

BETH, E. W., (1959) *The Foundations of Mathematics*, Amsterdam, North-Holland Publ. Co.

BUNGE, M., (1967) *Scientific Research*, 2 vols., Berlin-Heidelberg-New York, Springer-Verlag.

BUNGE, M., (1967) *Foundations of Physics*, Berlin-Heidelberg-New York, Springer-Verlag.

BUNGE, M., (forthcoming) *Meaning and Truth in Science*.

CARNAP, R., (1958) *Introduction to Symbolic Logic and its Applications*, New York, Dover.

CURRY, H. B., (1963) *Foundations of Mathematical Logic*, New York, McGraw-Hill.

HATCHER, W. A., (1968) *Foundations of Mathematics*, Philadelphia, W. B. Saunders.

HENKIN, L., SUPPES, P. and TARSKI, A. (eds.) (1959) *The Axiomatic Method*, Amsterdam, North-Holland Publ. Co.

HILBERT, D. and BERNAYS, P., (1934–1939) *Grundlagen der Mathematik*, 2 vols., Berlin, Springer (Rev. ed. of Vol. I: 1968).

KLEENE, S., (1952) *Introduction to Metamathematics*, Princeton (N.J.), Van Nostrand.

KLIBANSKY, R., (ed.) (1968) *Contemporary Philosophy*, vols. I and II, Firenze, La Nuova Italia Editrice.

MACLANE, S. and BIRKHOFF, G., (1967) *Algebra*, New York, Macmillan.

MOSTOWSKI, A., (1965) 'Thirty Years of Foundational Studies', *Acta Philosophica Fennica, XVII*.

POPPER, K. R., (1959) *The Logic of Scientific Discovery*, 2nd edition, London, Hutchinson.

RASIOWA, H. and SIKORSKI, R., (1963) *The Mathematics of Metamathematics*, Warsaw, Państwowe Wydawnictwo Naukowe.

ROBINSON, A., (1956) *Complete Theories*, Amsterdam, North-Holland Publ. Co.

ROBINSON, A., (1963) *Introduction to Model Theory and to the Metamathematics of Algebra*, Amsterdam, North-Holland Publ. Co.

SMULLYAN, R. M., (1961) *Theory of Formal Systems*, Princeton, Princeton Univ. Press.

STOLL, R. R., (1961) *Set Theory and Logic*, San Francisco and London, W. H. Freeman.

SUPPES, P., (1967) *Set-Theoretical Structures in Science*, Stanford (Calif.), Institute for Mathematical Studies in the Social Sciences.

TARSKI, A., (1956) *Logic, Semantics, Metamathematics,* transl. by J. H. Woodger, Oxford, Clarendon Press.

TARSKI, A., MOSTOWSKI, A. and ROBINSON, R. M., (1953) *Undecidable Theories,* Amsterdam, North-Holland Publ. Co.

WOODGER, J. H., (1937) *The Axiomatic Method in Biology,* Cambridge (Mass.), Cambridge Univ. Press.